37

CLAAS

CW00818791

CLAAS

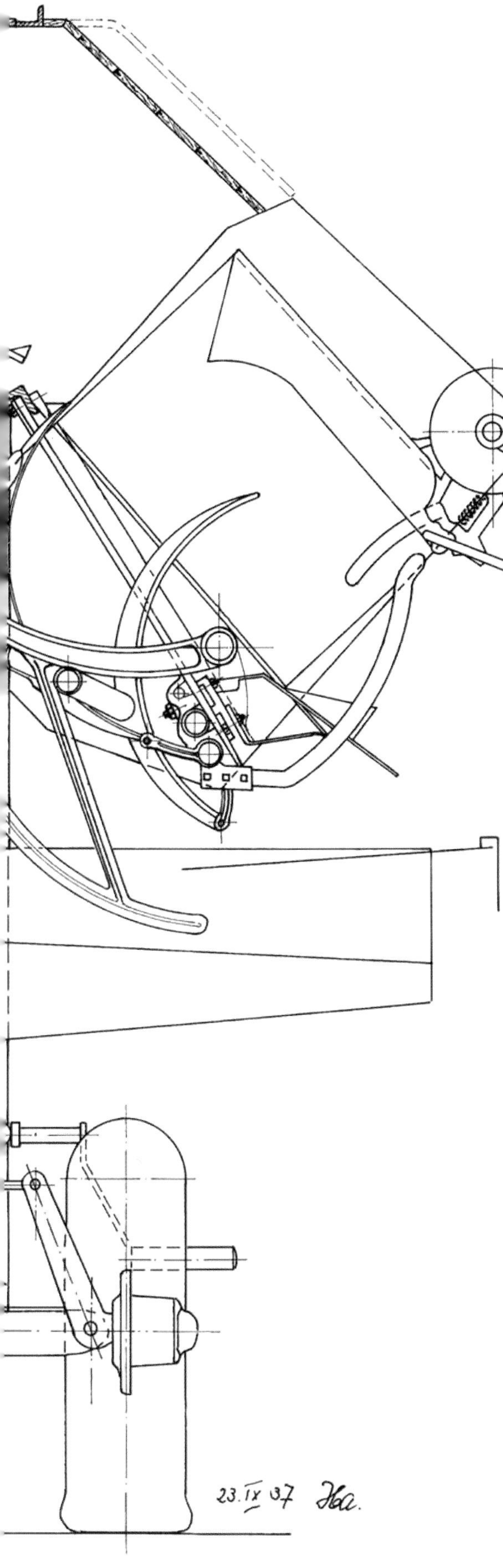

GEBR. Claas

1913 1940 1950 1960 1970

The major European brand

CLAAS

CLAAS-CHRONICLE

A History of this unique Engineering Company
from 1913 to now

Published by:

Horst-Dieter Görg and Wilhelm Kemper

Editorial team:
Martin Beckmann, Horst Biere, Ludwig Caspers, Eberhard Weller

English version:
William Howard

With contributions from:

Bernd Albrecht, Hasso Bertram, Bernd Blömer, Stefan Böttinger, Hans Budde, Paul Budde,
Gerhard Clostermeyer, Johannes Dammann, Christian von Davier, Erik Eckermann,
Günther Ellermann, Astrid Enge, Nils Fredriksen, Jacques Gouet, Franz Heitjann, Heinrich Hemker,
Klaus Herrmann, Wolfgang Hornberger, Wilhelm Isenberg, Hans Jansen, Ernst Klinger, Heinz König,
Josef Löchte, Rolf Meuther, Gerd Meyer, Gerhard Meyer, Jens Möller, Norbert Ortkras,
Hillrich Otten, Meinolf Reiher, Heinz Reinharz, Heinrich Rinklake, Heinrich Roderfeld, Karl Ruprecht,
Günter Schinkel, Günter Schlagenhauf, Johannes Schwörzer, Wilhelm Strothmann,
Dieter Tasch, Manfred Wagner, Ludger Wiemann

An introductory message from Oliver Walston

My first contact with a *Claas* combine was the wood and cardboard model which my father kept on his very large desk. It had been given to him by August Claas in 1946 when my father was running agriculture in the British Zone of Germany. Many decades later my father and I used to visit German farms every year and if ever we were in Westphalia we would pay a visit to Dr August. On the last occasion, when he was a very old man, he offered us before lunch a glass of the famous local black schnapps, *Schwarzer Steinhager.* After pouring us each a glass he hesitated. At this point Frau Claas reminded her husband that the doctor had forbidden this type of refreshment. Dr August paused again, sighed deeply and, on this occasion anyway, proceeded to ignore the medical advice.

When I started to farm myself in the early 1970s I learnt to drive a *Claas Senator* and sat outside in the dust wearing a silk handkerchief round my face like an outlaw from a western movie. Then came the first combine cabs – which were too hot with the doors shut and too dusty with the doors open.

In the mid 1970s we invested in an *Apollo* grass drier and a *Jaguar* forage harvester and for the next five years much of my time was spent sitting in windy fields of Lucerne watching the steam rise from the *Apollo.*

I have always been interested in new technology, which probably explains why we bought one of the first *Rollant* balers in England. It might also explain why I once decided to buy the new *IH Axial-Flow* combine to accompany the three *Claas* machines we were running at the time. Sometime during the summer Helmut Claas paid one of his state visits to Thriplow and must have been surprised to see a red machine among the green ones. Instead of asking me why I had been so stupid, he remained completely serene, cheerful and polite. Two years later the red machine was sold. It had not been a success. I suspect that when he heard this, Helmut might have allowed himself a private smile.

Today we run only a single combine at Thriplow. Our *Lexion 580 Terra Trac* is quite a machine. The output is incredible but – even more important – thanks to the *Laser Pilot* steering even an incompetent combine driver like me is now an expert. Instead of leaving 500 centimetres at the end of my knife this device ensures that I leave a mere ten. Which is why on some days this harvest, when the regular driver was drilling oilseed rape, I was able to cut forty hectares in a single day. And as I sat there watching the crop flow over the header I occasionally dreamed of that little wooden and cardboard model on my father's desk.

Oliver Walston

1 *Oliver Walston*

Foreword by Richard Godwin

The first time I found out about *Claas* equipment was as an agricultural engineering student during the harvest of 1967 when conducting a combine performance survey in Oxfordshire and Berkshire. I was impressed by their design and performance and this led to a continuing respect for *Claas* products.

Some thirty years later I was asked to nominate a suitable candidate from the agricultural engineering industry for the award of an honorary *DSc* from *Cranfield University* at Silsoe. Many machine manufacturing companies which had started out as family run businesses were by then public companies with less easily identified corporate leaders. A little thought then led to the name of Helmut Claas, a man of great integrity, drive and technical prowess with substantial business success.

The more I researched the background of both Helmut and the *Claas* company the more impressed I became. This was exemplified by the fact that in 1998 the *Dominator* combine, which had been on sale for 25 years, was the most successful combine harvester model of all time, the recently introduced *Lexion* was the most powerful combine in the world and the *Jaguar* forage harvester had an excellent reputation for forage harvesting productivity. So in July 1998 I had the honour of reading the citation for Helmut and asking our Chancellor to award him the Degree of *DSc Honaris Causa.* The following year Helmut invited Bill Radley (Head of *Cranfield University* at Silsoe at that time) and I to Harsewinkel where we discussed the formation of the *Claas* Foundation with the aim of providing financial backing to students with interests in agricultural engineering, economics and related disciplines.

I have had the honour since then of working with Helmut and his colleagues in the establishment of the programme for the foundation. This activity initially supported students studying in the UK (Silsoe, Harpur Adams and Cirencester) as well as a number of German Universities. With improving student mobility across Europe, *Claas* is now supporting students from the enlarged EU and Russia to study in other countries. These aims are totally philanthropic, without longer term commitments by the students to the *Claas* organisation. However, one has to acknowledge that an underlying agenda is to ensure that if we have well educated and knowledgeable young professionals entering into agriculture and agricultural engineering it will help to ensure the survival of European agriculture and the demand for quality engineered products.

This book is a testament to the companie's drive in developing engineering excellence in agriculture over a period of nearly 100 years.

DICK GODWIN

2 *Dick Godwin*

Welcome from Helmut Claas

Over 90 years of agricultural machinery from *Claas* – a dramatic period and reason enough to publish this *Claas Chronicle*. The *Claas* company saga is dominated by innovations, many of which were major breakthroughs. We have come a long way to reach the top and we often found ourselves in the situation of being first mover. We have always seen ourselves as pioneers and have gone our individual way. This is the main explanation why over these 90 years we have achieved the position we have in the market today. This process was enhanced both by Westphalian values such as hard work, commitment and persistence in the face of opposition as well as the personal characteristics of the *Claas* founders with their vision, decisiveness, technical skills and the right feeling for the market coupled with lots of optimism.

Those same success factors valid since 1913 still hold true in the future. *Claas* today is one of those companies which is prepared to chart its own course – despite obstacles – when necessary and is prepared to take risks to reach those new shores whilst investing substantial amounts of energy, creativity and financial resources into product development. Efficient and rational production processes are just as important a focus as worldwide distribution and service back up. Our success is dependent on qualified and highly motivated employees since success depends on people.

This book describes the company's development. It's designed to preserve our tradition to which we as a family company are committed. The historical development of our products takes pride of place in this book which is due to the agricultural and technical orientation of our founding fathers and their offspring.

I wish to thank all of those involved in interviews or who have contributed themselves. This enabled us to make a representative cross – section of the company's history right up to the present day. In addition let me extend my thanks to the publishers, the editorial team, the authors, translater and the numerous helpers for their efforts in studying so many files and documents.

Helmut Claas
Chairman of the Supervisory Board of the CLAAS KGaA mbH

3 *Four generations can be seen here. Helmut Claas and his daughter Cathrina standing in front of the photo with August Claas seated in front of a painting of his father, Franz Claas Senior*

Preface from the Editorial Team

As a leading agricultural equipment manufacturer *Claas* has consistently broken new ground with important developments in the world of farm mechanisation. The history integral to this book is therefore very interesting in view of the wide variety it contains.

We have gone to an enormous amount of effort sifting though historical documents, pictures, brochures, statistics and stories, facts and figures whilst questioning people who can still remember the way it happened and have come up with an appealing company work of reference. If you're looking for the definitive *Claas* product history, then you will not find it here. Our objective as editorial team was to highlight the background surrounding key events including less familiar aspects of the remarkably diverse corporate history.

We too would like to thank everyone who played a part in producing the *Claas* Chronicle. Individual names are listed at the end of the book.

We would be happy if this book helps lay the groundwork for the further extension of the *Claas* company archives and museum, as well as helping other agricultural museums as a reference book for their work.

So all it remains for us is to wish you a good read!

Martin Beckmann | Horst Biere | Dr. Ludwig Caspers

Horst-Dieter Görg | Wilhelm Kemper | Eberhard Weller

4 *The editorial team on a Hercules in the museum of the Technoparc: Horst-Dieter Görg, Wilhelm Kemper, Horst Biere, Eberhard Weller, Dr. Ludwig Caspers, Martin Beckmann. (From left to right)*

Index

The growth of a Family Company

The Distribution Network then and now

Claas Advertising and Public Relations

Keeping the Tradition alive

Appendix

5 *Claas straw trussers could be used with all makes of threshing machines and were awarded the silver DLG medal in 1924 and won a further award at the Barcelona World Fair in 1929*

The Origins of Harvest Mechanisation

6 *One of the first American style combines*

The story in a nutshell: farming of cereals and harvesting by hand established themselves in Mesopotamia some 4000 years ago. The first combines were built in America in 1830, pulled by teams of up to 40 horses or mules. Then self propelled machines evolved as steam and internal combustion engines came along. The origins of the Claas history are to be found in the manufacture of centrifuges used for skimming milk. Franz Claas Senior entered harvesting as a contractor, building up invaluable experience he was able to pass on to his sons.

Agriculture in Mesopotamia

The introduction of farming was the spark that set off the creation of what is now known as the cradle of civilisation. As a production-oriented activity it supplemented or replaced the hunter / gatherer mentality which had the disadvantage of decimating wild animal stocks. As population grew this activity led to forced migration and nomadic people have rarely left any traces of cultural achievements in their tracks. Tilling the soil and tending livestock increased food output and yields whilst encouraging in its wake early urban construction based on a permanent site. This in turn created the environment for higher material and intellectual aspirations and new levels of cultural accomplishment.

The creation and continuity of city states in Mesopotamia was dependent on an efficient food supply. Mesopotamia, by the way, is defined as the country between the Euphrates and Tigris rivers in Babylon, the land around the lower courses of the twin rivers, Assyria, the country around the town Assur, and in Akkad. This constituted the first major kingdom in history, encompassing the current regions of Iraq and Syria. The city states between the Persian Golf and Mosul emerged between approximately 3000 and 2400 BC after the acquisition of land by the Sumerians.

The prevailing natural and civilisation conditions meant that the Sumerian and Assyrian farming community was able to feed the growing population although less and less people were actively involved in farming (typically by becoming traders, priests or government officials). The mud deposits from Euphrates and Tigris made the region the most fertile plain between the Indus in the east and the Nile in the west. However, the lack of rainfall (between 10 and 50 cm a year compared to Munich with 96 cm) in the southern areas made irrigation necessary. The water conveyance and channelling system installed over a lengthy period of time was an outstanding technical and logistical achievement. It matches other highlights of Babylonian culture such as its religion and its legislation, speech and writing, plus literature, art and scientific observation, architecture, administration and organisation.

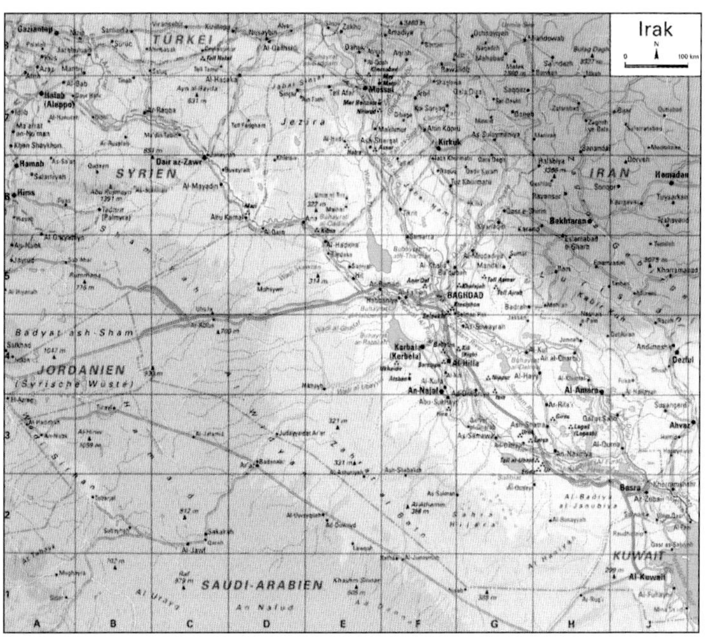

7 Map of Iraq with antique sites

The origins of food supply are buried in the mists of time. The early people used everything they could get their hands on for food by gathering, fishing and especially hunting. Hunting methods became more and more sophisticated – pits, lances, spears, bows and arrows – to the extent that they started disrupting the ecologic balance for the first time. Wild animal populations were not able to regenerate due to overhunting. The tribes had then to follow the animals; sometimes entire folk migrated and frequently hostile disputes over hunting grounds broke out and people were displaced. These negative achievements are a recurring theme throughout human history, although the triggering factors have changed.

The people of the ancient world started to become sedentary from about 9000 to 6750 BC. Hunters and gatherers became farmers and cattle breeders joined forces to form village communities. The Neolithic Revolution marked the transition from a hunting to food producing society and is just as significant a part of early history as the Industrial Revolution which occurred from around 1820 and was set in motion by the steam engine. The ancient revolution prospered in regions with domestic animals and cultivatable wild plant varieties and where the average rainfall amounted to more than 20 cm a year.

That was the case in a few areas in Mesopotamia, part of the fertile crescent which stretches around the barren Arab desert and valleys in

Egypt and Israel, Lebanon, Syria, Turkey, Iraq and Iran. There is enough rain, primarily during the winter for rain-induced farming, the oldest form of agriculture.

Since Mesopotamia's individual areas each had their own particular landscape, climate and vegetation, farming practices had inevitably to adjust to variable conditions. It can generally be said that the area of rain-induced farming lies to the north of an imaginary line between the town Hit on the Euphrates and Samarra on the Tigris, some 110 km north of Baghdad. The oldest agriculture emerged as winter rain induced farming in the edge zones of the (Persian) Zagros mountains.

South of this line we find the alluvium, alluvial sediments of Euphrates and Tigris Rivers. The Karkheh and Karun rivers flow into them from the Zagros mountains. In this fertile alluvial soil, the rainfall only amounts to 5 to 15 cm a year and is therefore insufficient for farming. Actually, to be able to engage in agriculture here, an irrigation system utilising the flood waters of Euphrates and Tigris had to be constructed. The seed was sown in September or October, but the Spring melt that caused the flooding only reached the alluvium in April or May. The cultivation of lower Mesopotamia is thus an "irrigation agriculture" depending on water conveyance and channelling.

Before giving a detailed description of the crops, domestic animals and farming utensils will be dealt with.

Seed finds as well as fragments of flints, mortars and millstones from the late Stone Age (Neolithic, 8000 to 7000 BC) indicate that fields were being tilled then. The assumption is that "mankind finally left the caves"[1] and probably settled in huts, for instance, in the valleys of the foothills in southern Kurdistan east of Mosul. Initially, it was most likely a type of garden farming (hoe bed) which then passed, with the beginning of the 7th millennium, into rain-induced farming. The villagers grew large grained, two row barley as well as wheat (emmer) cultivated from wild varieties. Apart from wheat, barley and millet which were the most important types of grain for several millennia, the early farmers also gathered and planted other plants such as lentils, garbanzo, vetches, horse beans and later sesame.

Also around 7000 BC, the keeping of domestic animals began with the goat, followed by dogs, sheep, cows and pigs. Cows and oxen became

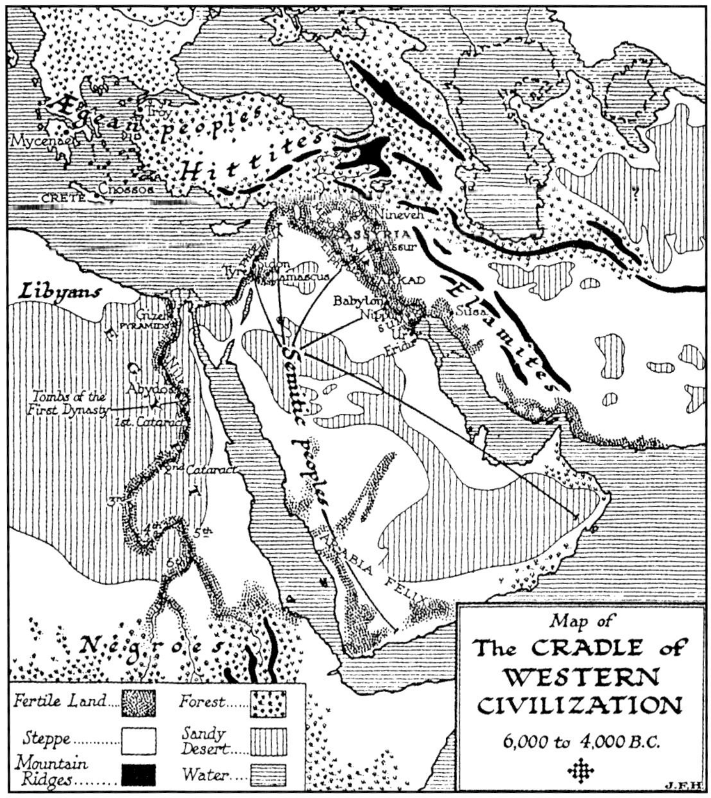

8 The cradle of western civilization with the fertile crescent – 6000 to 4000 BC

indispensable domestic animals for the farmer. They had to pull the plough, the harrow, the threshing sledge and later two wheel carts that were used to bring in the sheaves and to haul the grain from the threshing floors to the granaries. Cows were also primarily used for stomping down the soil after the flood waters and after the first ploughing; sometimes mules, wild donkeys or male goats were also used. Horses were less commonly used since the claws of the cows were more suitable for field work than the hooves of the different kinds of horses.

The plough was the most important agricultural implement, and it was only invented in this region of the world during the time of transition from field agriculture to irrigation farming in the 4th millennium. It was preceded by manual tools for digging (spades and shovels), hacking, beating and hitting (axe and "adze", an axe with a transverse blade). With its various functions, the field roller was still pulled by hand while harrows and ploughs were pulled by cows.

In the ancient Orient, a distinction was made between two types of plough. Firstly the deep cutting plough for the early tillage (seed bed preparation) in September and October. Then there was the furrow sowing plough for the cultivation of untilled land taking advantage of the flood water in May and June. It was then used for ploughing the actual furrow. The seed

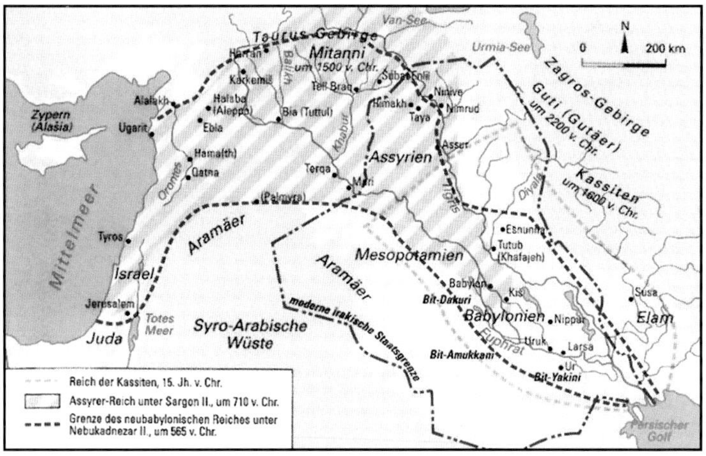

9 Mesopotamia at the time of the Assyrians. 2nd to 1st millennium before Christ

was sown with the help of a seed funnel integrated into the plough. This special furrow sowing plough and the quality of the ground meant that only a small amount of seed material was needed.

The blade of the plough was made of beaten copper which began to be processed for implements in the 4th millennium before Christ. Bronze was preferred by the 3rd millennium and iron took over in the 1st millennium. All other parts of the plough were made of wood. When something broke, the sowing ploughmen obtained spare parts from tradesmen, which demonstrates how an economy with different work disciplines had gradually emerged. Apart from sowing ploughmen, there were grain carriers, threshers, water drawers, water regulators and other "professions" and jobs in the farming field. These tasks had to be performed by independent and semi-independent farmers and workers, by women, slaves, prisoners of war but also children as helpers. Depending on the social status and epoch the Twin River region – unlike Egypt whose history remained largely undisturbed from the outside – exhibits a confusing historical sequence of events to this very day. Wages were paid either in grain rations or money.

Back to irrigation agriculture. The Roman historian Pliny the Elder, considered the Mesopotamian alluvium as "the most fertile field of the entire Orient".[2] To gain this distinction, the Babylonians not only had to work harder than their neighbours but also had to overcome mathematical, technical, logistical and of course financial challenges. The reason for this is that the flood waters had to be used both for flooding the fields as well as the irrigation of fields and meadows, gardens and parks, canals and reservoirs, weirs, sluices and bucket elevators. They even built an aqueduct in 690 BC, making this the oldest man-made water line in human history.

Some city states such as Larsa, Lagash and Umma were principally irrigation districts. The irrigation network required land surveying, earthworks and dam construction. Canals and basins had to be kept regularly clear of residues and maintained, building materials had to be procured in large quantities. At peak times, each project involved up to 5400 workers who had to be supplied with work assignments, accommodation, meals and wages.

At certain times, kings considered it their divine duty to irrigate the land and to produce foodstuffs. Farming therefore acquired a religious status which can be compared to an extent with today's subsidies to their farming industries ac-

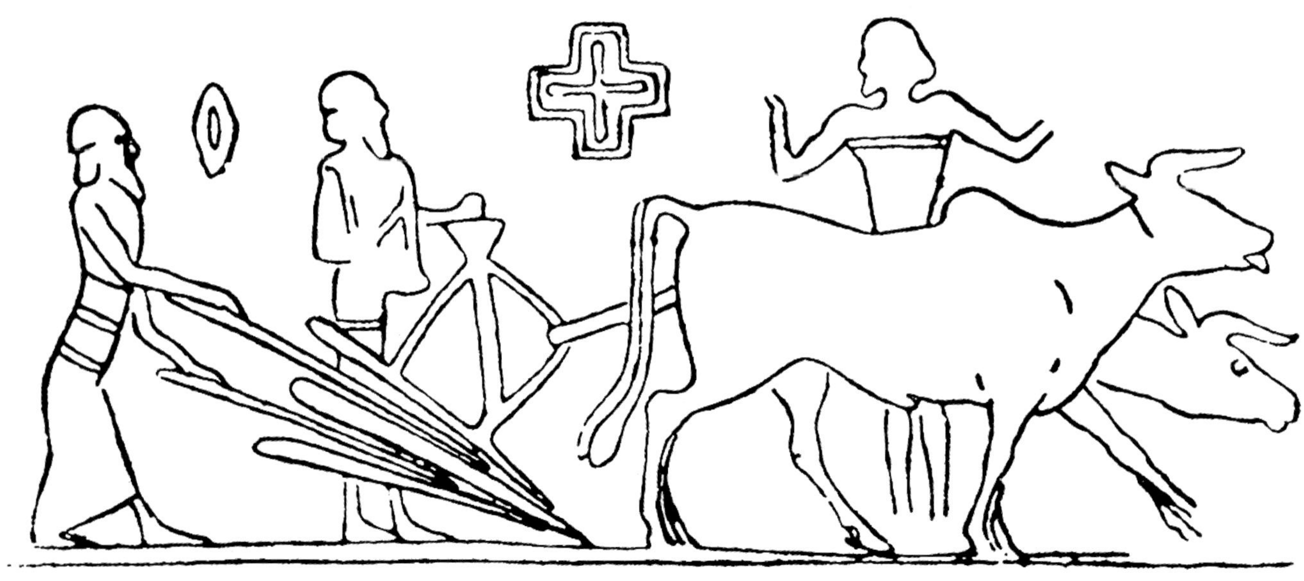

10 Babylonian furrow sowing plough with seed container, in whose funnel a sowing ploughman filled the seeds which fell into the furrow under and behind the blade. A second ploughman guided the plough, a third one the cows on the yoke (not shown)

11 Arab ploughman with a camel as draft animal

corded by the EU and the US administrations. But the irrigation system gradually became obsolete: the Euphrates and Tigris rivers moved their riverbeds thus changing topography and fertility continuously. Approximately every 20 to 40 years, the Persian Gulf is pushed one kilometre to the southeast. This explains for instance why the port city of Ur, founded around 4000 BC, is now on the mainland roughly 160 km away from the coast. Arabic Islam (from 634 AD) and the Mongolians, invading in 1258, however, busied themselves with power struggles and not with agriculture.

The biggest handicap, however, was and still is the salt pollution that had already began at the time of the Sumerians. Not only the salts contained in the river water but also additional dissolved salts from the ground are deposited on or near the ground surface due to the high evaporation in dry hot climates. If the salt reaches the root area of the plants, it disturbs their water absorption causing them to die. Today, 60 percent of Mesopotamia's land area is considered to be too saline, primarily due to excessive irrigation and lack of drainage - another disturbance of the ecological balance due to human intervention. Incidentally, fertilizers were not used in the old Mesopotamia.

Today, just as thousands of years ago, wheat, barley and vegetables are planted. There are also cotton crops and date plantations. But in spite of reconstitution of old irrigation areas in the 20th century and a land reform in 1958, modern Iraq (since 1921) cannot feed itself, not even in times of peace.

Erik Eckermann

Literature:

Armas Salonen: Agricultura Mesopotamica, Helsinki 1968
[1] p. 21; [2] p. 26: ager totius orientis fertilissimus

R. J. Garde : Irrigation in Ancient Mesopotamia, in : ICID (International Commission on Irrigation & Drainage) Bulletin, July 1978, Vol. 27, No. 2

Karl Graf von Klinckowstroem: Geschichte der Technik,Berlin, Darmstadt, Wien

H. G. Wells: The Outline of History, London 1925, Vol. I and II

Karl-Rolf Schultz-Klinken: 9000 Jahre Landwirtschaft, in: Bild der Wissenschaft, issue 11/1977

Wolfgang Gockel: Iraq, Cologne 2001

12 Later major civilization also struggled with the development of harvest technology as can be seen by the model of a pushed Roman "mowing machine with harvesting cart"

American Harvesting and Machinery

The 19th century illustrated book entitled *"Das Ganze der Landwirtschaft"*[1] describes the harvest as the prime goal of the whole farm: it must crown the labor of a year...". However, soil conditions, weather and availability of manpower influence the crop yield. In the race against time, the first harvesters, each designed for a particular purpose, helped speed up the process. After thousands of years of traditional use of reaping hooks, scythes[2] and simple threshing equipment, they were a major step forward and formed the basis for combining many work processes in one machine. Today's self-propelled combine harvesters are complete harvesters – they reap and thresh the grain, clean and retrieve the corn and chop the straw.

The impetus for the mechanisation of farming, particularly that of harvesting, was provided by Scottish, English and American farmers. American farmers had to cultivate larger areas with less manpower at their disposal than their European counterparts. Whereas the yield per area was a major topic in Europe, American farmers focused on increasing the productivity per man. In addition, the North American topography was more favourable for mechanisation. In those times farm machines required a surface as flat as possible which were just not available in much of England or Scotland. It is therefore not surprising that farming machines from the U.S. and Canada very soon gained recognition internationally.

However, even in North America, the beginnings were primitive. Many years after 1800, a farmer was still typically farming with a wooden plough, harrow, hoe, hay fork and rake, mostly of poor design and often home made. The first major improvement, beginning in 1825, was the cast iron plough which, just like in industrial production processes, speeded up the pace of development.

Countless farmers and mechanics turned their hands to making their own inventions – the reaper is a good example of this trend. A harvester built in 1826 by Patrick Bell in Scotland was one of the first to feature moving knives and a rotating reel. The reel bent the stalks toward the scissor-type knives and onto an inclined collecting apron from where they were stored either on the right or on the left side of the machine. Bell's machine gained little acceptance in Scotland or in the United States. However it incorporated some the most important features of modern combine harvesters: front cutting unit, a reel, it was pushed not pulled (horse power was later replaced by engines), it had a big front ground wheel, automatic reaper and was operated by one man.

Soon afterwards the Americans Obed Hussey and Cyrus McCormick succeeded in selling their first machines, Hussey in 1834 and McCormick in1839. Hussey's *reaper* was designed for grass with a robust chassis and cutting unit to enable mowing close to the ground with its undulations and stones. In comparison, McCormick was able to make his harvesting machine more easily. because the knives and fingers cut at a height of ten or more cm from the ground. The customers

13 Bell's 1826 reaper with two front wheels under the cutting unit and two big wheels to drive the cutting mechanism and reel. Pushed by two horses, steered by the farmer using a drawbar extension. One of these is on display at the Science Museum, London

14 McCormick's 1831 reaper. A rider and a so called forker who raked the cut grain from the platform produced as much as five cutters per day. Additional workers bound the stalks to sheaves and stood them up. In Europe this job was mostly done by women

of these machines were gentlemen farmers, who considered mechanised harvesting as an interesting experiment.[3]

The population pressure of European immigrants, the completion of the Erie canal from Albany on the Hudson to Buffalo on Lake Eric in 1825 and the construction of railway lines through the Appalachians starting in 1843 moved the frontier of farming toward the West. New towns and population centres sprung up. The increasing mechanisation of farming was another factor behind the shift of the bread basket from the Buffalo-Rochester region in New York state to the Mid-West with Chicago as its centre. When McCormick visited the "newly-opened prairies"[4], which is how the Americans paraphrased the expulsion and extermination of Indians and buffalos, he concluded that a reaper would be considered a luxury in his home state of Virginia whilst it was a necessity in the West.

Consequently, *McCormick* opened a factory in Chicago (1847) where he manufactured reapers on an industrial scale. He installed a production line and steam engines and practiced an aggressive business policy with hire purchase, professional advertising and priority processes. By 1860, he had become the biggest manufacturer of reapers. The iron and steel industry of the region was also significantly boosted by farming.

Following the introduction of steel ploughs by John Deere in the 1840's the hard prairie topsoil could be properly tilled. The area under cultivation expanded in line with the effectiveness of the harvesters. The average size of the two million American farms around 1850 – which coincides with the advent of mechanical harvesters and the cultivation of the prairie – amounted to approximately 25 *acres* (10 ha). By 1910 the area under cultivable had gone up five times to some 125 *acres* per farm with four million farms. So, with the mass production of affordable farming tools, companies like Cyrus McCormick, John Deere, Jerome Increase Case and later Henry Ford gained not only a dominant position compared to thc competition, but also boosted the national economy – according to the Austrian-American national economist Joseph Alois Schumpeter, the dynamic entrepreneur achieved "new combinations" *(= innovations)* thus bringing about an upturn of the economy.

To avoid time-consuming and cost-intensive manual work, lots of efforts were made to design a single machine to handle the various harvesting functions. Over the intervening years[5], the reaper assumed additional tasks such as depositing the cut stalks on a tilting belt (Bell 1826, Hornsby 1865), on a platform, on the ground (= automatic reaper, 1851) or discharging untied bundles of stalks onto the ground.

Reaping and binding machines were to become the temporary development peak of the humble reaper. Initially, one or several workers riding along on the machine manually tied the bundles into sheaves (from 1853), after that, binding devices followed for twine, wire and straw in 1905. However, while reaping and binding machines began to displace the reapers which were pulled or the headers which were pushed, the next step to the development to the combine harvester, a combination of mowing and threshing machine, began to emerge.

The origins of the threshing machine go even further back than those of the reaper. First of all, most attention was devoted to the transfer of the traditional threshing

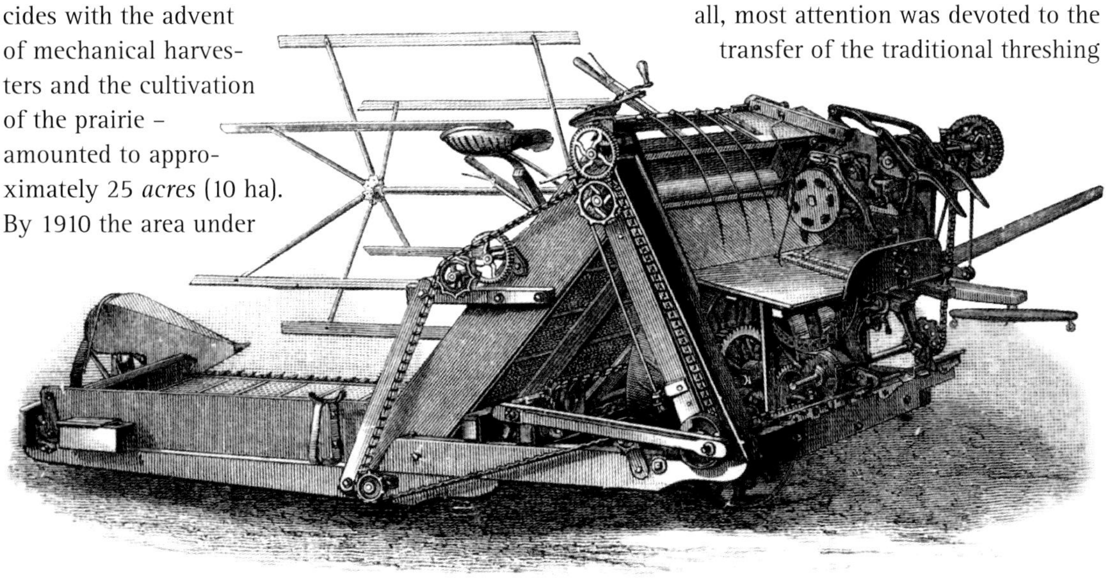

15 *Reaper / binder around 1885. The automatic reaper turned into this complex reaping and binding machine. This one has left hand cutting for use with a team of horses. The mowed grain is transported from the reel on the platform. This is covered by a belt driven by the ground wheel. It reaches the trussing table where it is bound into sheaves by the binding device and dropped off at the right*

methods dependent on human or animal muscle power such as stamping, pressing, hammering and rolling into the industrial age. Today's threshing is still closely tied to Scotsman Andrew Meikle's patented machines from 1788 with their rotating rasp bar drum. This threshed the grain in a basket. Preceding this by a wide margin are the grain cleaning centrifuge blowers invented in China in the 3rd century B.C. which only found their way to Europe in the 15th century.

The first threshing machines and newer blowing fans were stationary devices, mostly under a roof. The grain harvested on the field was bound into sheaves, stayed a few days in the field on crouches to dry. Then, it was brought in and threshed in winter by hand, horse-gin or water powered threshing machines. Depending on the equipment, the grain could be separated and cleaned and the straw could be stored or chopped. In contrast with mobile threshers, most threshing machines on wheels could thresh during harvest and costly storage of the corn sheaves could be avoided. Around 1800, the first portable steam threshing machines appeared in the east of England. However, they were reserved for the biggest estates for many decades.

The first threshing machine introduced in North America originated from Scotland in 1788. It was not portable, had to be operated by two men and produced 70 *bushels* (1 bushel = 35.2 litres) a day, ten times that threshed with a flail. Scottish and English machines dominated the market up to the 1820's and were then replaced by American designed ones.

In 1822 and 1826, *Savage* and *Douglass* replaced the European style rasp bar drum with a peg

16 *Mobile steam threshing unit from around 1890 with steam engine, threshing machine and straw elevator. In the threshing housing under the work platform, the threshing drum with basket, adjacent straw walkers, sieves, fans and bagging stand. Drive through steam engine with extra high funnel together with spark catcher and extra long driving belt to avoid fire*

drum thresher which became a typical feature of North American threshing machines. In 1843, Case combined the thresher, blower and horse pedal drive into a combined thresher and soon became the biggest threshing machine manufacturer in the world. Attempts to combine mowing and threshing processes into one machine proliferated as was apparent by the patents issued by the *Patent Office* in Washington from 1828.

The development of this combined harvester is attributed mainly to Hiram Moore (built in 1834, patented in 1836) whose machine design became the benchmark for following generations of combine harvester: the knife unit moving to and fro cut the corn, a reel pressed the stalks on a platform, the threshing drum separated the grain from the stalk whilst a fan fitted behind got rid of the chaff. With a normal cutting width of 12 feet (3.65 m), the machine was pulled by approximately sixteen horses hitched in pairs, cutting was to the right and a team of six men was needed. In addition, three to four men on the machine kept an eye on the mowing and threshing mechanism. This was set in motion by horse power from the drive wheel through cog wheels and controlled by levers. Moore / Hascall's combined harvester was proclaimed as a "great invention ... for the needs of a great country"[6] but the initial design failed to impress in the cool and humid climate in Michigan. It should be added that Moore considered himself more of an inventor than a businessman.

In 1854, one of his machines made its way from Michigan to the arid state of California. It went via Cape Horn since there was no direct link yet across the continent. During the 1880's, following some years of amateurish production the industrial process took hold with Stockton declaring itself the combine capital of the world. Names like Daniel Best, Benjamin Holt and George Stockton Berry emerged whose combined harvester of 1886 appeared almost visionary.

The horses had gone, replaced by a steam engine whose boiler was fired using the harvested straw. The prime mover could be driven forward and backward and could be converted into a tractor for other purposes when the harvesting devices were removed. In 1888, the 22-foot (6.70 m) cutter bar, with up to 60 cm adjustment was superseded by a 40 foot header (12.20 m), making it the biggest of its time. It enabled mowing and threshing of 100 acres (40 ha) a day and even had headlights for night work. A second steam engine fuelled by the boiler of the main machine powered the threshing unit for stationary threshing.

Berry was able to sell a few of these self propelled machines and his reputation as a pioneer held for decades. The Californian combine harvesters, which also turned up in other U.S. states and Canadian provinces sporadically, remained horse drawn for the time being. The horse drawn era came to an end with World War I. The war increased the demand for wheat which required more cultivable land but at the same time deprived farming of seasonal workers as the men were called up for military service. From 1917, the sale of combine harvesters increased steeply, even outside of California, and some were still horse drawn or more often powered by steam engine or gasoline tractors, depending on the price and the harvest area. Cutting and threshing units were driven either via ground wheels, auxiliary engines or tractor PTO shafts. Between the wars the combine population grew at a rapid pace, opening up more land for farming and ensuring the reliable supply of food to the growing population. None of the American combine producers showed much interest in Europe yet, and hardly noticed when *Claas* started developing the European style combine in the 1930s.

However the Second World War had even more serious repercussions on American farming. A further increased demand for wheat and other field crops was accompanied this time both by a new labour shortage as well as steel rationing which curbed the American combine harvester production which collapsed from 54,296 in 1941 to 29,219 in 1943. This encouraged the development of *interstate custom combining* between 1942 and 1947 as independent contractors turned combine threshing into a paid service for farmers. With their machinery they followed the harvest times from early crops in the South to later maturity in the North, moving about 15 miles a day. The custom combining circuit formed a corridor on the east of the Rocky Mountains from Texas and Oklahoma to Saskatchewan.

But above all, World War II gave a big boost to self propelled combine harvesters. Increasing crop yields coupled with savings in personnel, tractors, fuel and operating hours were the key factors in this development. The Canadian company *Massey-Harris*, in agreement with Canadian and American officials, succeeded in initially supplying threshing contractors with 500 self propelled machines in 1944. The Self Propelled Harvest Brigade of *Massey-Harris* was

17 Berry's self-propelled combine harvester, 1886. The world's first self-propelled combine with plenty of innovations. Individual steam engines for travel and harvesting functions. Probably the first U.S. straw burning steam engine. First machine with forward and reverse drive, modular design (useable as tractor without harvester) and night work (1888)

a unique harvesting endeavour operated with military discipline which became part of American history. It convinced officials, farmers and other companies to start producing Self Propelled Combines: After *Massey-Harris* in 1938, *International Harvester* followed in 1942, *Deere* in 1947, *Oliver* in 1949, *Allis Chalmers* and *Gleaner* in 1951 and *Claas* in 1953. *Massey-Harris-Ferguson* opened its third European subsidiary in Eschwege Germany in 1954.

The introduction of the combine harvester in Germany was a laborious procedure. American machines imported from 1927 turned out to be unsuitable for German and European conditions. These machines had wide headers suitable for extensive grain production and low yields in the U.S. American combine harvesters cut just under the ears and left up to 50 cm high stubble behind. Straw and chaff remained on the field. In Germany and Europe on the contrary, crop densities were much higher. Straw and chaff were needed here as feed and litter on cattle farms.

All the straw had to be processed then by the combine harvester. This in turn called for technically modified threshing drums and straw walkers. In addition, there were economic and political circumstances – with the release of short term foreign loans in Germany which were invested in long term development projects from 1923, Germany was particularly hard hit by the world economic crisis (1929 to 1932). Investment activity came to a standstill and the benefits of saving personnel with combine harvesters in times of high unemployment lost any economic interest. Nevertheless, from 1930, *Claas* and the *Deutschen Industriewerke* carried out

18 Holt's horse drawn combine around 1904. Up to the 1920's, combines were pulled by horses or mules, even in the hilly landscape of California. High up on an overhanging seat, the driver hovers above a team of up to 40 animals. Additional 3 to 5 workers were necessary for general supervision, cutting height, sieves and bag binding. The harvesting unit was driven by the ground wheel

some experiments with combines in Spandau. In 1936, *Claas* released a pull type combine harvester and binder and the first European self propelled machine followed in 1953. The later chapters cover this fascinating period in great depth. The visions of Bell, Meikle, Moore and Berry, just to mention the most well-known, also became a reality in Europe though it took a long while and was impaired by the constraints of two world wars.

Erick Eckermann

Notes

[1] *Wilhelm Hamm: Das Ganze der Landwirthschaft in Bildern. Leipzig 1872, S. 64*

[2] *The vallus, a two-wheel mowing cart with container mounted on the axle, remained apparently limited to a few Gallic farms in the 2nd and 3rd century B.C. Its rake-like front end with its iron spikes was thereby pushed into the grain field by horse or cow from behind the axle; the ears were broken off and swept by a helper – with the help of a rake – into the container. A second man behind the horse steered the harvesting machine and kept the spike arrangement at the proper height.*

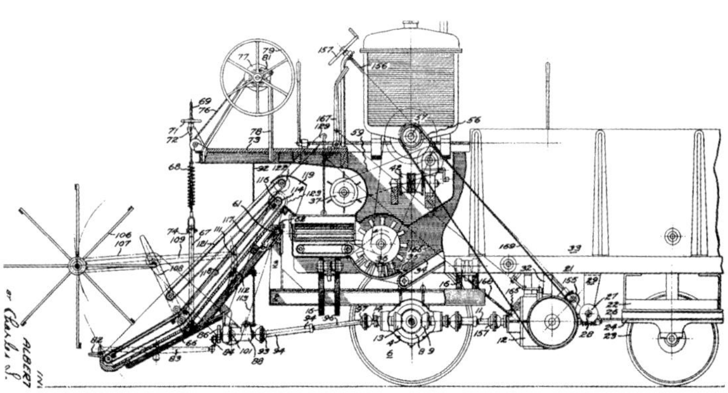

19 One of the countless American patents on self propelled combines from 1927. This one shows the engine under the floor and front wheel drive. The cutting unit is operated through a propeller shaft, the threshing cylinder through belts

[3] *Jan Kuuse: Interaction between Agriculture and Industry. Göteborg 1974, S. 232*

[4] *Graeme R. Quick; Wesley F. Buchele: The Grain Harvesters. St. Joseph, MI, 1978, S. 32*

[5] *The dates quoted are approximate and may not necessarily tie in accurately to the actual year of patent registration or introduction.*

[6] *Quotation is attributed to the American narrator James Fenimore Cooper (1789-1851), taken from (4), pages 89 and 90*

Sources:

See notes 1, 3 and 4, further:

Manfred Baedeker; Ralf Lenge: The CLAAS Combine Story, Münster 2001

Wilhelm Berdrow: Buch der Erfindungen, Leipzig 1901, Düsseldorf 1985

Percy W. Blandford: Old Farm Tools and Machinery, Fort Lauderdale 1976

Alfons Eggert: Von der Mähmaschine zum Mähdrescher, Münster 1991

Harold U. Faulkner: Geschichte der Amerikanischen Wirtschaft, Düsseldorf 1957

Johann Christian Ginzrot: Die Wägen und Fahrwerke der Griechen und Römer und anderer alter Völker, München 1817, Hildesheim / New York 1975

International Harvester: 25 Jahre IHC-Werke in Neuß, Neuß 1934

Thomas D. Isern: Custom Combining on the Great Plains, Oklahoma 1981

Harris P. Smith: Farm Machinery and Equipment, New York und London 1937

Walter Söhne: Bodenbearbeitungs- und Erntetechnik, Frankfurt / M 1992

Reinhold Thebis: Erntemaschinen, Berlin 1948

Ulrich Troitzsch, Wolfhard Weber: Die Technik, Braunschweig 1982

Peter Wacker: Mähdrescher verändern die Ernte, in: Agrarhistorische Zeitschrift / Deutsches Landwirtschaftsmuseum, issue 7, Hohenheim 1997

Hermann Walz: Mähdrescher-ABC, Würzburg 1972

L.A. West: Agriculture – Hand Tools to Mechanisation, London 1967

Franz Claas Senior – His Life and Times

Franz Claas was born in 1859 and as adult he had a wide range of interests which led him to start making farming equipment in 1880. After getting his qualifications as a veterinary healer he started making centrifuges in large numbers. In addition he ran a sawmill and flour mill and did contract threshing. Franz Claas was both a good teacher for his four sons and set them a good example to follow.

The history of the *Claas* company wouldn't be complete without the inclusion of Franz Claas. He was the father of the Claas brothers who later set up the company and he was born on the 17th of March 1859 as the only son of Heinrich Claas and his wife Katharina, née Brüggemann in the farming community of Heerde, close to Harsewinkel. Heinrich was a farmer with 12.5 ha of arable land and pasture plus a sawmill, a contracting operation with several threshing machines and a workshop with smithy to round it all off. In addition he was a respected and busy vet.

Mechanisation was still in its infancy in those days on the farms but Franz developed an unusually strong interest in all things technical, much to the annoyance of his parents who showed little interest. Apparently his mother destroyed a lathe he had built himself so he built a new one in the nearby woods and made spinning tops with it to the delight of his school friends.

When he was 16 and school time was over, his parents then arranged for him to take up an apprenticeship with a vet called Dr. Kaspar Steinkühler in Glandorf. His training lasted three years and he was able to learn a lot, qualifying finally as a veterinary healer. In his spare time he would visit a local blacksmith who made special hooves for lame horses on orders from the vet. The young Franz soon made friends with the blacksmith, a friendship which was strengthened when he related his lathe building adventures. He was then able to learn about forging techniques as time went by.

His father died around this time so Franz Claas went back home to Heerde where he spent his time running the farm and building up his veterinary practice. However his technical leanings still left his mother unimpressed.

Franz Claas with his broad scope of interests loved his job and was really dedicated to his practice. He held weekly consultations in and around Harsewinkel and went out on horseback or pony and trap to visit sick animals on neighbouring farms. His strengths lay clearly both in healing sick animals and in technical matters, whilst the business management side wasn't his cup of tea. He found it embarrassing to ask for money for his services and didn't keep good records on outstanding debts. Neither could his wife Maria, née Prövestmann, be of much assistance.

Franz spent most of his spare time playing around with technical things and his mother's resistance faded gradually as she began to understand her son's predilections. Early in the 1880's he set up a workshop on the farm where he started producing centrifuges for skimming milk mechanically from 1887. This first development of his was such a success that he could

20 *Franz Claas Senior, 1859 to 1928*

21 Maria Claas, née Prövestmann 1861 to 1922

hardly keep up with demand as orders poured in from the region and even from overseas. Farmers' sons from the region who had emigrated to Canada ordered *Claas* centrifuges from Heerde for themselves and their neighbours. The *Triumph* was patented and was offered with hourly throughputs of 80, 90, 130 and 170 litres. This product line formed the foundation of the regional centrifuge industry.

The explosion in demand led to serious new competition and competitive pressure gradually eroded the company's profitability, whilst patent disputes were irritating and wasted a lot of time. Finally he decided to look for a new challenge and stopped producing centrifuges.

In 1885 Bernhard was born, the natural successor, and he was followed by August and Franz in 1887 and 1890, then Theo in 1897. The daughters Käthe, Lisbeth and Alwine rounded off the happy family. The Claas sons had a technical interest laid in their cradle, growing up in their father's workshop where the company's manufacturing skills had made the name *Claas* well known in Westphalia and beyond for the first time.

During the 1890's Franz saw one of the first reapers to be imported into Germany in action in nearby Wiedenbrück. One year later another example of Claas engineering skill was standing in the family farmyard complete with a patented laying device. Franz Claas produced 600 of them in the following years and this design was later even built in America where it was christened as a windrower.

Meanwhile Franz had turned his hand to building threshing machines, initially with treadmill drive. In the early 1880's he made small ones which increased in size progressively as the centrifuge production declined. He also examined potato lifting techniques whilst his sons Bernhard, August and Franz turned to him for guidance as they got involved in the business which had 20 to 30 employees.

At the turn of the 20th century straw trussers started to appear from England. Franz Senior set out to be the first to build such a machine which he did. It made its debut in 1907. The knotting devices of both machines – the English one and the German one – were much too complex. They were more like precision tools than working parts and their spring tensioning made them temperamental in the cold. The answer was to push them into a warm barn overnight,

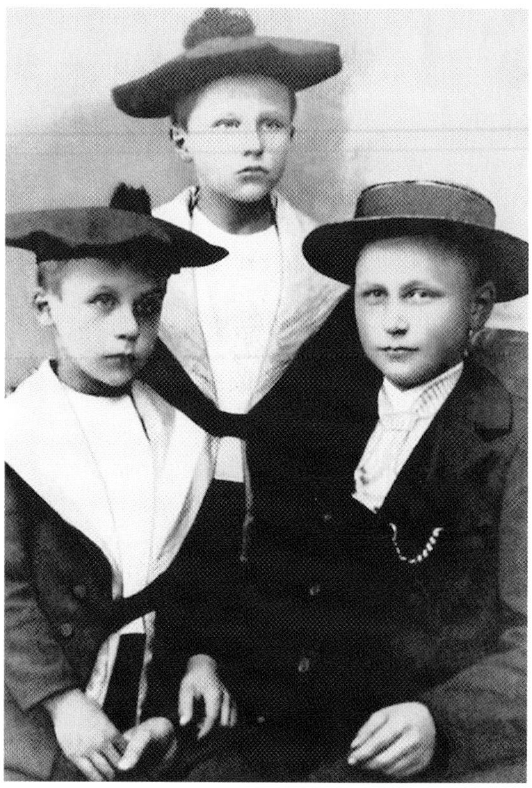

22 Franz, August and Bernhard in their young days

23 Theo, the youngest son

24 Käthe and Lisbeth, the two elder girls

then everything was fine. They were nicknamed "Libbethken" which could be translated as Little Lizzy.

In later years Bernhard Claas often mentioned this trusser which was used in quite large numbers in Westphalia: "When we saw a farmer or a labourer approaching the house, we knew at once what was up. Then August was called out to look over Little Lizzy, because he knew it better than anyone".

In or around 1900 Franz Senior set up as a threshing contractor, firstly with one machine going from farm to farm. The number of machines went to three then four, all of them home made and fitted with straw trussers.

Some time before *McCormick* had come out with a new knotter for their sheaf binder with only about one third of the moving parts of the complicated *Deering* knotter. It worked much better. As a result of the repeated problems with the trussers working in Germany, August Claas took a close look at this design and set out to make the *McCormick* version useable on local machines by adding an extra moveable lip. These efforts failed first time round and the final answer had to wait till the end of the First World War when it was finally patented. The "*knotter*" as it was later termed was to make the name of *Claas* known around the world.

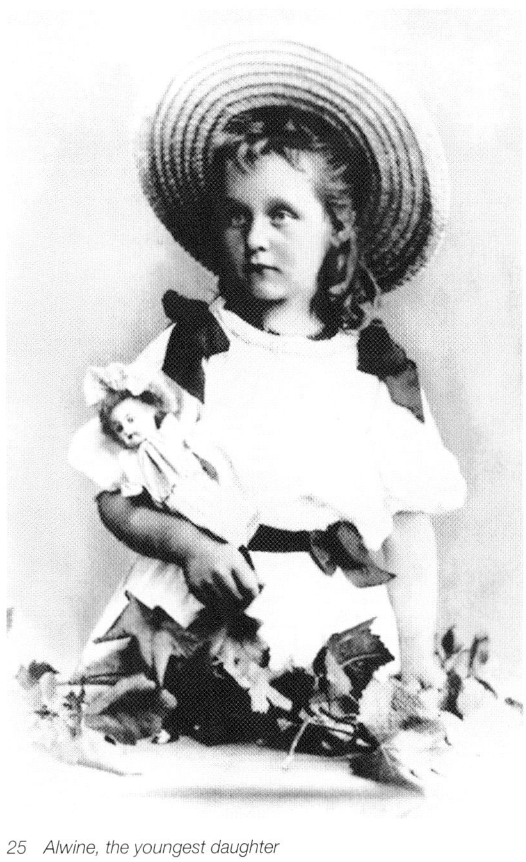

25 Alwine, the youngest daughter

PATENT-URKUNDE

Nr 130171.

GESETZ v. 7. APRIL 1891

AUF GRUND DER ANGEHEFTETEN PATENTSCHRIFT IST DURCH BESCHLUSS DES KAISERLICHEN PATENTAMTES

an Franz Claas in Clarholz i. W.

EIN PATENT ERTHEILT WORDEN.

GEGENSTAND DES PATENTES IST:

Ablegvorrichtung für Grasmähmaschinen zum Mähen von Getreide.

ANFANG DES PATENTES: 15. Juli 1900.

DIE RECHTE UND PFLICHTEN DES PATENTINHABERS SIND DURCH DAS PATENT-GESETZ VOM 7. APRIL 1891 (REICHS-GESETZBLATT FÜR 1891 SEITE 79) BESTIMMT.

ZU URKUND DER ERTHEILUNG DES PATENTES IST DIESE AUSFERTIGUNG ERFOLGT.

KAISERLICHES PATENTAMT.

26 Oldest surviving patent document from Franz Claas Senior

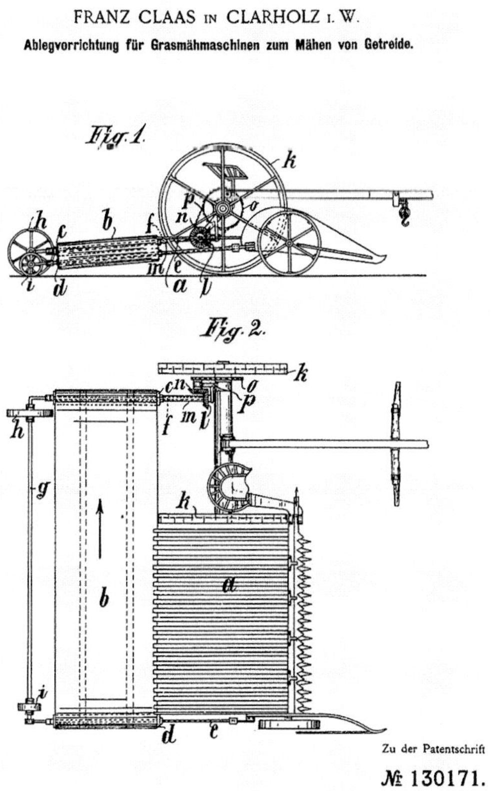

27 Diagrma of the laying device from Franz Claas' patent application – 15th of July 1900

recognition of his contribution to the centrifuge business.

At the end of the war, the *Claas brothers* all returned to the parental home safe and sound and concentrated on building up their fledgling company. They had saved up their soldier's pay and had amassed a reasonable working capital. They made a fortunate choice in buying up a defunct brick works in 1919, finally setting up their company founded in 1913 in the new location.

Their father was now able to indulge his passion for engineering, which had been so successful in the past. He took part actively in the company's rise to fame and was also happy to lend a hand. For instance he set up a big lead acid battery storage centre and not only cast the cell plates with the company electrician Wittenbrink but also assembled the cells.

When he died in 1928 aged 69 he knew perfectly that he had passed on his technical skills to his sons. Without doubt he enjoyed being part of his sons' success and being in Harsewinkel. This year was when August Claas made the statement "*Sonne über Harsewinkel*" – the sun over Harsewinkel. This emblem graced the inside cover of

August Claas set up his own business in 1913. In 1914 the company *Gebrüder Claas* (Claas Brothers) was registered in Rheda together with brothers Bernhard and Franz. War broke out shortly after and all three were called up immediately. The development of the trusser was put to one side for the duration. Even worse was that in their absence Franz Senior got into serious financial trouble and despite all his efforts lost his farm as a result.

The family moved then to Harsewinkel which was a small village at that time. It is located on the other side of the river Ems and has a history that goes back one thousand years. Theo meanwhile had found a new job in the *Briest* airplane company – later *Heinkel* – near to Brandenburg. He then moved on to *Rumpler Aircraft Works* in Berlin and then worked for a Berlin based bridge builder called *Hein & Lehmann* on a bridge project over the Wileica river near Vilnius in Lithuania before being called up finally in 1916.

Franz Claas Senior limited his activities to the animal healing side and this was more than enough to pay the bills. He turned down the support offered on behalf of the Centrifuge Manufacturers Guild by *Carl Miele* in Gütersloh in

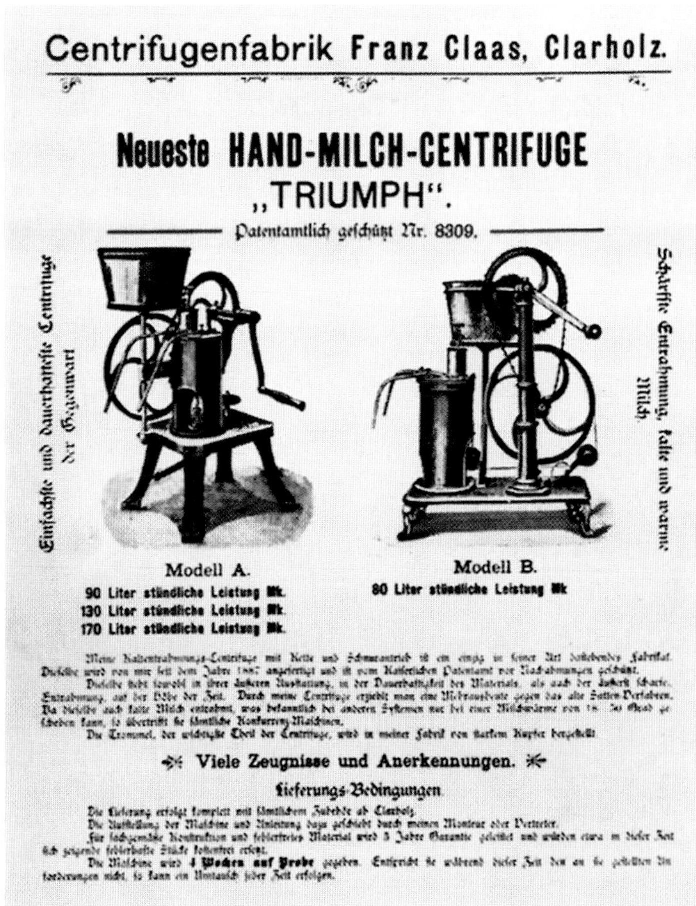

28 A selection of Claas centrifuges

29 "The sun over Harsewinkel", first cited by August Claas in 1928

the company paper (*der Knoter*) from the end of 1951 always accompanied by a preface written by the company boss.

Horst-Dieter Görg, Wilhelm Kemper

Sources:

Sonne über Harsewinkel, unpublished CLAAS company journal from Paula Claas and Walter Werland, Harsewinkel 1962

Der Knoter – company journal, volume 4 , Christmas 1953, 12th year, page 18

30 The Harsewinkel brick factory

The Claas Brothers pave the way for the first Combine Harvesters

31 Lanz Bulldog and Claas MDB at work

In 1913 August Claas formed a company to make straw trussers. This later turned into the Gebrüder Claas company – Claas Brothers – with the participation of his brothers Bernard, Franz Junior and some years later Theo. After the end of the First World War the purchase of the brick works in Harsewinkel was the basis for building up the company's activities commencing with straw trussers, balers and spreaders. The export business was launched on the back of reparation demands. The company became well known following granting of the knotter patent in 1921. In 1930 Professor Vormfelde gave Claas Brothers the required impetus to get going on the development of the first European combine harvester and binder which went into production seven years later. The real breakthrough into the combine business came to Claas after the Second World War with the pull type Super.

Foundation of the *Gebrüder Claas* company

The company we know today was founded originally by August Claas in 1913 after he had finished his education and military service. His brothers Bernhard and Franz joined him one year later. When Theo Claas joined them later *Claas Brothers* were complete and all were included on the list of owners of the company. The brick works in Harsewinkel were taken over in 1919 and a production plant for straw trussers was built there as well. Balers and spreaders were later added to the model range.

August Claas ended his active military service in 1909 as armoury master and rejoined his father's factory. In view of the financial trouble his father was in he felt it prudent to set up on his own in 1913 in Clarholz-Heerde. On the 7th of June 1913 he registered with the authorities "with the utmost respect a business with effect from the 8th of April 1913. I employ 2 mechanics, 1 assistant and produce straw trussers."

On the 12th of January 1914 the authorities were further informed that the company had become from then on *Gebrüder Claas*. It is unlikely that his mother was in favour of him taking on his brothers Bernard and Franz Junior in the new company which traded as an unlimited partnership. Theo Claas joined the ranks of the owners in 1935 when Bernard pulled out due to his lack of an heir.

Back in 1914 the brothers didn't have much time left to build up the business with the outbreak of war a few months later. August, Bernhard and Franz were called up and the firm was left on hold. During their absence there was nothing they could do to prevent the compulsory sale of their father's property in Heerde due to debts to a local farmer amounting to 85 Marks and to a local carpenter who was owed 196.30 Marks. The whole property went to a coal and wood dealer in nearby Warendorf for 50,000 Marks including both the complete inventory, both livestock and other objects.

Whilst the sons were at the front Maria Claas couldn't arrange a stay of trial at the Bielefeld county court. To this day it remains a mystery why such a paltry amount had to be claimed with such ferocity. The judge also followed the strange reasoning that it was impossible to tell whether the property to be sold compulsorily would achieve a higher price after the conclusion of the war and it was equally unclear if the three sons would come back intact.

In later years August Claas would often refer back to these nasty circumstances for the family, a sign that they had left an indelible impression on him. Theo was called up in 1916 and when

32 The Claas brothers around 1950: Theo, Franz, August and Bernhard (from left to right)

they all returned safe and sound from the war, it was typical for August that his only interest was the future and so he rolled up his sleeves and began to breathe life back into the company.

An old brick works in Harsewinkel

Franz Claas's brother-in-law August Prövestmann arranged the move to nearby Harsewinkel, where they rented a house at Gütersloher Landstrasse 266. There stood an abandoned brickworks and a site of 1,500 m2 just outside town on the way to Greffen. August Claas judged this to be suited for the planned new venture and it was bought for 13,000 Marks on the 7th of July 1919. Their first order came from the former owner – Weserhütte – for dismantling the installations not included in the transaction.

August Claas acquired a next-to-new drilling machine from his former comrade-in-arms, Hans Petznick. Then two lathes were added, gauges, a plane, a milling machine and a band saw which enabled them to produce the whole straw trusser themselves. The three threshing units rescued from the Heerde liquidation auction were reconditioned and everything, apart from a steam engine needed to drive machines in the plant, was sold. The income was used to buy more machine tools and raw materials to fill up the first of the newly erected assembly buildings.

August Claas had sold a straw trusser to *Reesink*, a farm equipment dealer, in Zytphen in Holland prior to the First World War. Later the first exports from Harsewinkel were another two trussers to the same customer. They were already fitted with the improved knotter with the moveable lip designed by August Claas which had been registered for a patent in Germany and abroad. *Reesink* paid promptly in Dutch Guilders, a welcome income because of the rampant inflation in Germany.

New products ensure growth

With the expansion of trusser production using the high reliability knotter, the imports from England ground to a halt. In other markets too, like France, Holland, Belgium and Switzerland, the brothers were able to win market share against the English competitors. Business was so brisk that they couldn't supply enough machines for a while. The knotters were sold on their own to dealers and repair shops who could promise Claas tying quality for other brands of trusser.

Handwerkskammer zu Bielefeld.

Prüfungs-Zeugnis.

Der Lehrling Aug. Claas
geboren am 15 Dezember 1887
in Clarholz Kreis Wiedenbrück
hat bei dem Herrn Franz Claas
wohnhaft zu Clarholz
das Maschinen-Schlosser Handwerk
in 3 Jahren vom 2 Januar 1901
bis 2 Januar 1904 ordnungsmäßig erlernt.
Betragen: gut

Nachdem der August Claas
am heutigen Tage vor dem unterzeichneten Prüfungsausschuß seine Gesellenprüfung im
Maschinen-Schlosser
genügend
bestanden, ist dieses
Prüfungs-Zeugnis
ausgefertigt und wird demselben mit den besten Glückwünschen für seinen ferneren Lebensweg hiermit eingehändigt.
Gütersloh den 4 Oktober 1907
Der Prüfungsausschuß für das Handwerk
G. Horstmann
Vorsitzender.
Meisterbeisitzer. Gesellenbeisitzer.
Aug. Claas
Eigenhändige Unterschrift des Inhabers.

33 Exam certificate from August Claas, 1907, certification as a qualified mechanic

August Claas said later: "advertising can play tricks with you. After the First World War I advertised parts for English trussers. We got so many orders we could only satisfy a fraction of the demand".

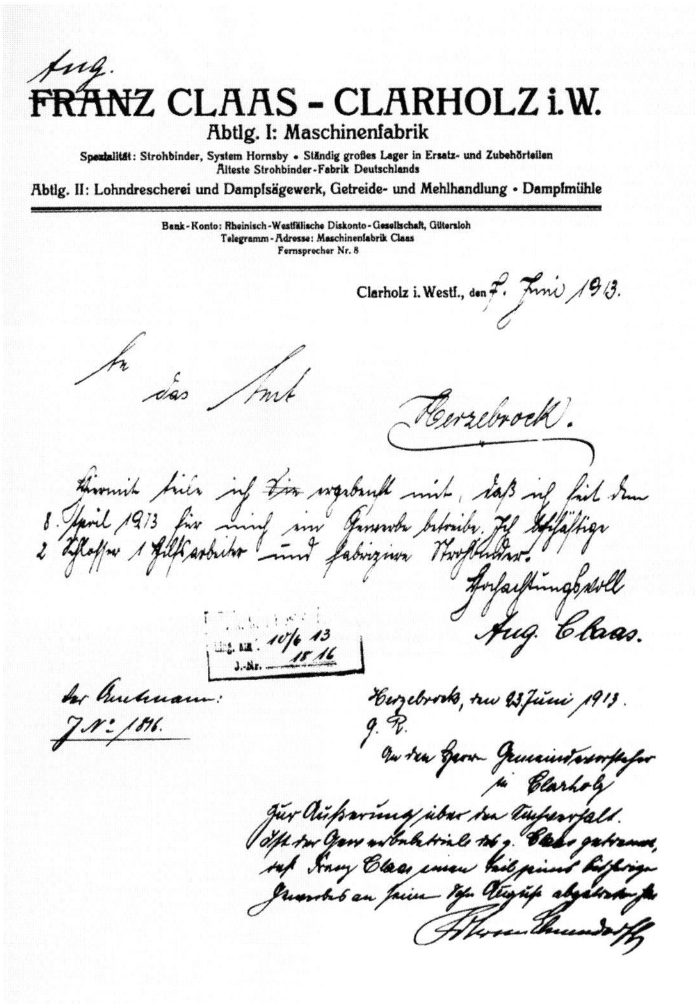
Aug.
FRANZ CLAAS - CLARHOLZ i.W.
Abtlg. I: Maschinenfabrik
Spezialität: Strohbinder, System Hornsby • Ständig großes Lager in Ersatz- und Zubehörteilen
Älteste Strohbinder-Fabrik Deutschlands
Abtlg. II: Lohndrescherei und Dampfsägewerk, Getreide- und Mehlhandlung • Dampfmühle
Bank-Konto: Rheinisch-Westfälische Diskonto-Gesellschaft, Gütersloh
Telegramm-Adresse: Maschinenfabrik Claas
Fernsprecher Nr. 8

Clarholz i. Westf., den 7. Juni 1913.

An das Amt Herzebrock.

Hochachtungsvoll
Aug. Claas.

Herzebrock, den 23 Juni 1913.

34 Company registration using father's letterhead in 1913

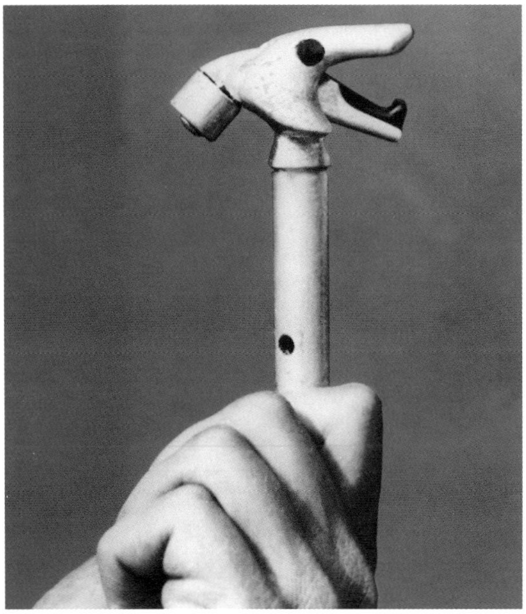

35 The patented knotter became the trade make and made Claas a familiar name round the world

War reparation contracts which came in from 1922 explain the early dominance of the company, especially in France. They boosted turnover and increased the profitability of the young company. The order quotas which were released by the government also went to companies which couldn't produce trussers and Claas then picked up even more business. Machinery and buildings had to be enlarged and the company managed to survive the period of chronic inflation since the expansion was carried out without going into debt.

Gebrüder Claas took up the production of fertiliser spreaders in 1923 and were granted a patent one year later. They were introduced as a completely new product in 1924 and sold in large numbers. In 1929 and 1930, despite the world depression, over 4,000 machines were sold and the patents registered in several European countries.

The evolution of the straw trusser led to the introduction of straw balers at the end of the 1920s and they officially became part of the product range in 1931. This gave the company another pillar to build on, in particular for the export business which accounted for 48 % of production and strengthened progress until the Second World War.

The pick-up balers for gathering and loading hay were introduced in 1934 and over one thousand had been sold in Germany by the time production had to be halted in 1942 with exports going far over the European borders to Canada and New Zealand.

The headcount in 1924 was just 45, and had climbed to 361 on the 15th of October 1935, the date on which the 20,000th *Claas* machine was built, the model "Westfalen". A year later 402 people were working there and on the 23rd of October 1937 another jump to 453 is recorded. The production start of the MDB combine in

36 The old brick works with the four new Claas production buildings

1936 contributed to keeping everyone busy at that time. By the way, these exact dates and numbers come from company festivals which took place until 1939. In May of that year there were 520 people on the *Claas* payroll. August Claas announced that he had set up a pension and dependents' fund with effect from December 1st 1938 for all employees.

Sand dunes to bricks

As the size of the factory grew and grew, in particular with the advent of combine production, the sand dunes surrounding the factory became an obstacle. *Gebrüder Claas* made a virtue of necessity and erected their own brick works in 1937 which started operations in autumn of the same year. The sand was used to produce the bricks whilst at the same time clearing the space for further expansion. Probably it wasn't thought of as a long term activity, but brick production kept going till 1958, no doubt as a consequence of the Second World War.

Company festivals ceased with the outbreak of war and many employees were called up. They were kept informed about their company and home with a circular sent to the front from

38 *Sand was loaded on wagons pulled by locomotives and brought to the brick works, around 1938*

October 1939. In October 1942 this was given the title of the *Knoter*, which became the house journal and survived until the 1970s and was then in turn superseded by *CLAAS Intern.*

Horst-Dieter Görg
Wilhelm Kemper

Sources:

Sonne über Harsewinkel, unpublished CLAAS company chronicle by Paula Claas and Walter Werland, Harsewinkel 1962

Knoter, the house journal number 4, Christmas 1953, volume 12, page 18

37 *August and Paula Claas with their children Helmut, Irmgard and Reinhold (from left to right)*

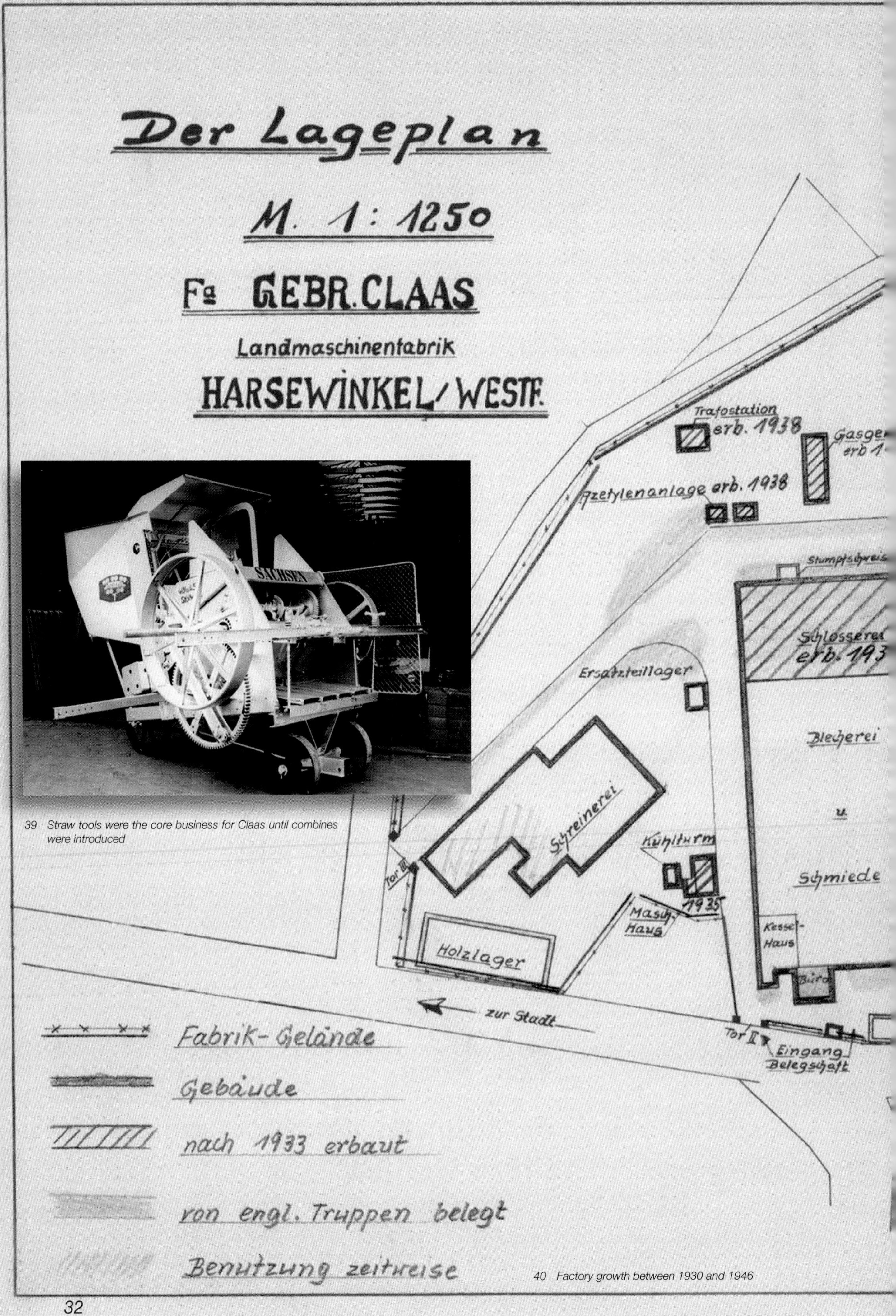

39 Straw tools were the core business for Claas until combines were introduced

40 Factory growth between 1930 and 1946

41 The newly erected brick works in the winter of 1941

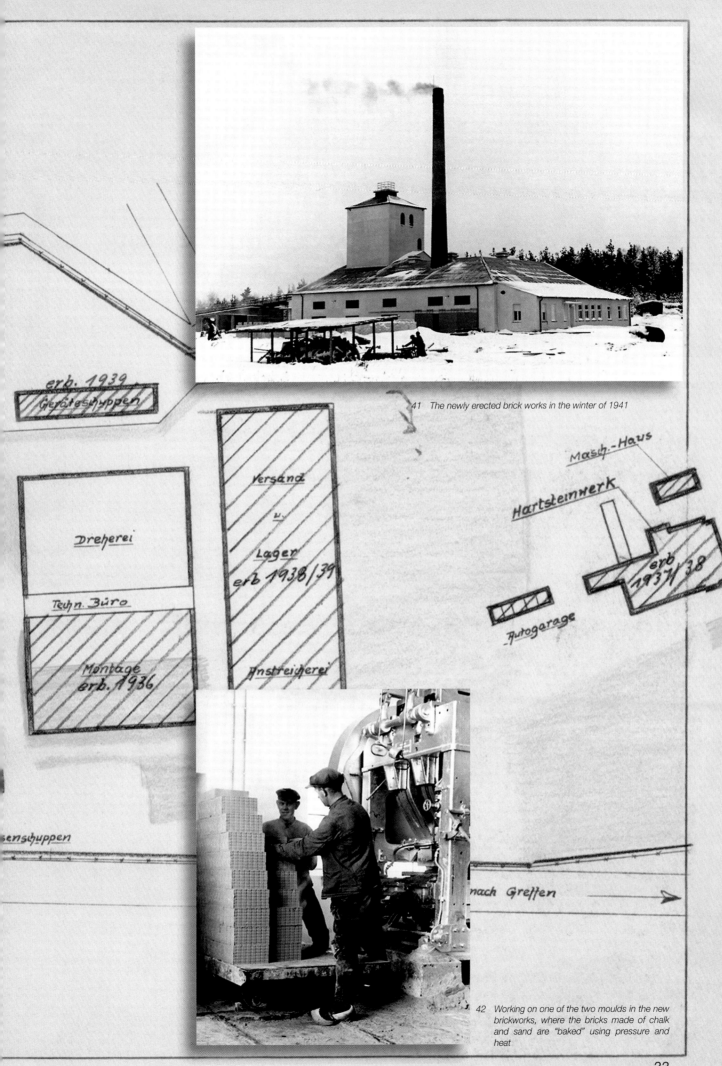

erb. 1939
Geräteschuppen
Versand
u.
Lager
erb 1938/39
Dreherei
Techn. Büro
Montage
erb. 1936
Anstreicherei
Masch.-Haus
Hartsteinwerk
erb 1937/38
Autogarage
nach Greffen

42 Working on one of the two moulds in the new brickworks, where the bricks made of chalk and sand are "baked" using pressure and heat

Trussers and Straw Balers

August Claas began in 1920 with the production of straw trussers. They turned out to be a big success, underpinning the financial foundations for sustained growth of the company. In 1922 fertiliser spreaders were added and then straw balers as the need for new farming solutions spread. The reparation programme following the 1918 defeat actually helped the company by creating many contacts for them around Europe. The willingness to look far and wide for business became part of the company way of life whilst technical prowess as witnessed by the knotter patents starting in 1921 ensured an innovative attitude from early on.

43 This photo commemorates the 3,000th trusser

From the first days of the company in 1913 the *Claas* company was involved in keeping the tying devices going on competitive products such as *Hornsby* and *Massey Harris* with the reliable technology the founders had pioneered. In fact the need for improved knotter reliability was heightened by the war, because the twine quality got steadily worse. August Claas came up with creative solutions through keen observation and dogged persistence.

Professor Karl Vormfelde, another visionary of the time, reported how he had observed the new knotter in action on a farm in Schildesche near Bielefeld in 1922 and followed it up with in-depth and endurance tests for the DLG. His comprehensive report explains how the *Claas knotter* worked impeccably with the worst imaginable twine qualities made of different natural fibres. This was a big issue in this period so the DLG carried out a trusser test in 1924 in Klein-Wansleben (East Germany) with nine participants including *Claas*. The eagerly awaited test results were announced during the DLG autumn conference by government advisor Professor Gustav Fischer who summed it up as follows: "the knotter from *Gebrüder Claas* in Harsewinkel is superior to all the others because it can use very fine twine as well as the thick stuff. This knotter is a major step forward with far ranging consequences for improved economics."

In view of the importance of this solution to farmers of the time it is easy to imagine how this news spread amongst the scientific and farming community. It translated into a major sales success with over 1,000 competitive trussers being fitted with *Claas* knotters by 1926. Then as now competitive efforts to copy the technology had to be protected by patent and this included the following innovations which were first registered – patent number 372140 in 1921 protected the twine clasping and cutting device, in 1923 patent number 412212 was approved and covered the legendary *Claas* knotter hook. What made this so special was the swivelling upper lip which enabled the tongue to move freely between the upper and lower lip whilst the knot was being thrown into place. This additional upper lip made it possible to handle different twine diameters without difficulty.

Patent number 460771 in 1926 was concerned with the twine squeezer which positioned the twine securely so it could be picked up cleanly by the knotter hook. From then on, further refinements were not needed and so the basic principles have remained unchanged to this day, despite higher throughputs, increased baling pressures and new operating conditions. These technical demands led for instance to the installation of two twine deflectors on the twine clasping wheel to improve the twine holding power. The knotter hook was beefed up for handling synthetic twine of up to 130 m/kg. Ruggedness and durability were enhanced by switching over to a majority of cast components.

For the first time *Claas* had solved a problem that had been a major preoccupation for farmers and stayed true to this problem-solving philosophy from then on.

Straw Trussers

Processing of the straw coming from the threshing machine was very hard work. Either the straw was stored loose or sorted by hand and tied. The need to reduce labour in the harvest was understood by Franz Claas who saw a market opportunity and decided to build a straw trusser in 1896.

The layout of the early straw trusser was similar to the reaper / trusser of that time in terms of design and function. The trusser was placed directly behind the threshing machine and was driven by the same unit. The straw dropped off the straw walkers into a funnel, was then grabbed by packer tines on a crankshaft which pulled it into the trussing chamber against the packing levers. The bundle was tied when the set size was reached, the knotter shaft made one turn with the needles moving up, first wrapping the bundle and then into the knotter. Once tied the finished bundle was ejected.

Whilst the first production run was in 1920 the real breakthrough only came in 1924 with the improved knotter, the validation by the DLG and awarding of a silver medal. The highest production volume was reached in 1929 with 2,960 units. Customers then as now appreciated the numerous features of the *Claas* product – value for money, high output, faultless tying reliability and energy efficiency with less than one horse power needed. In addition there was a broad product range with six different models in different outputs and widths, with single or dual tying. From 1931 a new technology superseded the trusser – the straw baler quickly cannibalised the sales of the trusser and finally replaced it completely.

Straw Balers

Not content with having the straw bound up tight, farmers were asking for more – more density and more consistent size. The straw baler was the answer and came onto the market in 1931. These balers were also set up separately at the exit of the threshing machine. Now the straw and chaff dropped onto the feed platform with rakes fitted either above or below the platform. They fed the straw evenly to the ram fitted in the baling channel and packed the straw densely, saving valuable storage space in the process.

The added features appealed to customers who appreciated the extra bale density and working speed. They responded by buying, so the production reached up to 3600 balers a year at its peak. Fifteen different models were on offer with channel widths from 0.85 to 1.6 metres and single, dual and triple knotters.

44 Cross section of a straw baler

In 1952 an integral baler for threshing machines with 1 to 1.5 metre channel width was introduced. This made it much easier to transport the traditional threshing machine, which was in turn reaching the end of its life cycle and was soon to make way completely to the combine harvester.

These early balers could be fitted with straw cutters in the feed area on an optional basis. With an extension slide the bales could be placed on the straw storage floor up to 4 metres high and at a distance of 15 metres. The output had now reached up to 4 tons of straw an hour, and the power required had gone up to 5 hp, although the density was very low in comparison with today.

When the combine harvester took over, integral lightweight balers could be fitted to them. They had 0.7 to 1 metre width and many early combines were so equipped, but this too faded with time as baling density continued to rise. Therefore their production at *Claas* ceased at the end of the 1960s.

Gerhard Clostermeyer

45 The slogan rhymes in German and suggests that "CLAAS tying reliability has world renown"

Birth of the First Combine

It was thanks to Professor Karl Vormfelde that *Claas* took up the development of the combine harvester in 1930 in the first place. The professor managed to convince August Claas that it was the right time to create a combine for European conditions and it says a lot about the entrepreneurial spirit of the founder that he was prepared to take on a venture of this magnitude. Dr. Walter Brenner came and joined him on the project as an assistant in Harsewinkel and with August Claas set about building the first combine in Germany. The rocky road took six years to complete. Only then did the dream became reality and the first successful field test went into the history books as the "Victory of Zschernitz" near Halle in East Germany in 1936. Accompanied by an exemplary customer satisfaction programme over one thousand combines were put into service before war broke out again three years later.

There were just 16 combine harvesters in the whole of Germany in 1928, most of which had been imported from the USA. Professor Vormfelde was an academic at the Agricultural College in Bonn and despite the overwhelming majority of informed opinion he was convinced that the combine had a future in Germany. He had reached this conclusion on the basis of world cereals export statistics which indicated that the export volume in the USA and Canada, Argentina and Australia had doubled to 28 million tons on average between 1925 and 1927 in comparison with pre-war levels[1]. He had deduced that this was due to increases in mechanisation, in particular the huge growth in the combine fleet and its beneficial impact on other factors including expanding the total area under cultivation. Professor Vormfelde tried to gain support from the larger German farm equipment manufacturers early in 1930 without raising much interest. In a talk to his assistant, Dr. Brenner, he then concluded that "we can forget the big companies, we'll ask the smaller ones. The *Claas brothers*, for instance, because the second eldest – August Claas – seems to be the right sort of person for us. August Claas is an optimist, he is very tenacious and doesn't shrink from taking risks". This is a strong indication that *Claas*, with its commercial and technical skills, had already made a good name for itself at this early stage in its development[2].

The creation of the first *Claas* combine is closely linked with the name of Walter Brenner. He was born in 1899 in Bavaria and then made the move north to Harsewinkel in 1930, based on a recommendation by Professor Vormfelde. His first effort appeared in 1932 in the form of a front cutting combine prototype which was demonstrated by invitation to other manufacturers on a nearby farm. This demonstration was a flop and the machine constantly came to a stop, so the guests drew their own conclusions and interest waned. August Claas also drew his own conclusions which confirm his fighting spirit and became part of the company philosophy for many decades: "If the others don't want to get involved, then we'll do it on our own".

46 to 48 The "parents" of the Claas combine (from left to right): Professor Walter Gustav Brenner, Doctor of Engineering, 1899 to 1973, August Claas 1887 to 1982 and Professor Karl Vormfelde, Doctor of Engineering 1881 to 1944

Walter Brenner documented his *Claas* memories for the 75th birthday of the founding father – August Claas – and this is a superb contemporary report on this most decisive phase of the company's development. Walter Brenner was the leading figure in the combine saga for over 25 years. Here's an excerpt: "*like everything else that becomes big, the beginnings of combine production and development were for us very small and hesitant. In the first years (1932 to 1934) we only brought out one or two trial machines which more or less worked so we could learn from them. In this first period we experimented with the basic threshing drum because this was uncharted territory at that time. We fed the drums from a 25 metre long belt and this gave us precise values similar to real threshing. This taught us a lot and gradually we could start discovering the relationships between throughput, fuel consumption, threshing efficiency and the best threshing drum design. Our objective was to make a small and low cost combine for our farmers to harvest local fields and the MDB turned out to be the right direction.*"

Once again the persistence of the company's founder paid off when most others would have given up. This is especially true in the face of failure with the front cutter bar prototype, although this design pre-empted many of the features that would later be used in self propelled combines. Walter Brenner and his helpers concentrated on the theme of a pull type combine from around 1935, inspired no doubt by the trends in North America. That same year the *Claas* R & D team was strengthened with the arrival of Erich Harmening who became the assistant of Walter Brenner. Before long the MDB (which means mower – thresher – binder) had taken shape, a revolutionary concept which accomplished all the tasks in one go in European type conditions. Testing facilities were very basic and much of the trial work was done in the surrounding fields and went on until darkness fell. August Claas would often go out and visit the testing team on his bike. This way the day's problems could be discussed and fixes worked out for the next step. Brenner and Harmening would have new parts built in the workshop the next day and the testing would continue.[3] This early form of simultaneous engineering became part of the company culture from then on.

The Victory of Zschernitz

The farm belonging to the Haberland family in Zschernitz close to Halle in the eastern part of Germany was where the final showdown took place. At last the new *MDB* combine came up

49 Photos of the first prototype ...

to expectations and production could begin. The MDB was later promoted as the machine that "does it all in one go" based on the "Dr. Brenner principle".[4] From now on the experts began to be impressed by the results. It reaped like a reaper, it threshed as well as a stationary thresher, it bound up the straw, cleaned the grain in two stages, disawned it and separated the chaff. The bundles of straw could be gathered and the MDB could be driven economically from the PTO of any normal tractor with no auxiliary engine required. The price was competitive and the performance matched that of the big American combines. Cost of operation was a leading factor in gaining acceptance for the new harvesting concept and the break even point was set at 62.5 hectares (slightly over 150 acres) with a work rate claimed by the factory of 5 hectares in 10 hours, a remarkable feat for this time.

A combination of factors helped the combine to take off successfully. In particular the unemployment of the depression had turned into a chronic lack of manpower for harvesting jobs, so the MDB was a godsend for the large fields which even then were a feature of the large

50 ... and field trials in Harsewinkel

51 The combine's victory at Zschernitz, 1936 ....

barley and wheat farms in the centre of the country. It took just three men to harvest 30 and even 40 tons of cereals a day with a single tractor and MDB combination. In the first harvest 420 tons were harvested and with more experience and technical improvements this went up to 510 tons a year later. The crops in Germany were dense and often laid flat and the MDB had been designed to cope with laid crops. The crop lifters had been borrowed from the reaper and ensured a clean crop entry into the machine. The ears which fell off went into the threshing drum and weren't left on the field as was usual, so losses were reduced.

The farm of Walter Haberland became a tourist attraction for other farmers who came from far and wide to see what the fuss was all about. He reported that "the farmers from the whole region came in droves to see the *Claas* combine harvesting method. It was new, fast and reliable." The new dimension in harvesting had also caught the eye of the regional press as this excerpt

53 ... and the second victory with another combine in 1938

from the weekly farming magazine in Sachsen - Anhalt demonstrates: "*the first MDB was put into service in Zschernitz in 1936. This combine harvester is a very cost effective machine for farmers who are trying to achieve higher yields, bringing the factors labour, teams, twine and repairs into balance. The MDB with the trailed chaff container needs a 38 hp Bulldog so, in addition to the tractor driver, two men are need on the combine and another two for transport of the chaff and wheat*". Articles like this became quite common. Since they were based on real experience the name of Claas soon emerged as a leader and MDB sales developed very positively. The Haberland family became an enthusiastic early adopter and by 1940 they had put another three machines into service. They harvested in close formation, maybe the first to do so.

52 MDB "new era" colour brochure in 1938

54 ... and was suitably toasted by the teams

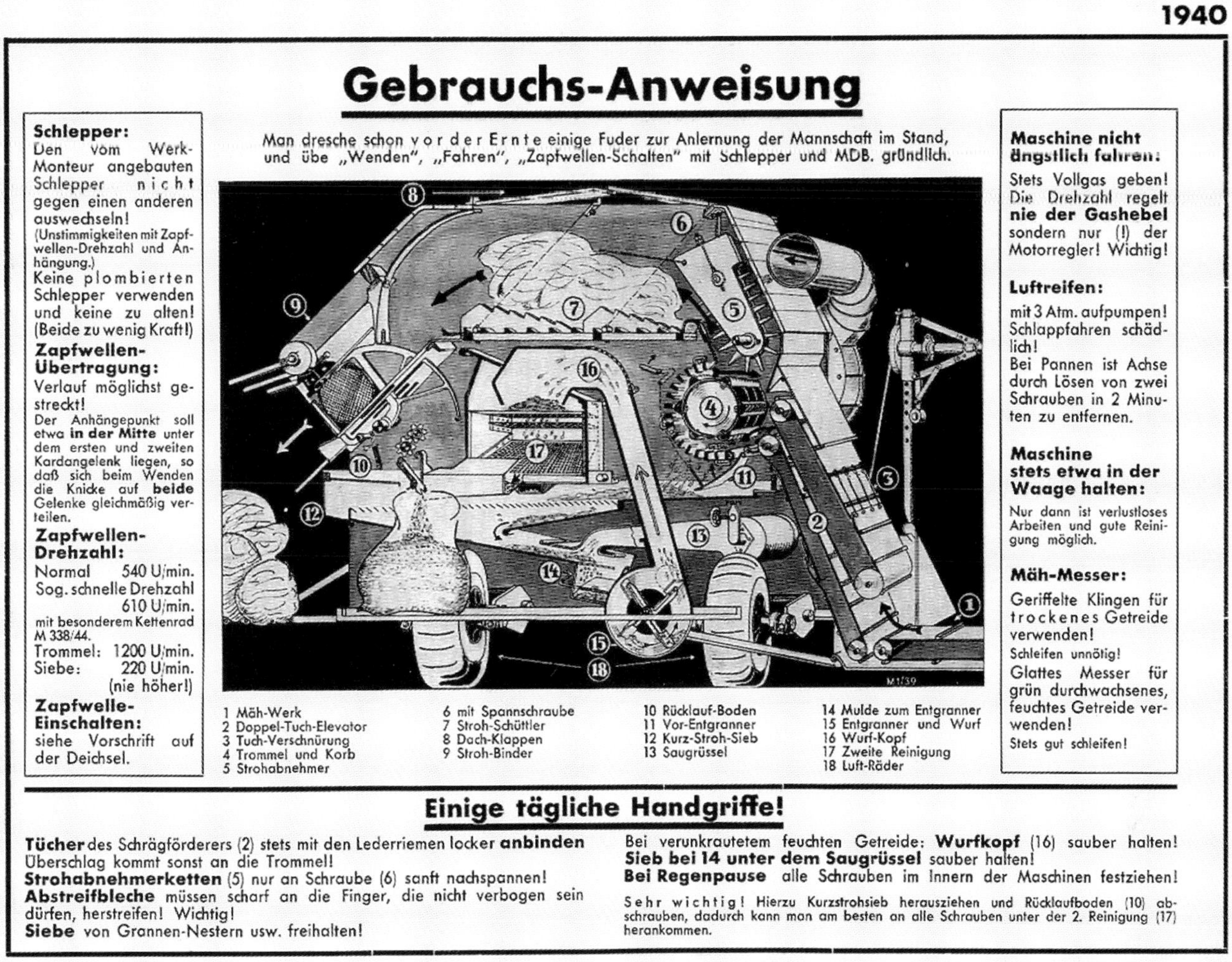

1940

Gebrauchs-Anweisung

Schlepper:
Den vom Werk-Monteur angebauten Schlepper n i c h t gegen einen anderen auswechseln!
(Unstimmigkeiten mit Zapfwellen-Drehzahl und Anhängung.)
Keine p l o m b i e r t e n Schlepper verwenden und keine zu alten! (Beide zu wenig Kraft!)

Zapfwellen-Übertragung:
Verlauf möglichst gestreckt!
Der Anhängepunkt soll etwa **in der Mitte** unter dem ersten und zweiten Kardangelenk liegen, so daß sich beim Wenden die Knicke auf **beide** Gelenke gleichmäßig verteilen.

Zapfwellen-Drehzahl:
Normal 540 U/min.
Sog. schnelle Drehzahl 610 U/min.
mit besonderem Kettenrad M 338/44.
Trommel: 1200 U/min.
Siebe: 220 U/min. (nie höher!)

Zapfwelle-Einschalten:
siehe Vorschrift auf der Deichsel.

Man dresche schon v o r d e r E r n t e einige Fuder zur Anlernung der Mannschaft im Stand, und übe „Wenden", „Fahren", „Zapfwellen-Schalten" mit Schlepper und MDB. gründlich.

1 Mäh-Werk
2 Doppel-Tuch-Elevator
3 Tuch-Verschnürung
4 Trommel und Korb
5 Strohabnehmer
6 mit Spannschraube
7 Stroh-Schüttler
8 Dach-Klappen
9 Stroh-Binder
10 Rücklauf-Boden
11 Vor-Entgranner
12 Kurz-Stroh-Sieb
13 Saugrüssel
14 Mulde zum Entgranner
15 Entgranner und Wurf
16 Wurf-Kopf
17 Zweite Reinigung
18 Luft-Räder

Maschine nicht ängstlich fahren:
Stets Vollgas geben! Die Drehzahl regelt **nie der Gashebel** sondern nur (!) der Motorregler! Wichtig!

Luftreifen:
mit 3 Atm. aufpumpen! Schlappfahren schädlich!
Bei Pannen ist Achse durch Lösen von zwei Schrauben in 2 Minuten zu entfernen.

Maschine stets etwa in der Waage halten:
Nur dann ist verlustloses Arbeiten und gute Reinigung möglich.

Mäh-Messer:
Geriffelte Klingen für t r o c k e n e s Getreide verwenden!
Schleifen unnötig!
Glattes Messer für grün durchwachsenes, feuchtes Getreide verwenden!
Stets gut schleifen!

Einige tägliche Handgriffe!

Tücher des Schrägförderers (2) stets mit den Lederriemen locker **anbinden** Überschlag kommt sonst an die Trommel!
Strohabnehmerketten (5) nur an Schraube (6) sanft nachspannen!
Abstreifbleche müssen scharf an die Finger, die nicht verbogen sein dürfen, herstreifen! Wichtig!
Siebe von Grannen-Nestern usw. freihalten!

Bei verunkrautetem feuchten Getreide: **Wurfkopf** (16) sauber halten!
Sieb bei 14 unter dem Saugrüssel sauber halten!
Bei Regenpause alle Schrauben im Innern der Maschinen festziehen!

S e h r w i c h t i g ! Hierzu Kurzstrohsieb herausziehen und Rücklaufboden (10) abschrauben, dadurch kann man am besten an alle Schrauben unter der 2. Reinigung (17) herankommen.

55 MDB cross section and quick user guide

Inevitably there were the prophets of doom who called the combine a stillborn child. Walter Brenner wanted to respond with counter arguments but was held back by August Claas, whose strategic point of view was rather different: "we'll do nothing because as long as this well known professor continues to run down our combine, nobody else will risk building a combine themselves. That way we keep the market to ourselves".[5]

The success of the MDB came only after many years full of obstacles. The front mounted cutter bar version fitted around a *Lanz Bulldog* was, for instance, a dead end because it was too awkward to handle. The cutting unit had to be removed to use the tractor again and this was very complicated. In his recollections Vormfelde wrote that he, Walter Brenner and August Claas realised this but none of them wanted to be the first to give in.

Walter Brenner and August Claas made a visit to the world fair in Chicago in 1933 at which Allis Chalmers exhibited a trailed combine. A further trip to an agricultural show in Paris at which they looked over the prototype of a French pull type combine by *Guillotin* – it never made it to production – made up their minds and a change of direction was agreed. The simplicity of hooking up the combine behind the tractor was the decisive reason. August conferred with brother Theo and *Claas* was on the right road at last.

During the design phase the acceptance of the new technology was cast into doubt repeatedly because there were six million people out of work at the time in Germany. The cost and risk of the venture lead to controversy inside the company as well. August Claas wouldn't be blown off course with his belief that things would improve as the economy picked up again. The historical events of that time proved him right as the construction and rearmament programmes instituted by the Third Reich transformed the employment situation, virtually overnight. The big farms in the centre and east of the country found themselves confronted by a serious shortage of manpower. The timing of the introduction of the MDB couldn't have come at a better time as the product was perfectly suited to the prevailing conditions. By 1939, the first hundred machines had gone into service and

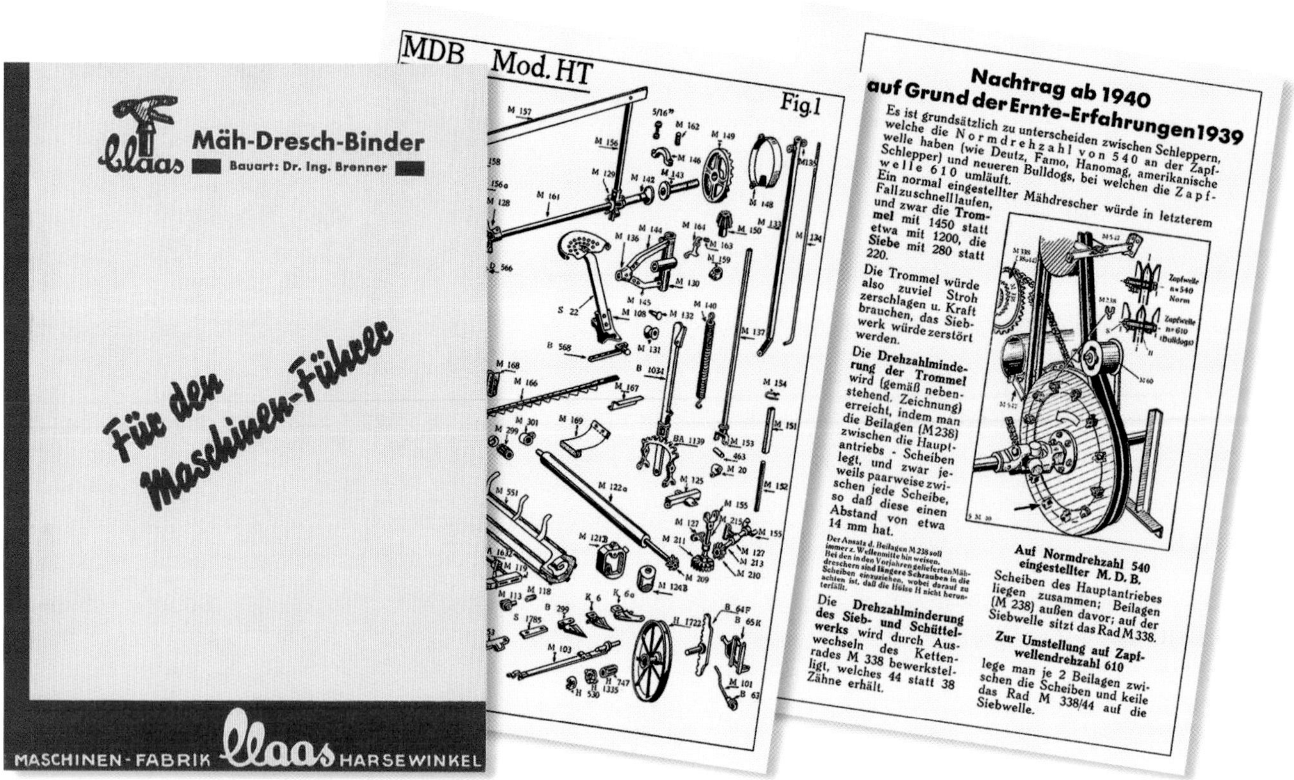

56 Operator's manual, parts list and update information

when production was forced to a stop in 1943, 1,400 MDB had been built. Some 1,000 of these were in Germany, the rest had been exported.

Even in the 1930s the company had paid attention to the needs of the neighbouring countries and so we still find evidence of English and French promotional material from that time as well as the order documentation to these countries. The promotional message was the encouragement of the "opening of a new era of cereals harvesting in Europe".

All round capability

The development team hadn't just designed the basic machine but had looked at all eventualities – an early example of a systems approach in harvesting. A long list of extras was made available for the MDB including a stationary version, sheaf gatherer, sack ramp, dual wheel fork with pneumatic tyres, pneumatic tyred chaff container and even compensation for working across slopes of up to 10 %. These were the HT models. (HT stood for high and low).

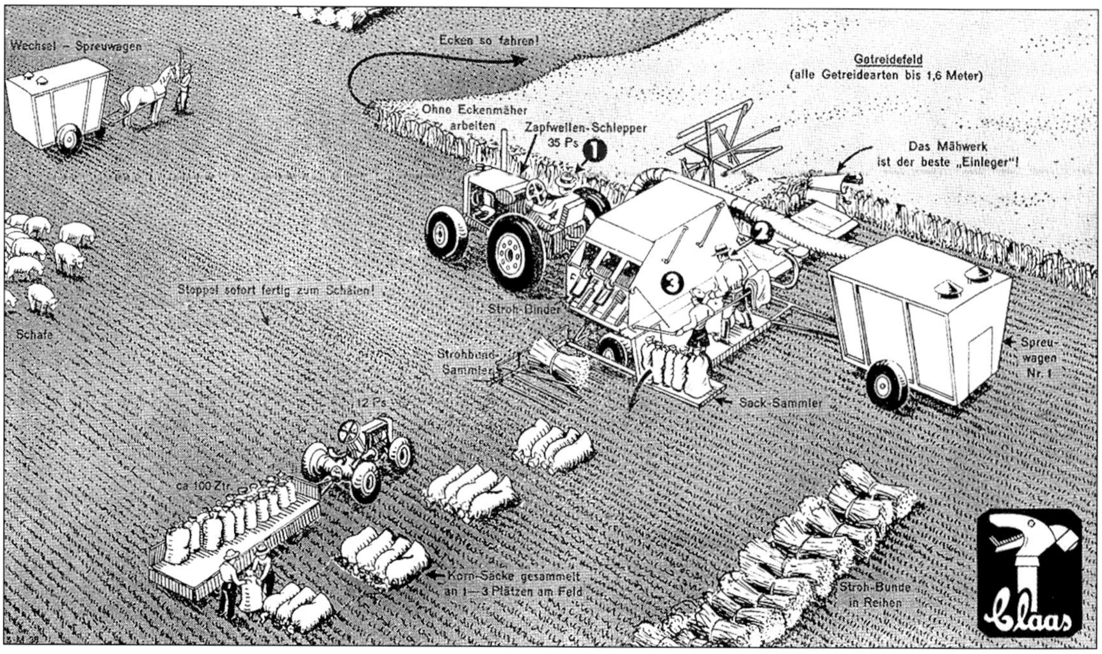

57 Illustration of correct utilisation of the MDB

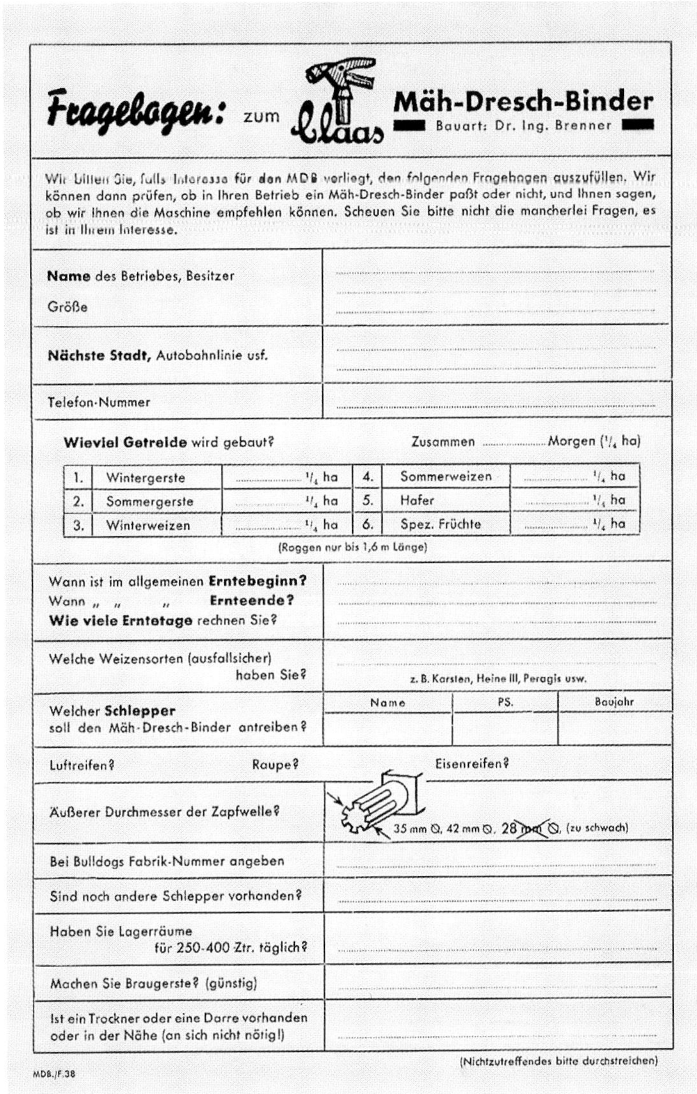

Fragebogen: zum Claas **Mäh-Dresch-Binder**
Bauart: Dr. Ing. Brenner

Wir bitten Sie, falls Interesse für den MDB vorliegt, den folgenden Fragebogen auszufüllen. Wir können dann prüfen, ob in Ihren Betrieb ein Mäh-Dresch-Binder paßt oder nicht, und Ihnen sagen, ob wir Ihnen die Maschine empfehlen können. Scheuen Sie bitte nicht die mancherlei Fragen, es ist in Ihrem Interesse.

Name des Betriebes, Besitzer Größe	
Nächste Stadt, Autobahnlinie usf.	
Telefon-Nummer	

Wieviel Getreide wird gebaut? Zusammen .... Morgen (1/4 ha)

1.	Wintergerste	.... 1/4 ha	4.	Sommerweizen	.... 1/4 ha
2.	Sommergerste	.... 1/4 ha	5.	Hafer	.... 1/4 ha
3.	Winterweizen	.... 1/4 ha	6.	Spez. Früchte	.... 1/4 ha

(Roggen nur bis 1,6 m Länge)

Wann ist im allgemeinen **Erntebeginn?** Wann " " " **Ernteende?** **Wie viele Erntetage** rechnen Sie?			
Welche Weizensorten (ausfallsicher) haben Sie?	z. B. Karsten, Heine III, Peragis usw.		
Welcher **Schlepper** soll den Mäh-Dresch-Binder antreiben?	Name	PS.	Baujahr
Luftreifen? Raupe?	Eisenreifen?		
Äußerer Durchmesser der Zapfwelle?	35 mm ⌀, 42 mm ⌀, 28 ~~mm~~ ⌀, (zu schwach)		
Bei Bulldogs Fabrik-Nummer angeben			
Sind noch andere Schlepper vorhanden?			
Haben Sie Lagerräume für 250-400 Ztr. täglich?			
Machen Sie Braugerste? (günstig)			
Ist ein Trockner oder eine Darre vorhanden oder in der Nähe (an sich nicht nötig!)			

MDB./F.38 (Nichtzutreffendes bitte durchstreichen)

58 *Application questionnaire in 1938*

This demonstrates the customer focus of the company from its earliest days, and this strength has given *Claas* the edge ever since. At exhibitions the aim wasn't just to sell a machine, the customer was interviewed to make sure that the conditions were suitable for the new technology. Whilst this type of application analysis is common nowadays, it was a revolutionary sales method back in the 1930s.

The questionnaire on the right provided the company with a customer harvesting profile whilst another one brought in right after the product's introduction requested customer feedback on experience and evaluation to enable improvements to be made. The customer satisfaction survey was born and also helped convince other farmers to join the club. The example of the Haberland family mentioned earlier was just one testimonial from many satisfied customers who came back repeatedly for more equipment.

Another smart idea was to routinely dispatch a *Claas* fitter to train the combine team on correct MDB operation and he would stay until everything was running to the customer's satisfaction. This was a vital step in assuring acceptance of the brand new technology and was supplemented by operator courses in the winter months to refresh their knowledge prior to the new season. The customer was issued with a comprehensive instruction guide and parts lists which were regularly updated with reports on new harvest experience, some examples of which are illustrated on these pages. What would now be called the loyalty programme was contained in a well illustrated book with information on every step from the machine's arrival, transfer from the rail station, set up, service, repairs and accessories plus winter storage. Then, prior to the outbreak of war, *Claas* offered incentives for the machinery teams to encourage them to get the most of their combine. Good results were rewarded with money prizes in varying amounts. Alongside brilliant technology Marketing ideas that were revolutionary in their time have always featured in the success story of the company.

Even the workmanlike appearance of the *Claas* fitters and engineers in the field was done for a reason - they were not there to give advice and stay warm and dry in the dust free zone, they had the task of getting the machine going however bad the conditions were.

Walter Brenner summed up the MDB as follows: "*the Claas MDB is not a magical tool that can transform a badly run farm into a well run one. It's also not a machine which will make the reaper and threshing machine obsolete at a stroke. However when it is correctly employed it will in its present form contribute without a doubt to ensuring the food supply. Its operating cost is an enormous benefit especially with a price that is not too excessive.*"[6]

This is a fitting tribute from one of the creators of the combine and a fitting end to this chapter.

MARTIN BECKMANN, HORST-DIETER GÖRG

Sources:

1 Karl Vormfelde: a new world order with the combine harvester, VDI journal 07.02.1931

2 Paula Claas: Sonne über Harsewinkel, unpublished Harsewinkel 1962. Page 81 to 85

3 See also "... dann machen wir es allein", history of Harsewinkel

4 Claas factory promotional flyer 1938

5 Erich Harmening in "Miterlebte Landtechnik", Max Eyth Gesellschaft Darmstadt 1981

6 Walter Brenner – harvest experience with the Claas MDB from "die Technik der Landwirtschaft" Volume 1, 1939

From the MDB to the *Super*

Although the country was at war, the combine creators in Harsewinkel were looking ahead to the advent of peace and ways of improving the MDB. These activities were kept quiet since officially every effort had to be focussed on warfare. This covert development saw the light of day very shortly after hostilities had ceased. In 1946 the transverse crop flow of the MDB was replaced by a right angle flow, the crop travelling first crosswise and then to the rear. This helped boost productivity at a stroke and the ultimate test was not long in coming. The new combine called the *Super* made a name for itself in the toughest conditions in an operation known as the Emergency Harvest Action in the Rhineland. This caught the eye of the English commanders who were running this part of Germany after the war. In 1953 the *Super Junior* was introduced for the countless smaller farmers who wanted to invest in mechanisation.

By the outbreak of war in 1939 one hundred MDB combines had been built. From then on the pace quickened in the following years with 450 combines leaving the plant in 1940 and once again in 1941. The added volume helped to build up experience and improve reliability. Production continued apace in 1942 despite material shortages. Sometimes a requisition order for steel would turn up late or there were no tyres available. Walter Brenner had come to grips with the problem urgently: "our aircraft type tyres were needed urgently for the air force. In autumn 1939 we didn't know how we could keep production going. Then we heard about 2,000 Polish tyres that had been requisitioned in a warehouse in Posen. We were fortunately able to get hold of them. This was a stroke of luck and meant we could keep our production licence and go on working for another two years. So this explains why for this period the MDB was fitted with Polish *Stomil* tyres."[1]

59 *Early version of the sales brochure for the Super 1949 style ...*

The reprieve ended finally in the early months of 1943 when the Nazi regime ordered the company to focus on compulsory production of articles for the military effort, such as shell cases. Farm equipment manufacturing was forbidden.

Despite the obvious constraints product development kept going and with the help of a few Russian prisoners-of-war who were fortunate enough to land in the calm surroundings of Harsewinkel the plans for the *Super* were drawn up, a handful of prototypes built and limited testing took place locally and on the farms of Saxony in 1943.

The biggest design change in the new range was the crop flow. Instead of being processed in a straight line crossways, the crop was now turned through a right angle so the straw walkers could be extended and the added separation increased the output.

The Emergency Harvest Action

When peace finally broke out, there were other more urgent needs than building combines in Germany. The machines that were left were put into service in the plains next to the Rhine. Then in 1946 the British military authorities approached *Claas* with an urgent request. The population in the region west of the Rhine was short of food and the cities had been largely destroyed, so the order had been given to save what there

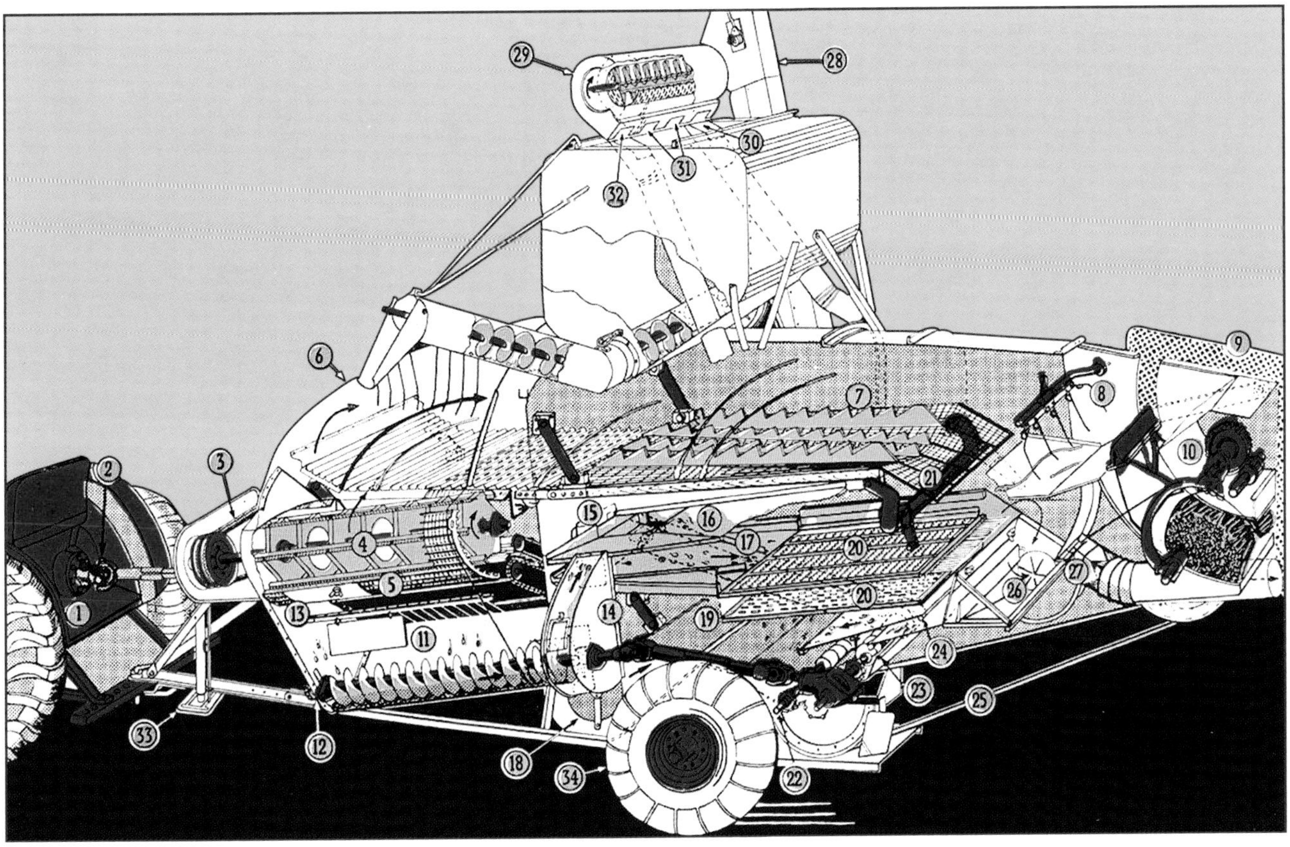

60 … and a functional cross section of the all round harvester

was of the harvest. The military rounded up eight R 40 *Hanomag* tractors and an unbelievable amount of diesel fuel and *Claas* was requested to provide the rest of the harvesting chain. Three *Super* combines were all there was and with customary enthusiasm and support, they were put in service into the area around Jülich, Düren and Aachen, which had been declared a disaster area. The conditions were extremely demanding but the combines matured to series production status in just one season.

Heinrich Rinklake took part in the operation under the captaincy of Walter Brenner and recalls it: "we travelled to the Rhine on the main highway which was fairly well intact and crossed the Rhine on a small pontoon bridge". The fields were full of bomb craters and the farmers desperate for help. They were so pleased when the teams turned up and were happy to share their last few crumbs with the visitors. Since there was nowhere to stay most of the time, they slept in the straw in one of the two chaff containers they had brought with them. The other one was used to carry the spares which had been put in the convoy because there was nothing available locally. The destruction was so extensive that many of the local residents had not returned home although the harvest was ripe.[2]

The three teams were in action 300 times over an eight week period. They harvested everything they could, including all types of cereals plus beans, rape, mustard, dill and clover with the previously untested machines. The harvest action was repeated in 1947, only the operating conditions had improved a lot by then.

The *Super* goes to England

During the summer of 1946 three military government officials turned up at the company's headquarters directly from London with orders to confiscate a *Super* combine and ship it back. This raised more than a few eyebrows because there were neither patent rights nor licence agreements on the new combine. One of the officers helpfully suggested the company should organise some kind of protection before the testing programme began in the UK. However the structures for registering patents were destroyed along with everything else. The French distributor at that time was Léo Trier in Paris and it was a sign of the continued good relations that outlasted the war years, as recalled by Paula Claas: "he registered the patents in France in his name and made a reciprocal contractual agreement to transfer the rights back to us. That was more than decent of him!"

Once in England the German combine was subjected to a wide range of tests by government agencies and came through with flying colours, beating both locally made and American designs.

61

Claas aid convoy in the destroyed city of Jülich, 1946

62 Hanomag R 40 and Claas Super in action with the chaff container

63 The map shows the action radius based on the only available road map and then duplicated

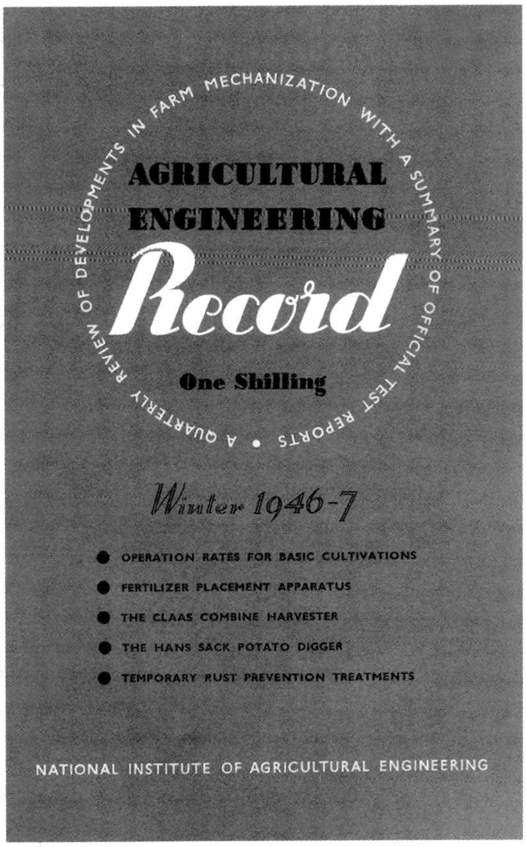

65 The NIAE Report with its positive appraisal of the Claas combine

The *NIAE (National Institute of Agricultural Engineering)* published its report in the Record of winter 1946 / 47 concluding that "the crop flow in the Claas combine is more than adequate for British conditions". Praise indeed from the experts![3]

This was followed by the first orders for *Claas* combines in July 1947. These orders were placed under military administration. The purchaser was *Mann & Son* based even then in Saxham, Suffolk. They had made a name for themselves as dealers for *Lanz* tractors and now became

64 The Super 500 brochure from 1955 has moved on

66 The Claas Super automatic with on-board hydraulics

67 *The 23 hp Volkswagen auxiliary engine could be engaged via a clutch*

Claas dealers as well. Several hundred more combines followed in 1948 and 1949, spearheading the post war export boom that helped Germany back on its feet. For *Claas* it was a new beginning that gave them the necessary resources for growth in manufacturing and product development at a watershed period in European history.

The engineers at *Claas* were now looking at turning the harvest into a one man operation and this design objective was the idea behind the *Super Automatic* combine. This machine featured a hydraulic circuit that could be operated by a valve on the tractor, increasing comfort for the driver. The connection was made with a quick connecting coupler so the driver could raise and lower both the cutter bar and the reel. This was an attempt to come closer to the operating efficiency of the self propelled combines that were now making their appearance on the market. The *Super Automatic* simplified the task of a clean crop entry into the combine and made lighter work of laid crops.

The *Super Junior*

In the aftermath of the war the export activity was the mainstay of the business, since German

69 *Early Claas Super-Junior brochure from 1953*

farmers lacked the wherewithal for major investments. Moreover, many of the big estates which had previously adopted combining were now behind the Iron Curtain. What the home market needed in the recovery phase was a smaller combine than the *Super* and therefore *Claas* responded with the *Super Junior* which came on the market in the summer of 1953. Although it had not been thoroughly tested, it was based on the proven technology borrowed from its bigger brother. In the first year 1,500 units were sold and no serious problems came to light in the field. Once again the company had listened carefully to the market and come up with the right product at the right time.

Heinrich Rinklake, Johannes Dammann

Sources

[1] *Paula Claas: Sonne über Harsewinkel, unpublished Harsewinkel 1962. Paula Claas and Walter Werland Harsewinkel 1962*
[2] *The "Knoter" – company journal, volume 3 1955, page 15*
[3] *The Claas combine harvester in NIAE "Report", York, England. Winter 1946-47, page 173 ff*

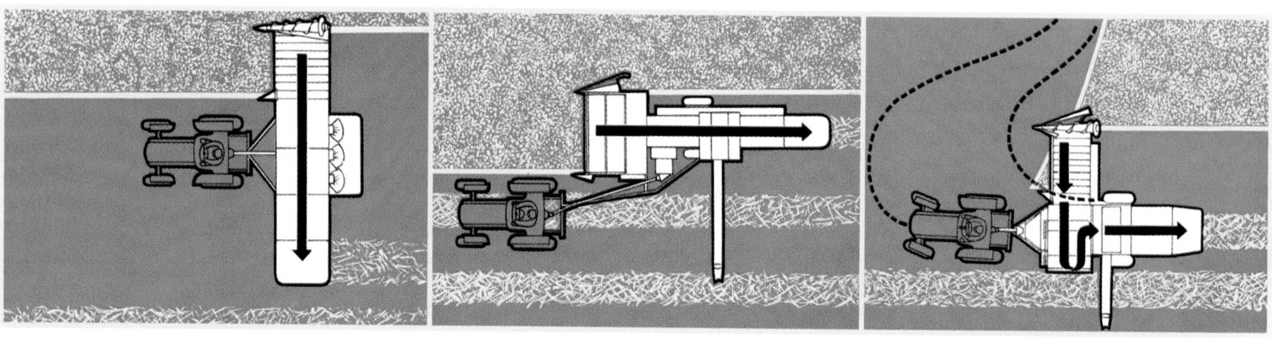

68 *These diagrams show how the Super right angle flow gives the best of both worlds*

Self Propelled Combines

70 The first Claas self propelled combine "Hercules"

As farm sizes increased combine work rates needed to grow in line. The company decided early on that they would have to keep innovating to stay ahead of the competition and that meant an early commitment to the self propelled combine. The first Claas self propelled combine came on the market in 1953 and was called Hercules. It was the first model with a straight line crop flow and set the stage for a whole generation of Claas combines with evocative names such as Matador, Senator and Mercator, names that every farmer has heard of to this day. It also gave rise to the Huckepack concept and later the Europa and Columbus ranges. The threshing machine had now had its day and gradually faded away. The Dominator was the next generation combine which spearheaded the company's development as a leading brand for big farms and contractors from the 1970s. The latest generation of Lexion combines was introduced in 1995 and reinforced the global technological leadership position of Claas into the 21st century.

The Arrival of the Hercules

In the early 1950s *CLAAS* found itself at the centre of the initial mechanisation phase of the family farms on the one hand and the demands of the large estates for higher work rates and improved productivity on the other. For these the self propelled combine was the answer, since this would be a much more efficient approach and the tractors could be employed on other jobs during the harvest. Originally launched as the *Hercules* the name of the first self propelled combine had to be changed shortly after to *SF* (Selbstfahrer = self propelled) to avoid a legal dispute. The first *CLAAS* combine with front to back crop flow was updated successively and finally made way for the *Matador*.

In 1953 *Claas* was one of a number of manufacturers who brought out self propelled combines to satisfy the demands of the growing number of large farms. The name *Hercules* had, however, been registered elsewhere and so the abbreviation *SF* was quickly thought up.

By now the *Claas* engineers had learnt more than enough about building machines, transmitting power and controlling the various functions of the combine harvester. The self propelled combine was a new challenge and we will now see that the prevailing crop structure had a permanent impact on the design of *Claas* combines, especially the intake area. Rye was an important crop and the stems were often 2 metres long, so the *Claas* combine had to do a better job in these conditions than the competition.

72 An early SF in the field

Claas
1953
Hercules
Der selbstfahrende Mähdrescher
Ein Meisterwerk moderner Mähdrescher - Technik aus den Werkstätten des bekannten Claas-„Super"!
Der „HERCULES" entstand in mehrjähriger Entwicklungsarbeit aus der Summe der Erfahrungen, die wir mit Tausenden von Mähdreschern in der ganzen Welt sammeln konnten!

71 1953 Hercules self propelled combine brochure

The American style self propelled combines had started coming in during the early 1950s and August Claas was quick to realise that the market would soon be asking for the product in larger numbers. The American combines were unsuited to local conditions with narrow and short intakes which threshed the long straw before it was cut. It was decided to adopt the open 1.25 metre wide threshing drum from the *Super*. This in turn determined the body and sieve box width. The width of the feed housing was matched to the body width and lengthened to handle the long and copious straw. The engineers had once again done their homework and with careful observation they realised that it was essential for the extra long stalks to be cut before the ears reached the threshing drum. Apart from this the *Super* provided the sieve box design and layout plus the side extensions on the preparation pan for hillside work.

This was a four straw walker machine with three steps and there was plenty of space above for the large volumes of straw. This ensured a smooth flow of straw through the secondary separation area and a reduction in losses.

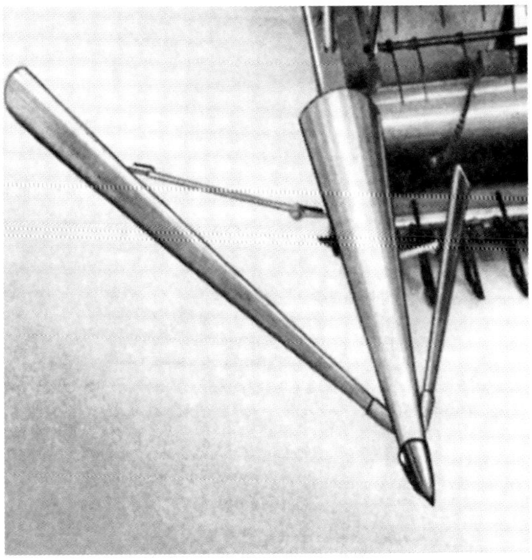

73 Crop divider

The sieve box performance was improved with a drum type fan and special attention was made to the quality of work in both standing or laid crops. The cutter bar table was extended forward to cope with long straw and the crop dividers separated the standing crop cleanly. Even in laid crops the *SF* could harvest 5 to 7 tons per hour with an outstanding grain quality, a remarkable performance for the era. The driver could control the reel and cutterbar independently from one another as the field conditions changed.

Hydraulics are nowadays an integral part of most machines – not then so it was a forward looking step when August Claas used the opportunity of the new combines to produce an in-house hydraulic system. The *Hercules* was the first to benefit with a gear type pump, piston actuator, a control valve and the hydraulic cylinders.

The hand operated control valve was designed specifically for the combine operator with four hose connections – (feed, return and 2 cylinder connections) and 5 positions (neutral, 2 x lift and lowering). It meant that the driver had one single lever operating in a gate for easy regulation of the constantly changing settings on the machine. This innovation became a standard feature of *Claas* combines for many years to come. This made the *SF* undoubtedly the forerunner of all the Self propelled combines which finally established themselves in Europe.

74 A straightforward drive line increases reliability. Several chains were replaced by silent belts

The *SF 55* upgrade model

In autumn 1954 the whole engineering team of some 15 people managed by Erich Harmening and Fritz Wallmeyer was working on an update for the *SF*. If you're wondering what the *55* in the name stands for, it's simply the planned year of introduction. A new transmission with three

75 The 1955 brochure, first year of the SF "55"

forward speeds and one reverse gear was to be fitted. The gearbox and the final drives were to run in an oil bath in place of the normal internal gears with grease lubrication or chain drives. The design was aimed at improving reliability and cutting down maintenance.

The engineers had learnt that dust and chaff flying around in the field often led to the radiator clogging up and this led to engine overheating, so special attention was paid to the radiator air cowl in the product update. This philosophy of steady improvement and quick reaction to farmers' concerns became a major success factor for *Claas* in the years that followed.

76 *The SF valve gate*

The *Claas LD 40* diesel engine

Someone came up with the idea of building a *Claas* engine because the dependency on the engine producers rankled among the independent minded *Claas* management. So it came about that a four cylinder diesel started to take shape in 1953 with 10 to 12 hp more than the *Perkins* engines fitted at the time. The *LD 40* was therefore the heavy duty option for hillside operation, high straw throughput or heavy soils where the extra power was of value. Overall 4,280 engines were built before production ceased again some ten years later. Supply was failing to keep up with the rapidly growing demand for combines and the steady increase in power required would have made a six cylinder version necessary. After engine production had stopped the production equipment was to be sold to *Perkins*, until August Claas intervened and blocked the sale, threatening to resume production if they tried to push up the engine prices!

More new features

The combine upgrade also had an impact on the variator drive – the gearbox was driven by a belt variator and the speed was changed with a hydraulic and spring loaded adjustment. The threshing drum had a variator drive with two normal belts and so called fan type pulleys which had to be made with cast iron.

The additional hydraulic functions led to a change in the control layout, with a new valve to run the hydraulic drive variator. An additional control valve was fitted for the threshing drum speed.

The demands on the hydraulic system had grown again and the valves had to be leak free, unlike the earlier versions. However there were no val-

77 ***Cross section of the self propelled combine***

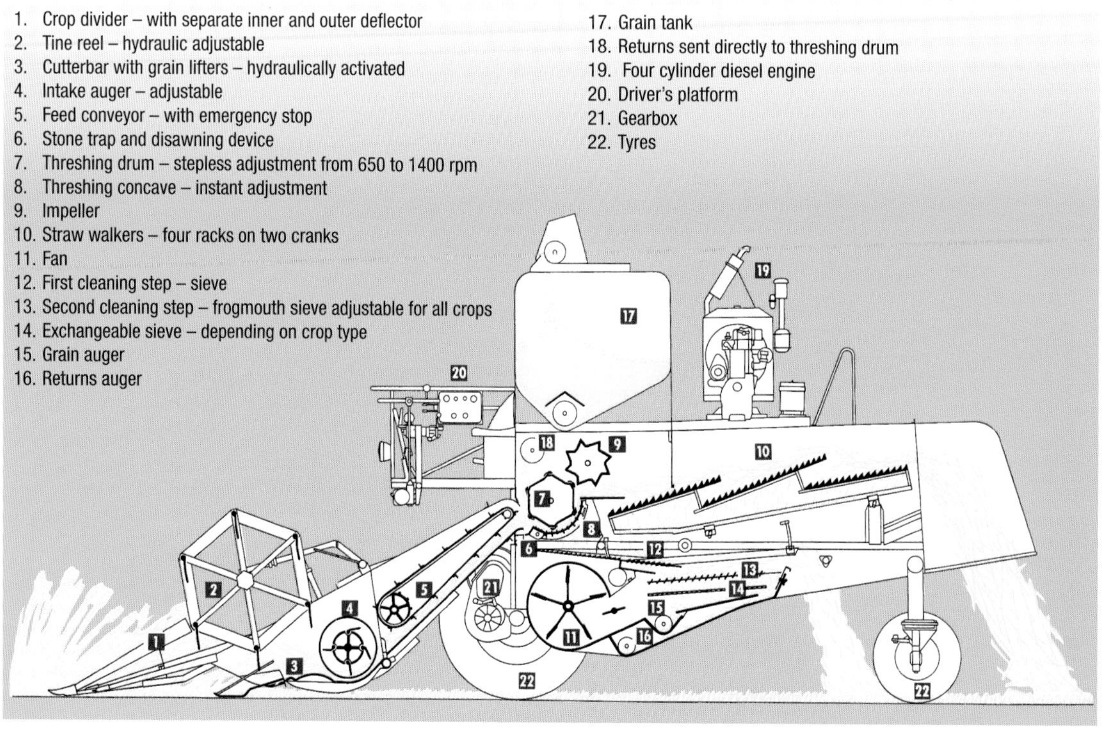

ves on the market which guaranteed leak free operation. The actuators were equipped with kickback valves which were made by *Claas* internally to overcome this.

The *SF 55* incorporated a whole row of customer requests as the sales brochure of the period shows:

- Reduced ground pressure with wider tyres
- Returns entry via augers over the drum
- Adjustable lower stop for the hydraulic cutter bar
- Slip clutch to prevent overload and damage
- Easy accessibility to all main points
- On board baler with the time proven *knotter.*

It was described as a machine for farmers – designed by farmers. The *SF 55* was sold in large volume and found much acclaim among farmers, contractors and machinery rings as a fine all rounder. This established the company's credentials in what became the most important market segment.

The self propelled *Matador*

The *Matador* saw the light of day in 1961 as the successor to the *SF* combine. It was to set new standards for the top customer segment and came with an 87 hp six cylinder diesel, once again adding another notch to the output curve. Spring suspended cutter bars became standard and now they'd reached a width over 3 metres, they had to be easy to remove for road travel on a trailer. Quick connecting couplings between the cutterbar and feed conveyor helped in this direction.

Tyre sizes increased and that meant longer feed conveyors. The hydraulic pressure and flow were increased to improve performance. The machines had become heavier and that led to the introduction of power steering. Claas engineered a compact system that fitted in the steering rod between the steering pivot and track rod so the control valve and cylinder were housed in one unit.

The grain tank became a standard feature – bagging was done for – whilst the machines were painted dark (Austral) green instead of silver metallic from 1964/65. It was all a bit too big for many smaller farmers in easy to harvest regions who were rewarded with the *Matador Standard* featuring a smaller four cylinder engine, shorter straw walkers and smaller grain tank capacity. At the same time the bigger combine was suffixed *Gigant* to accentuate its gigantic size.

In all some 35,000 *Matador* combines left the plant and a further landmark in this period was the 100,000th combine from *Claas.*

Plastic bushes reduce maintenance

Early in the 1960s, the order came from the owners to find ways of reducing maintenance dramatically. It was always wise to take such orders seriously because there was sound reasoning for them, although the project may not have sounded very exciting. At the time each combine had multiple grease points with different service intervals, varying from three times a day, daily, weekly, monthly or annually, so nobody could ever memorise the whole routine.

If it were possible to eliminate the maintenance of the various bushes and bearings, then the

78 *Matador Gigant with extra large cutter bar and higher output*

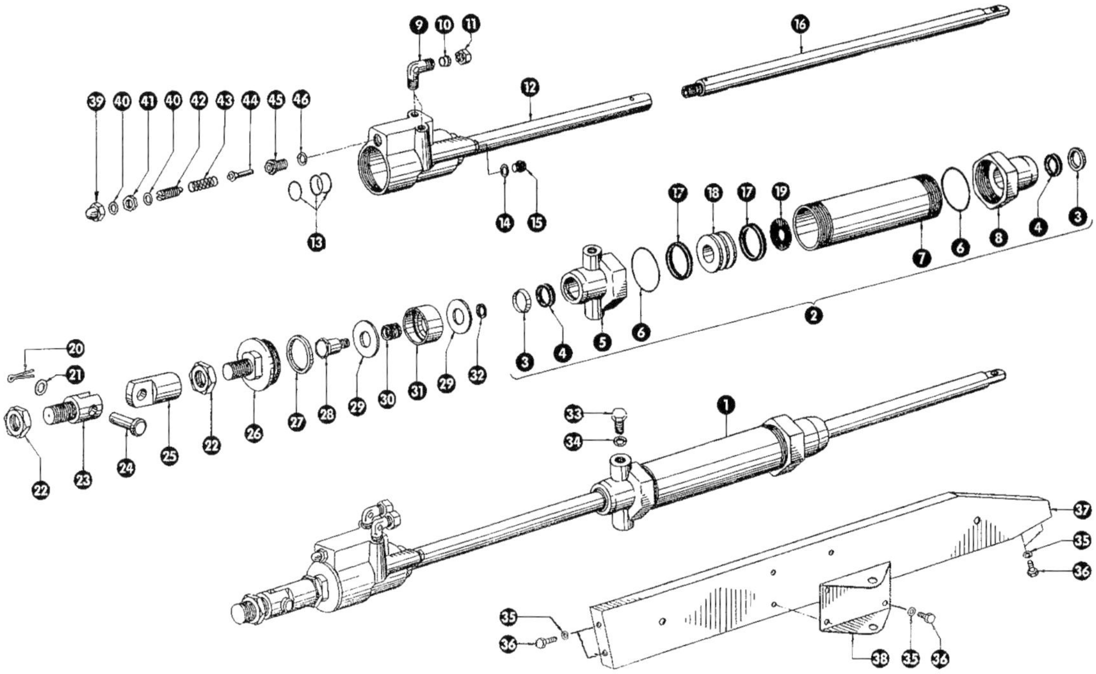

79 The hydraulic power steering in parts and fully assembled

customers would be able to save time, repairs would be needed less often and overall productivity would go up.

Close investigation revealed that the bushes had to be greased frequently because of the entry of aggressive dust and sand particles, juices from the crop and silica in the rice harvest. This was aggravated by high pressure cleaning prior to winter storage.

The use of plastics to solve this problem was bound to be controversial, despite the advantages. The bushes could be formed without any machining or added sealing needed and the material was therefore tested in dusty and hot conditions in the company to see where the limits lay. However there could be no doubt about the changeover in customers' minds, so extensive testing had to be done over a period of time.

80 Claas SF combine field demo

Field tests in the Dutch polders

A large scale test operation was organised in the Polder region of Ostflevoland next to the Ijsselmeer. This farming region covers some 54,000 hectares and they were an early fan of *Claas* products with one hundred machines in service. A large proportion was then switched to the new plastic bushes and the results were analysed each year.

The new style *Claas* bushes were fitted to combines and balers as standard starting in 1962. They were used on tubes, tensioners, levers, pedals, pulleys and spring cylinder mounts. After a few years several million plastic bushes were in service and ever since there have been no problems due to the material.

The engineers are particularly proud of the floating dual necked bushes inside the control pulley, because they can be fitted without tools whilst the thin walls and a lengthways slit reduce expansion due to a heat to a minimum. An example of the unrivalled attention to detail of which *Claas* engineers are justly proud.

The inconspicuous plastic bushes have proven themselves over time and have been retained right up to the present day on the Lexion range. All of these bushes have retained a high pressure grease nipple, which is there to inject a layer of grease for the winter to prevent corrosion. Typically *Claas*.

Johannes Dammann, Heinz König, Norbert Ortkras, Heinz Reinharz, Heinrich Roderfeld

Huckepack, *Columbus* and *Europa* for the Individual Farm

The idea behind the *Huckepack* (Huckaback) was to create a machine that was both combine harvester and implement carrier making it a machine that would pay its way on the farm all year round. The idea was sound, but it didn't catch on. On the other hand, the *Europa* and *Columbus* combines were both based on this design and became top selling models after their launch in 1958. The *Consul* was the first combine with a monocoque chassis and completely spot welded.

Once the *SF* combine had been launched Professor Brenner turned his attention to a farmers' combine. The price was in the forefront and was targeted at under 10,000 DM. The chassis was borrowed from a *VW* transporter with the maximum speed reduced to 20 km/h. A combine ran about 200 hours a year and there were still many farmers who didn't even own a tractor. Logically it made no sense to have a complete combine chassis lying around unused for most of the year, although its basic combine parts accounted for about half the total machine cost and could be used elsewhere.

If the threshing assembly could be split from the chassis, then the prime mover could be freed up for round – the – year operation. When the cereals harvest was due, then the threshing assembly would simply be piggybacked onto the chassis. Now the idea had been born the engineers could think of ways to make this economic, all round farmer's combine and tractor.

In 1956 the pre-series was presented with a single cylinder 12 hp *Hatz* diesel for the ground drive and a 27 hp *VW* petrol engine for threshing. The two wheel ground drive was via a *Hurth* transaxle with a steered front axle.

As the development project continued a *ZF* transmission made its entry along with a 15 hp *MWM* flat twin diesel. The engineers were also influenced by developments like the *Lanz Alldog* implement carrier. The *Claas* chassis had a patented threshing insert with a lengthways channel which could be removed. The prime mover could move in under the threshing unit with no time wasted and the combine function was ready to go in 30 minutes or so. Whilst the carrier had steering up front, the combine faced the other way and the driver's seat swung around by 180°. The pedals stayed in the same place so they too were back to front. The little *VW* engine had a *Claas* speed governor and was started by hand.

The implement manufacturers were all very interested, or so it seemed and there were numerous enquiries from companies making potato harvesters, seed drills, sprayers and choppers asking how their products could be fitted above, below, in front or behind. As long as they had three point mountings, it was quite straightforward. Combinations fitted between or over the axles were much more complex.

81 The Huckepack as implement carrier and mowing bar

82 The Huckepack as a combine harvester with bagging stand and the straw baler, common in those days

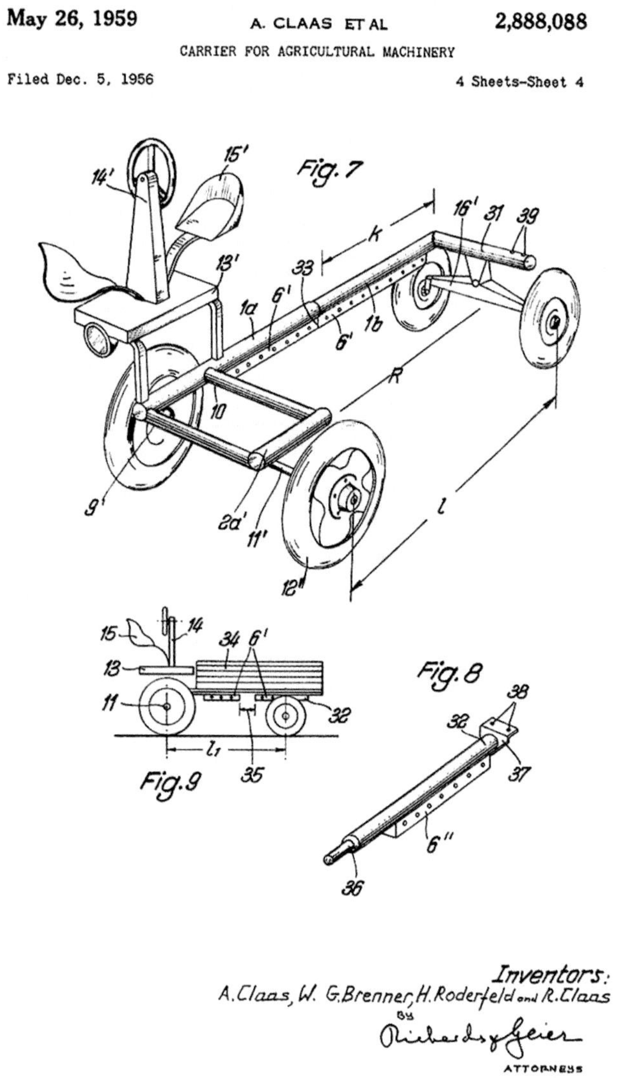

May 26, 1959
A. CLAAS ET AL
2,888,088
CARRIER FOR AGRICULTURAL MACHINERY
Filed Dec. 5, 1956
4 Sheets-Sheet 4
Fig. 7
Fig. 8
Fig. 9
Inventors:
A. Claas, W. G. Brenner, H. Roderfeld and R. Claas
ATTORNEYS

83 *Diagram of the Huckepack with the removable channel section as documented for the US patent application*

However the customers still wanted to have a dedicated machine with the *Huckepack* threshing system and were prepared to accept the low annual utilisation and the tied up capital that this entailed. As a result the company developed the *Europa* combine which did just that. In 1958 700 were sold whilst the *Huckepack* found only 150 buyers. Its days were numbered from then on and the great debate began on why it flopped. There are several factors:

- Not enough traction power, even after the engine had gone from 10 to 15 hp.
- Whilst the changeover was quick in theory, many of the bits and pieces for fixing the two sections together had disappeared in the meantime.
- Diesel and petrol engines on one unit were not acceptable.

The *Europa* combine was originally fitted with a *Daimler Benz* diesel engine from the *Unimog*, but was changed to *Perkins* following cooling problems, the same as the *SF*.

The *Columbus* with a petrol engine from *VW* came a little later, now endowed with an electric starter. The lower power versus the *Europa* was unusually never an issue, probably due to the shorter straw walkers and cutting width which was one metre less. It matched the farmers' requirements very well. Between them *Europa* and *Columbus* became the best selling *Claas*

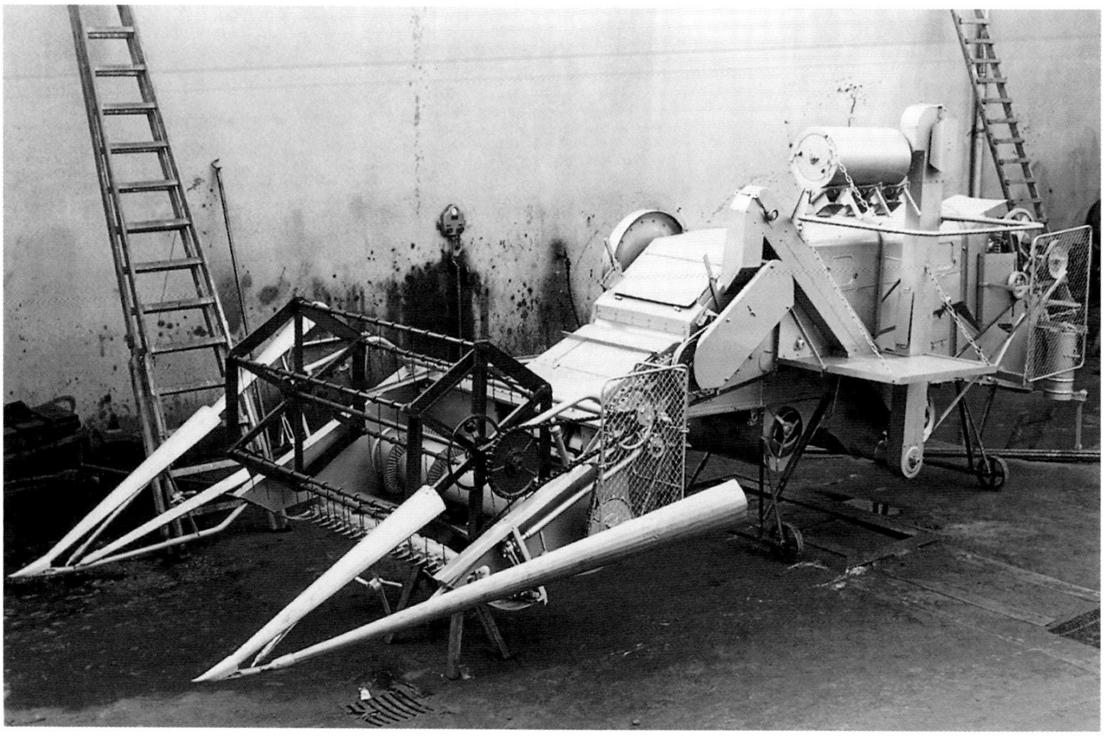

84 *The Huckepack combine set at rest*

Claas
PATENTED SELF-PROPELLED COMBINE HARVESTER
THE "EUROPA"
CLAAS
The Self-propelled Combine Harvester suitable for the most difficult European Harvest conditions - constructed to the exacting standards of the proved range of Claas machines - simple and giving easy accessibility to all parts - manufactured by the oldest and best known specialists in Combine Harvesters in Europe

85 *The Europa was claimed to be Europe's farmers' combine*

combines of all time with the highest daily production rate of 75 machines a day.

Up till this period endurance testing was carried out over the sand dunes close to the factory, a time consuming process which was speeded up with the inauguration of a 25 metre diameter concreted circular test track next to the plant. The combines were run non stop without a driver over the bumps and were checked for damage on a regular basis.

The sand dunes were the scene of a most remarkable archaeological discovery. Whilst running a combine around the dunes a dark object was noted on a steep slope and closer examination revealed it to be the remains of a funeral urn. The experts at the Bielefeld branch of the *Prehistorical Museum* have dated it as being from the 6th century B.C. The urn contained remains

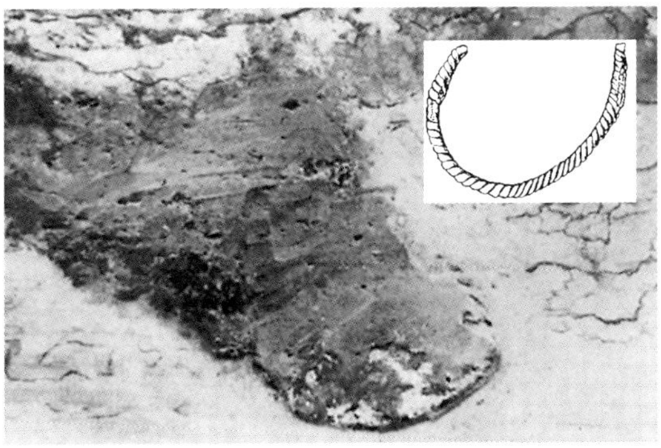

87 *Keen observation by Johannes Dammann unearthed the historical burial site*

of bones, charcoal and a bronze clasp for the deceased. Nobody had realised what a historical place Harsewinkel was!

Back to the near future, where we find the *Mercur* which was added in 1963, Its extra straw walker filled a performance gap between *Europa* and *Matador Standard*. It featured a wide threshing drum belt with manual adjustment.

86 *The Europa in the field*

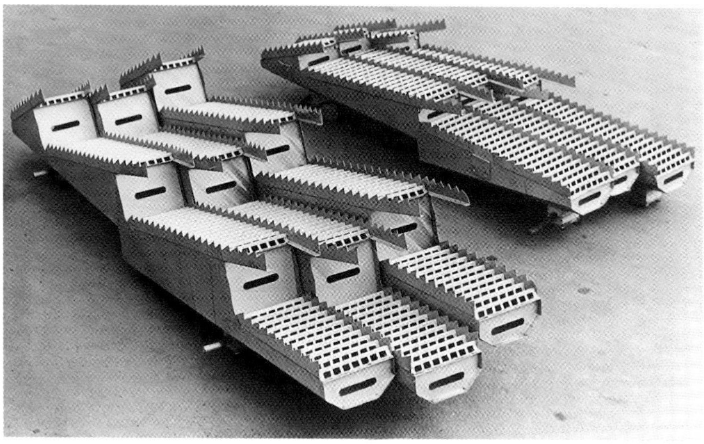

88 *Different straw walker lengths with Europa on the left and Columbus on the right*

91 *The Consul was the first Claas combine with a monocoque chassis*

The *Mercur's* place was taken in 1967 by the *Consul*, which was full of new functional and manufacturing ideas. The straw walkers were now fitted with enclosed return floors, the air blast was speed controlled and the discharge auger could be swivelled into position without loss of grain and at different discharge heights. The chassis was now a spot welded monocoque design and the machine had a new look.

Connecting shafts with conic connectors

Up until 1967 *Claas* usually fixed shafts in place with cotter pins, and the *Consul* used circlips.

Combines need a number of long shafts which go across the machine where they are held in place on the side panels. The stubs of the shafts are then retained in position at both ends. If the shaft or the bearings need attention, it must be possible to remove them easily without damage to the shaft mounting. This led the engineers to the creation of a new type of mounting with axial tensioning. The drawings below show how it is designed. It consists of a cone shaped ring, one each end. The shafts were threaded at each end to bolt the two conic rings. Mounting directly to the shafts is firm and solid, and essentially removal and fitting are facilitated by the open slit.

These conic rings have given excellent service ever since, they are now in use for 35 years, and have made their way to the *Lexion* combines. This design is typical of how the *Claas* engineers come up with simple and practical solutions.

After the introduction of the *Consul* the *Europa* and *Columbus* were both updated and became the *Cosmos* and the *Comet*, later the higher powered *Corsar* was added.

After the demise of the *Huckepack*, Heinrich Hemker got approval for a test department and introduced reports on test results, complete with diagrams, as far back as 1957. He began immediately to measure grain throughput in tons per hour, rather than the hundredweight measure used previously. This old unit had to do with the sacks used on the bagging stand, which had now lost their relevance. This was a bit of a shock for his colleagues since a combine which produced an impressive 40 hundredweights per hour was now devalued – on paper at least – to 2 tons per hour. Such is progress.

Heinrich Hemker, Heinz König, Heinrich Roderfeld

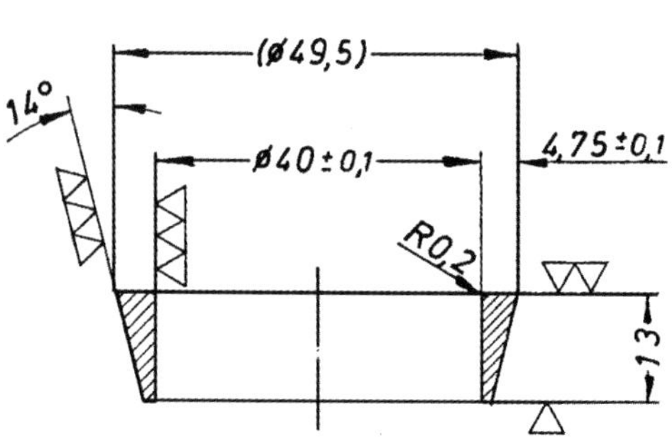

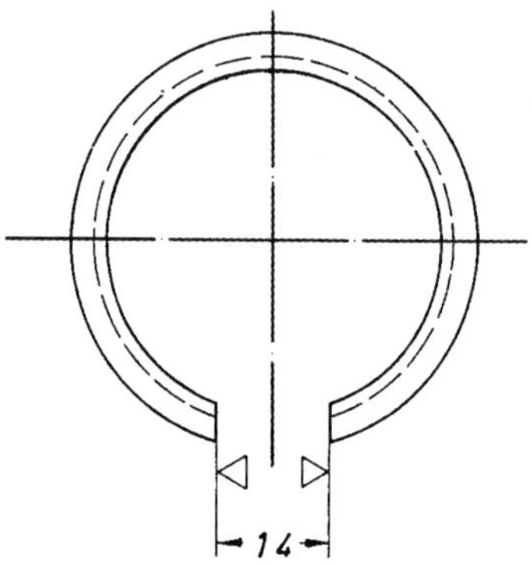

89 / 90 *Technical drawing of the conic ring …*

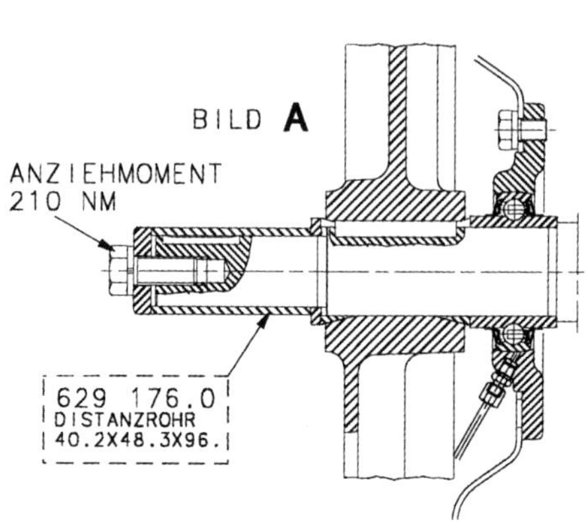

… and cross section diagram of the connection

The Senator and Mercator set new Output Standards

The *Senator* was launched in 1966 and the *Mercator* and *Protector* models completed the range. The *Senator* was a landmark product which ushered in a new design and a fresh new livery. Powerband main drive came in place of the traditional belts, whilst hydrostatic steering improved driver comfort.

Not much attention was paid to the exterior of a combine at first. After all it was a working tool. Protective panels where skimpy and positioned just where needed to prevent injury. Replacement sieves carried on the machine even doubled up as protection.

When the *Senator* came onto the market, this was the beginning of a major change in philosophy. A design consultant (Igl in Rosenheim) worked on the looks of the machine which not only had increased performance, it also was to show it to the outside world. The lines sloped away to the rear and gave it a clear contour. The grain tank and engine cover had a line to them. The new driver platform featured an adjustable steering column and the drive controls were now located just below in the driver's range of vision. Operating levers were in easy reach to the left and right of the driver who was positioned on an upholstered seat with an armrest on the right. Seating position and suspension could be adjusted and there was space for a second person next to the driver.

As combines grew in number and in size accident protection became a big issue. Large, easy to open panels covering the drive lines provide safety and became an integral design element.

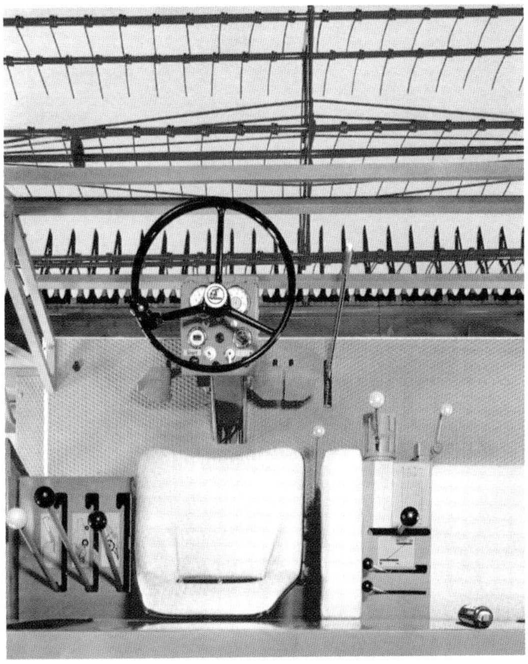

93 The Senator driver platform, the first ergonomic design

Along with the *Senator* came the familiar fresh looking seed green paintwork we know today, and this went really well with the new styling.

92 A new style Senator offloading in the field

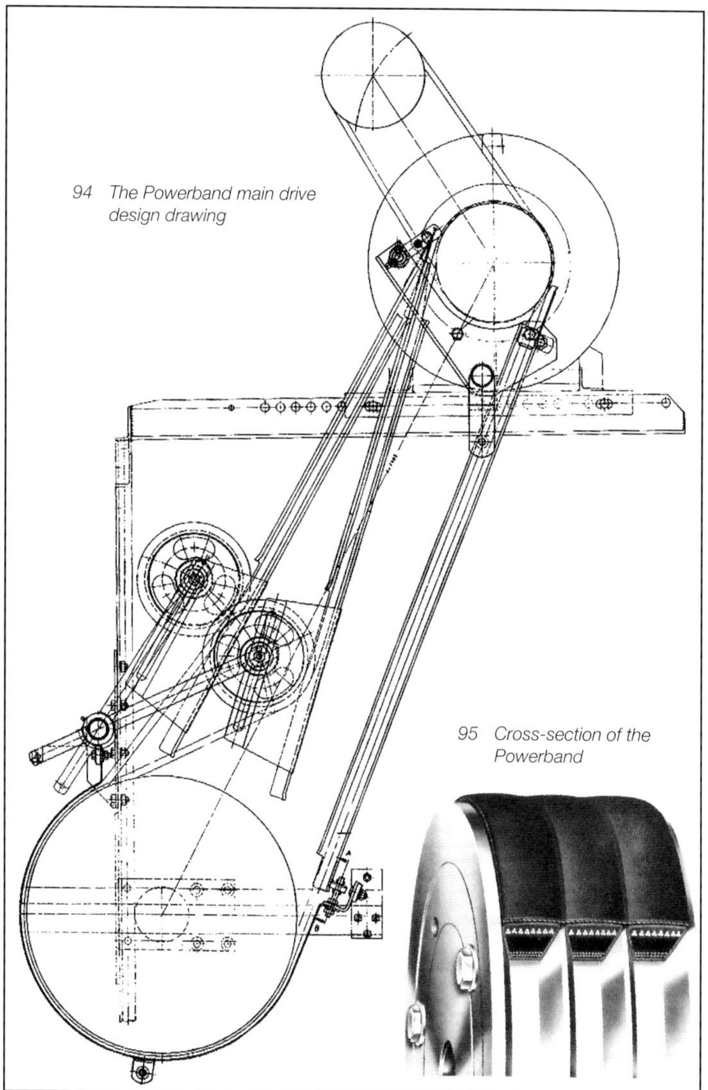

94 The Powerband main drive design drawing

95 Cross-section of the Powerband

In conjunction with the increased combine performance, cutterbar widths had now all gone over the 3 metre limit and had to be removed for road travel. This made the feed conveyor part of the machine.

Hydrostatic steering became a standard feature and the old linkage was a thing of the past.

96 Diagram of the hydrostatic steering from a 1967 training document

Hydraulic pipes now transferred the turns of the steering wheel into steering cylinder pressure and the corresponding movement of the steer wheels. Hydraulic brakes were also included.

The powerband was another innovation in the drive line of the *Senator*. This was a new type of drive composed of several identical belts fixed to a neoprene cover belt.

The changeover from the old belts was the main technical challenge to the designers at this time. This is why: when these belts were at idle they hung loose on the engine pulley and in addition they had lateral guidance. To prevent the powerband from burning due to friction from the engine pulley they had to be taken out of contact. The problem was solved with a new type of belt guide with an engagement shaft. Although the power flow was much increased and the pulley size reduced, the powerband was still only half as wide as the previous belt assembly, so it was a real advance. In addition the belt pre-tensioning and force required for engagement were both reduced considerably due to the positive grip of the belt grooves despite the engine power which at 105 hp had passed the 100 hp level for the first time.

Claas was the first combine producer world wide to introduce the switchable powerband drive approach. It took the other manufacturers up to 10 years to catch up with this innovation, which was a real customer benefit. Nowadays composite drive belts are a standard feature on all agricultural machines when a high power transfer is needed. *Claas* uses belts today up to 9 metres long and capable of transmitting up to 600 hp reliably and smoothly.

The *Mercator* came out one year later, equipped with a slightly smaller six cylinder engine in line with its lower work rate for smaller farms. The design was however cloned from the *Senator*.

The model range was completed with the addition of the *Protector* in 1968. This had a four cylinder engine to start with and a six cylinder option was added later. The *Protector* had a fixed 2.7 metre cutterbar and was designed as an entry level model with lower specs, including fewer features for the operator.

The names were proliferating so a clean up was ordered with *Mercator* remaining. The *Senator* turned into the *Mercator 70*, the *Protector* turned into the *Mercator 60* and *50*.

97 A Senator harvesting rice in Italy, 1968

Following a product update the *Mercator 70* got the intensive separation system as well as the hydraulic discharge auger from the new top - of - the - line *Dominator* series, at which point it became the *Mercator 75*. Finally the Dominator range was extended downward and the *Mercator* range was discontinued after 15 successful years.

Ludwig Caspers, Heinz König, Heinrich Roderfeld

98 The Protector rounded off the model range

From the *Dominator* to the *Mega*

With pressure growing on *CLAAS* to regain the technological lead at the end of the 1960s a new combine family was developed in record time. The *Dominator* was created in a matter of months by a team made up of production and development engineers. It featured a further jump in output and incorporated a completely new approach to manufacturing and shipping. The combine was designed in modules which were pre-assembled and after many facelifts and updates the *Mega* range was launched in 1993, the first *CLAAS* combines fitted with the *APS* threshing system.

The *Senator*, *Mercator* and *Consul* models were sold in the USA under the *Ford* label as the *640, 630* and *620*. This entailed a different blue and grey livery. These products enjoyed only limited success since they weren't accepted by American farmers when it came to harvesting soy beans and maize (corn).

Meanwhile the structural changes in Europe were continuing apace with farming operations gaining in size. Farmers and particularly contractors wanted higher capacity, higher performance and needed machines that would handle maize harvesting, a trend which also considerably lengthened the annual combine use.

A *Matador Gigant* was widened in the workshop with the addition of a straw walker to test the potential of wider combines. This move up into higher spheres of output used the narrow walker width of 250 mm as basis for the 5 and 6 straw walker combines. Instead of modifying the design of the *Senator / Mercator* range a new futuristic design was created with all the drives and elevators concealed under a rounded exterior.

99 Claas Senator as Ford 640 front page of a 1967 / 68 brochure

The machine was designed for rail transport and to stay within the gauge the grain tank was no longer near the top. Saddle tanks on either side of the machine provided the required capacity. It created a major sensation when it was presented at the 1970 DLG show where it was kept out of reach by a fence around it. It inspired competitors to copy the look but the project was abandoned when the tooling cost was worked out.

100 The so called "dustbin" with a six row maize header

Project 12

The decision for a new combine generation fell on the 6th of December 1969. Helmut Claas, who was then Technical Director outlined the design parameters:

- Suitable for maize harvesting
- Monocoque chassis
- Modular design for container transport
- Easy to build and repair
- Maximum parts commonality
- Intensive checks at all stages of production built in
- Value for money engineering
- Low manufacturing costs.

Willi Kemper, who was the Production Manager in those days was given the job as Project Manager. This was in order to ensure close cooperation between the R & D team with Erich Harmening and Franz Stein as Chief Foreman and the production people, a process now known as simultaneous engineering. This joint effort meant that that the first machines were built and out in the field a few months later in the early 1970 Spanish harvest and a hundred pre-series combines were in the field for the main European harvest – the *Dominator* was born.

The manufacturing approach was clearly defined with the spot welded, self supporting body. The riveting process which was part of the Mercator manufacturing method was becoming totally unacceptable with a noise level of over 100 dB (A) in what was dubbed the "concert hall". The health and safety authorities had been up in arms about this for some time and extensive sound deadening investments had been made.

The disappearance of beams in the chassis opened up more space for the sieve box and this in turn helped boost the cleaning system's performance. The air blast was speed controlled.

The open straw walkers taken from the *Consul* helped reduce overall height and the walker racks became lighter. The engine was positioned between the cab and the grain tank in the interests of a short, direct main drum drive with the impeller in between.

To fit the machine into a container shipment it could be split up into following assemblies:

- Threshing housing with drive axle and driver platform
- Straw walker housing and straw walkers
- Steer axle with cleaning system including the fans
- Grain tank
- Cutter bar.

These assembly groups made it possible to pre-assemble them at a right angle to the main assembly line. Machines could also be shipped in CKD or SKD form so that customers in overseas markets could fit local components as needed or where tariff restrictions applied.

This service friendly approach brought for instance the famous flange mounted threshing drum. This was designed so that this drum could be removed to the front without having to take the drive line apart, if damage occurred. This was the realisation of a dream for many combine mechanics who had long asked for a better solution. This was it.

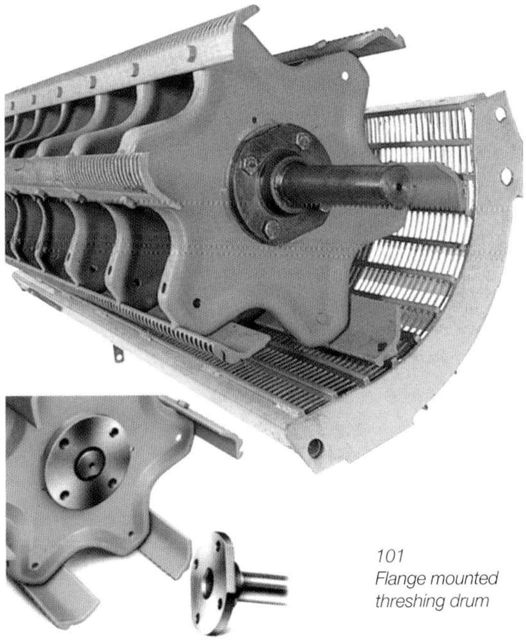

101
Flange mounted threshing drum

The parts commonality objective was achieved by the use of a maximum of identical parts across the model range in its varying widths.

The pre-assembly layout in the plant enabled each sub-unit to be thoroughly tested. Reliance was placed on autonomous testing procedures to reduce the workload at the final testing station. The *Dominator* range was the highly successful heart of the line range for many years, due in no small part to the value for money and high performance each and every model offered to farmers and contractors, in Europe and around the world.

The five straw walker *Dominator 80* with 1.32 metre drum width was introduced in the 1971 harvest. The six straw walker *Dominator 100* had 1.58 metre threshing width and followed a year later.

102 The Dominator 80 at work

The *Dominator 80* had been earmarked for the cooperation with Ford in USA as is visible from details in the first series such as the smaller diameter five piece reel and the open top grain tank with the inclined tank auger fitted in the middle. This open design wasn't appreciated in Europe and a tent style cover had to be offered, followed by a proper cover on the *Dominator 100*. The *Dominator 80* now had a hydrostatic drive option which was standard for the *Ford* combines. The *Dominator 100* came equipped with a hydrostatic drive from the outset.

Travel speed was varied by a hand control which changed the pump setting. The reverse gear was no longer required because the flow of oil in the pump could be reversed by passing the plate angle in the pump through neutral and reversing the flow.

Maize harvesting was an essential attribute in America and was gaining in importance in Europe so the *Dominator* range had to be capable of operating with the extra weight of 4 and 6 row maize headers and tough enough to withstand the longer operating season.

103 Dominator 100 in the Hungarian maize harvest

Endurance testing was concentrated on Hungary. This choice was based on two reasons – firstly large quantities of *Dominator* combines had been sold there as a result of component supply agreements. Secondly the large state farms such as Babolna with 15,000 hectares were places where 1,000 hours of harvesting in maize could be reached. The conditions were tough and the hours were long – often 15 hours a day – so that engineering limits were tested, ideas tried out and improvements could be incorporated rapidly.

The *Dominator 100* had reached a size previously unheard of so new technology was called for. Engine power was higher and the forces needed to couple up moving parts were growing beyond the manual stage and hydraulic operation was needed.

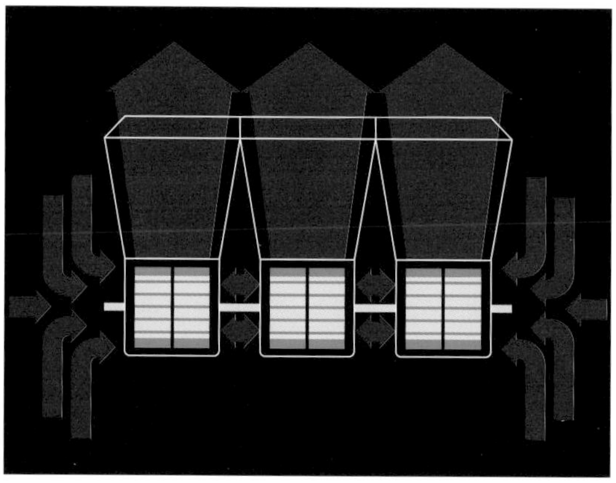

104 Turbine fans with air flow

The *Dominator 100* had also outgrown conventional drum type cleaning fans with their air intake from the sides. In their place turbine fans were developed with three sections, each with multiple paddles on both sides and individual intake and outflow channels to provide a new level of cleaning performance.

Straw walker difficulties emerged with the *Dominator 100* in the 1972/73 harvest. The straw flow was irregular and the material landed heaped to the left. It wasn't possible to spread the chopped straw evenly either and customers started to complain. Trials were made with guide plates in the straw walker housing and the straw walkers themselves, all to no avail. Once again, a keen eye was needed to pin down the problem and the engineers noticed that the left side panel was spot clean whilst the right panel was coated in dust. This was the clue they needed because the straw walker shafts and straw walkers were arranged in parallel and this simultaneous action had the effect of creating a sideways swing to the material. New straw walkers were fabricated to modify the middle section from 120 to 240 degrees counter clockwise.

The 1973 harvest was the next opportunity to see how the new layout worked and the results were positive. The shafts were then changed across the board and this new arrangement was registered as a patent. It was difficult to explain how it worked to the patent engineers and they were only convinced when Hans Dammann visited them and demonstrated with a pencil in a wire model how it only moved to one side as the rotation occurred.

Intensive separation

The separation of the remaining grain in the straw walkers was usually the limiting factor in combine performance at this time, a factor aggravated when there was a high proportion of leaves in the straw. The intensive separation system was designed to improve performance in this area. Sets of agitation tines above the straw walkers grab the straw in the same way as a hay rake and loosen the mat of straw so that the last grains can drop down more easily.

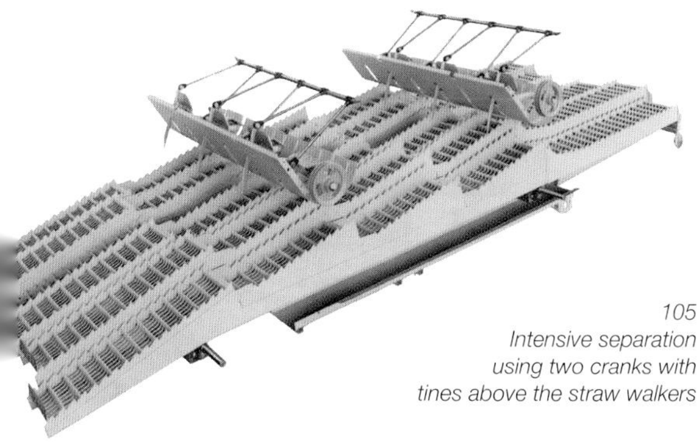

105 Intensive separation using two cranks with tines above the straw walkers

106 The Dominator 96 with integral cab

The hydrostatic drive machines were fitted with a switch in the drive lever to lift and lower the cutter bar.

By 1978 the *Dominator* family had been extended downwards and the *Mercator* range was finally phased out.

Driver's environment

As both output and the harvest season stretched into the cooler time of the year as a result of the added maize usage the driver needed more protection from the elements. The first cabs were add-on fixtures and *Claas* led the way yet again by making them a part of the design with the introduction of *Dominator* 6 series upgrade. The cab became an integral feature from then on.

The driver had a right to be protected against the cold and damp in the autumn harvests whilst being insulated from the summer heat and dust. To keep the dust out, the cab needed a gentle pressure difference without creating a draught. Fresh air was admitted by the large filters in the cab roof and despite the use of heat insulating glass, the air temperature was the same inside as out. The logical step was then to combine the heating with a cooling system, and so air conditioning made its debut.

Temperature is one major aspect, the other is noise. The cabs were sound insulated, separated from the platform by rubber mountings and trimmed with sound deadening panels. Since hydraulic valves tend to make unpleasant noises the multiple control valves which were a typical *Claas* feature were moved out of the cab. They were now activated by a control column with a gate.

107 Driver platform with drive lever and control column both located to the right hand side of the driver

CS system

The straw walker combine was reaching its performance limits, with no combination of height, width or length able to contribute to an improved performance. Helmut Claas suggested the development of a forced separation system which was then fabricated in the test workshop by Franz Tophinke. The straw walkers were substituted by eight separation cylinders and concaves fitted in a row to the rear of the combine. This layout increased the performance in the same package size and the forced straw flow had a positive impact when working on slopes since it no longer drifted downhill.

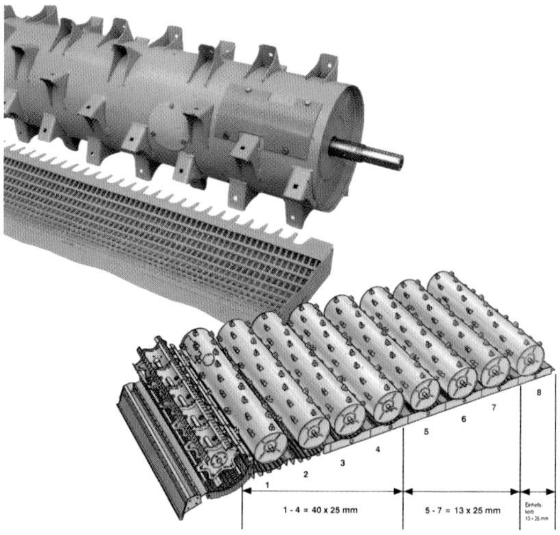

108 The CS system (separation drum and concave) and system layout

3 D cleaning

When combining across slopes the grain drifts to one side and guide plates on the sieves and feed pans are an inadequate solution. When the slope is too steep the classic cleaning system starts losing grain, and this effect is made worse by the free passage of air where the crop is missing on the uphill side. The 3 D system was created to generate a counter force against gravity. The sieves were set up with an additional uphill swing in addition to the normal to-and-fro action. This explains the three dimensional name given to the system.

The amplitude of the sideways swing is determined hydraulically in proportion to the slope angle by a pendulum.

Electronic control and monitoring

The machines belonging to the *Matador* generation were equipped with basic electrics to run the engine and road lighting. Instruments were limited to a drum speed indicator and the gearbox rpm equivalent to travel speed. The driver soon got to feel what 5 on the dial meant in second gear.

That all changed with the enclosed and soundproof cab. The driver could no longer hear a belt slipping or smell the smoke when something jammed. For a start, function monitors were installed inside the cab and when rpm dropped somewhere the driver was warned by a light.

The throughput monitor

The combine's work rate can vary considerably in the field, depending for instance on the crop type and the weather conditions. Since straw walker machines start losing grain rapidly above a certain output, conscientious drivers tend to stay well below the potential output to avoid losses. The throughput monitor was an early contribution to working closer to the limit by showing when losses start to go up.

Higher performance went hand in hand with driver comfort and the *Dominator 8* series upgrade in the mid 1980s went a long way in setting new ergonomic standards and improving maintenance.

At this point the multifunction control lever joined up the drive control with switches for a variety of other key functions.

The manually operated hydraulic valves made way for solenoids mounted conveniently in a single block at the side of the combine.

The individual indicators spread all over the cab were grouped together in a single information

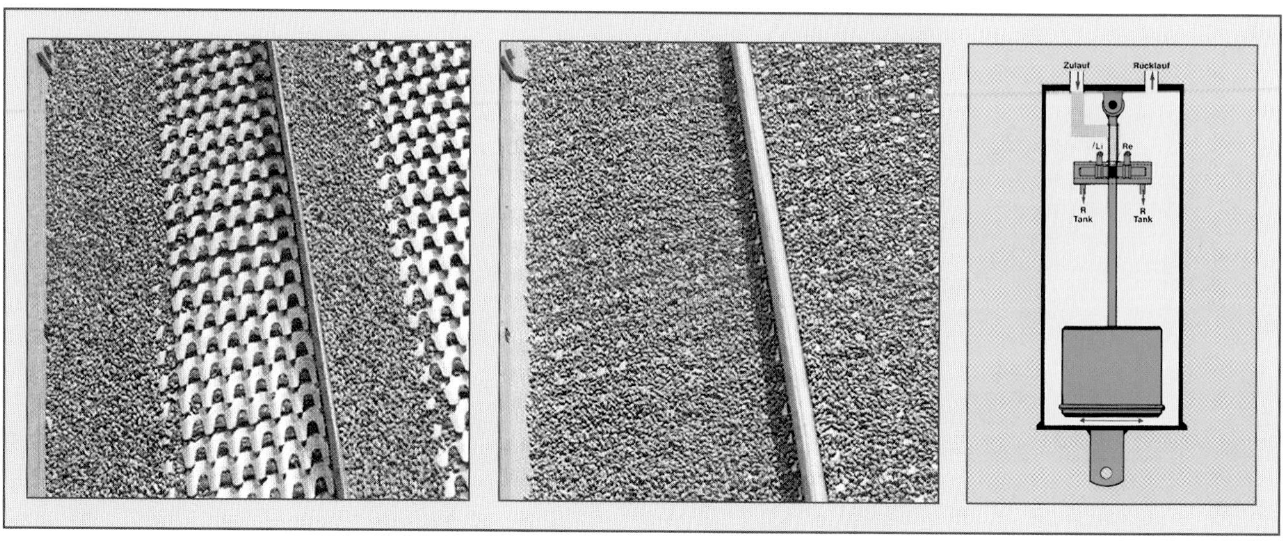

109 Sieve box crop on a slope without … … and with 3 D effect and … … the control pendulum

110 The multifunction control lever for travel speed and direction, reel lift and lowering

monitor mounted centrally under the steering wheel. This gave the driver all the information needed on how the machine was running.

The *Mega* and *APS*

When you put different assemblies together in a new combination, they can often add up to improved performance. The *Mega* combine range with *APS* (Acceleration and Pre-separation) is a good example of how this works in practice. In this highly successful model range a crop accelerator with a concave was fitted directly ahead of the main threshing drum. This had a highly positive impact on the crop flow, smoothing out the passage of the crop so the machine ran much more quietly whilst improving throughput, thanks to the early separation of loose grains before they reached the threshing drum.

111 APS threshing system with accelerator drum first fitted to Mega combine range

The cutter bar

The early types of cutter bar used on the *MDB* and *Super* resembled those of the reaper with a textile feed conveyor. The self propelled combines introduced the wide intake and six piece reel with controlled tines. The intake auger was fitted with four rows of retractable fingers in the transfer area, controlled by a cam plate. The knives were driven by a wobble drive mounted to a drive shaft taken off the main cutter bar drive. The table had fixed skids for passage over the field and was suspended by hydraulic cylinders with pre-tensioned coil springs.

The *Dominator* with its wider cutting widths gave rise to numerous modifications in these areas as weight and throughput rose steadily. For instance the single finger knife holders were replaced by double ones with more lateral stability. The drive was carried out with an eccentric and angle lever.

The feed tines were now driven by a crank and the cam plate disappeared. Following that the auger flights were made higher, feed tines now spread across the full width and the auger diameter increased. An oil bath drive with built in flywheel is now a standard part of the knife drive.

Increased cutting widths plus higher speeds meant that even more had to be done for the driver if output was to be maintained close to the limit. Automatic lowering and ground pressure control led finally to the development of *Claas Auto Contour* system. Hydraulic and elec-

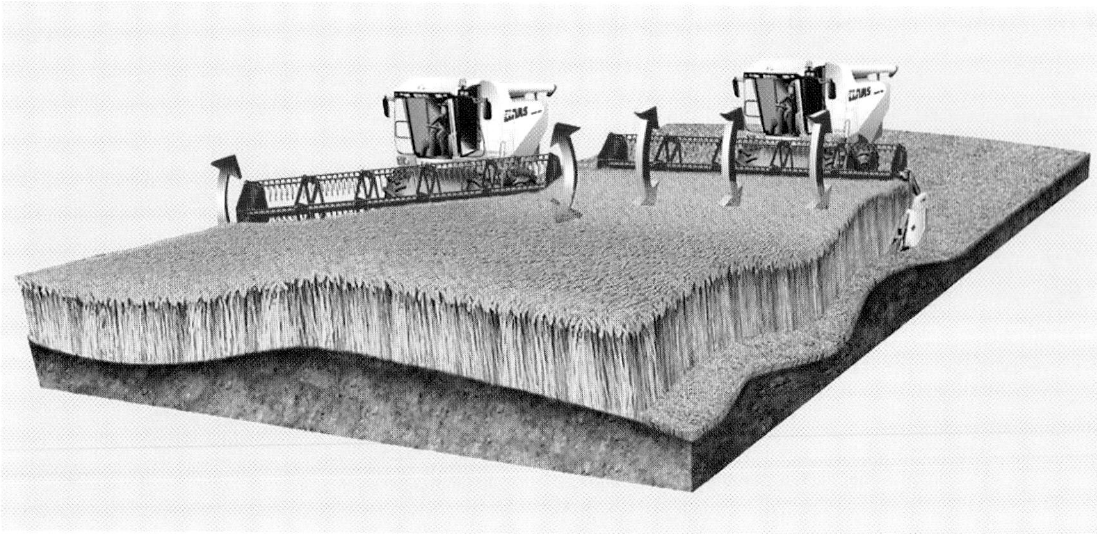

112 Claas Auto Contour enables the cutter bar to follow ground contours faithfully, regardless of the angle of the machine

tronic controls were blended to keep the cutter bar in line with the field contours, independently from the angle of the combine, giving a consistent short stubble height. An important step forward as farmers became more conscious of the need for correct straw management.

The Vario cutter bar

The Vario cutter bar was developed with a hydraulic table extension in response to the need to adapt quickly to changing field conditions. It also offered a convenient solution for oil seed rape harvesting with a second stage extension using insert plates.

Folding cutter bars

Virtually all combines have cutter bars which are over 3 metres wide. These have to be removed and loaded on a trailer for road transport, a common and time consuming task in areas with smaller farm structures. The table, intake auger, reel and knives on the *Claas* folding cutter bar are split in the middle and can be swivelled through 90° hydraulically to the front. In this position it stays within the 3 metre width limit.

Ludwig Caspers, Hans Dammann,
Wilhelm Kemper, Karl Rupprecht

114 The folding cutter bar shown half way between its transport and working position

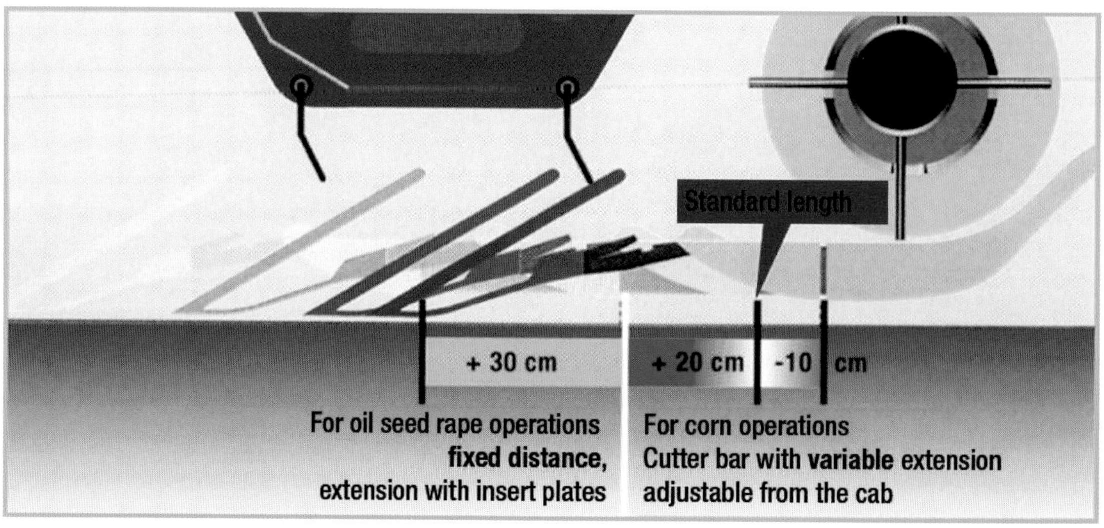

113 Illustration of the Vario cutter bar with adjustable table length

Lexion – King Size Combines

The introduction of the *Lexion* combine range is undoubtedly one of the most significant milestones in this story. The basic ideas were laid out in the early 1990s to help farmers and contractors to success as farm structures were once again subjected to rapid change. Introduced progressively from 1995 they covered the upper performance range with APS threshing systems as standard, whilst the top-of-the-line model featured a new rotor separation system which opened up the performance range into truly new dimensions. The current top model is the *Lexion 600*, the world's highest performing combine, keeping *Claas* in the technological lead for some time to come.

The hybrid threshing system was started in 1980 in Franz Tophinke's test lab at *Claas*. Later Franz Heidjann took over this project as chief engineer. The system was made up of a conventional threshing drum, an impeller to feed the crop on and secondary axial rotor separation. On the first units the straw walkers were replaced with twin axial mounted rotors and a common straw flow. Close attention was paid to the shape of the rotor flights and early trials in 1981 showed that additional engine power would be needed.

Next a three drum arrangement with matched speeds was tried out in a wider body. However, very dry and brittle straw led to blockages in the feed drum, problems which were soon sorted out. Extremely moist conditions such as grass seed revealed shortcomings which were solved by fitting spiral saw teeth profiles, a design which was retained in the final product. Bolt on retainers were welded onto the drum casing for bolting on the wear parts. Many hours were spent experimenting with the size of the concave perforations because of its importance for efficient grain separation without blockages in the packed straw.

If that wasn't enough, a single rotor Dominator combine with turret auger discharging was built and shown to a group of interested users from the USA in German harvest conditions. This combine layout was typical for the US market and was then run in the rice harvest there with the aim of building up a business relationship with IHC, but these efforts came to nothing.

The feed drum flow was improved by changing from three to six slats and then in 1992 two single rotor combines were built and thanks to close cooperation which was usual in these cases, the machine could be run in Spain in time.

The Lexion family

The combine development team under the leadership of Dr. Hermann Garbers began work on a project for a new family to replace the *Dominator* range with the support of the test lab with Chief foreman Franz Jungnitz. A twin rotor machine was designated as the top-of-line successor to the CS cylinder separation combine.

115 The Lexion 480 with cutting widths of up to nine metres

The project definition needed plenty of foresight and included:

- Increase of 20 % productivity for straw walker combines
- Inclusion of a rotor concept in the Lexion family
- Comfort and handling improvements to increase hourly operational performance and add to annual acreage potential
- New high impact design
- Integrated control and information systems
- Yield metering

The *Lexion 480* was the first of the new range to go into the market and was declared the world's highest output combine. With cutting widths of up to nine metres in heavy European crops, this was an amazing feat. The threshing drum width was 1,700 mm and the long established 450 mm drum diameter made way for a 600 mm version, together with a beefed up APS system. At that time there was a tiny market for machines of this size, but the time was right and volume sales exceeded all expectations as large farmers recognised the unique operating cost advantages of this king size combine, often replacing several smaller combines with just one *Lexion 480*.

The *Lexion 480* had APS plus the rotor separation, linked by a feed impeller which divided the straw into two flows as it enters the rotors. The crop then moves spirally to the back with high centrifugal forces acting on it, so the grain flies out and through the perforations in the casing. The rotor speed could be adjusted to the prevailing conditions, whilst the engine output of 305 KW (415 hp) was matched to this built in performance.

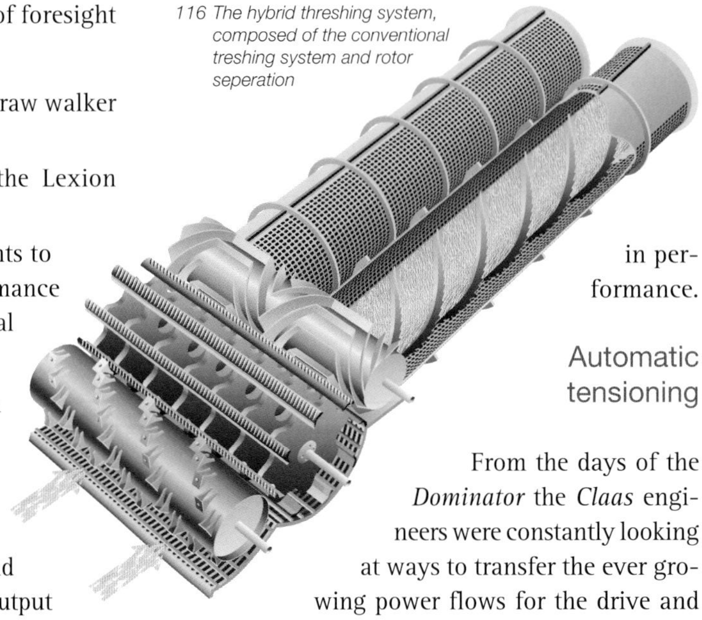

116 The hybrid threshing system, composed of the conventional treshing system and rotor seperation

Automatic tensioning

From the days of the *Dominator* the *Claas* engineers were constantly looking at ways to transfer the ever growing power flows for the drive and drum systems reliably, whilst not abandoning the familiar variable speed belt drive. This led them to the creation of the automatic tensioning device which was registered for a patent on June 30th 1976.

This works by tensioning the wide drive belt with a combined pressure mechanism in the drive, based on a combination of spring pressure and torque. Most of the pressure is generated by the spring, the rest comes automatically.

This system enables power peaks to be handled, even extreme variations, in a dust filled environment whilst ensuring a long belt life since the power flow occurs smoothly in relation to the torque demands.

What makes it different to other designs is that both pulleys are held firmly in position by a key shaft. The pressure amplification is introduced by the two pulley flanks, reducing the response

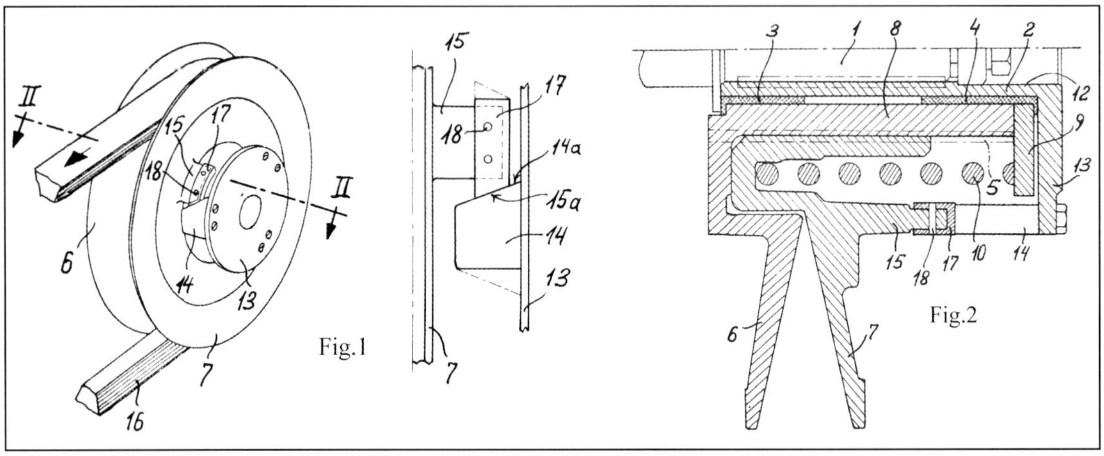

117 In the conventional drive assembly, (fig. 1 and 2) the fixed and variable pulleys are connected by a key shaft (5). The plate (9) is bolted to the hub (8). The pulley (7) can move lengthways and is tensioned by a pressure spring (10). In the patented version the complete control panel package consisting of the two pre-assembled pulley halves including the pressure spring is free to rotate on the hub (2) of the pressure flange (13) and fixed lengthways. The pressure flange hub is coupled to the drive shaft (1). When the drive comes under load the power flows via the three sliders (17) of the variable pulley onto the three curved pressure pieces on the pressure flange of the drive shaft.

118 The VISTA CAB with the air suspension seat in the middle of the new operator control centre

time when violent loading changes occur. The two belt side walls (16) are equally loaded and there are no additional stretching forces.

This patented tensioning device has stood the test of time now and is a standard feature on all *Claas* combines, including of course the *Lexion* family.

The cab design was revolutionary in that everything was done to enable the driver to work closer to the limit and do this for longer. This was a novel approach to improving machine output and relied on intelligent control systems. Driver comfort was part of this as demonstrated by the air suspended seat with the multifunction control lever now integrated into the armrest.

The man / machine interface was christened *CEBIS* or *Claas Electronic on Board Information System* and a display shows the driver the operating status of the combine without having to look away from the line of sight. This use of modern electronic control is one of the remarkable steps forward achieved by *Claas* engineers within the *Lexion* project. Yield metering was incorporated with the Quantimeter after many competitive attempts at developing a viable system had led to nothing. An on board printer and chip card were fitted for data transfer and storage. This system is the hub of yield mapping applications which is the foundation for modern precision farming.

The design team wanted to move away from the principle of just achieving a high tons per hour throughput because this was often misleading, since it could only be attained for a brief time under ideal conditions. Instead *Claas* engineering and marketing were in favour of a harvesting system approach which promised a higher daily and annual productivity and prior to launch extensive tests were carried out to back up this rather more intellectual approach. The driver was the key and improving productivity here was a new and challenging product strategy, but one that only a technology leader could credibly provide. In addition, set up and maintenance times would be cut adding to the productive hours of the combine. The customer could use fewer large machines or one huge combine to do the job.

The cutter bar is a decisive component in any performance enhancement project. The *Auto Contour* guidance system was taken over from the former range and the *Vario* cutter bar was added along with automatic reel positioning and speed. The cutter bar was fixed at four points with a single locking lever. The hydraulic connections were now leak free with a central coupler which also joined up the electrical circuits.

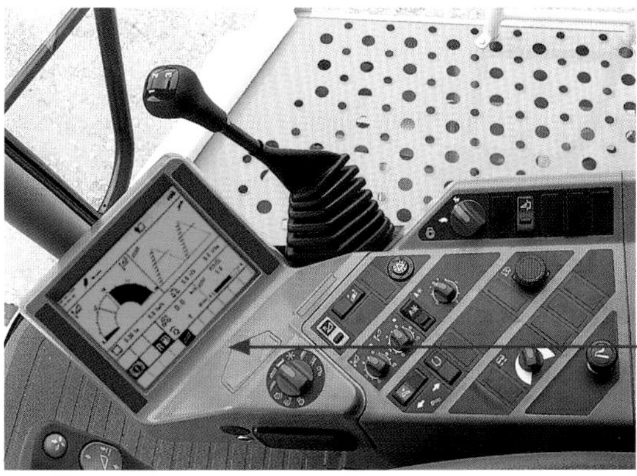

119 Instrument panel with CEBIS display

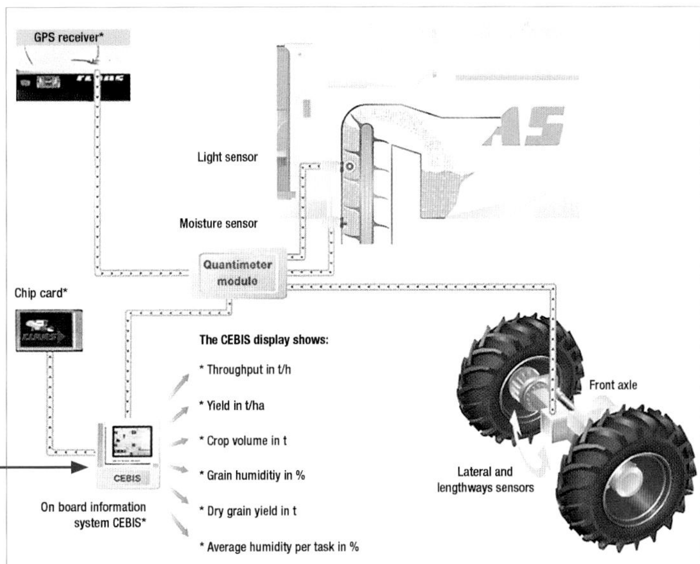

120 Precision farming, technology and cost reduction in one

121 Laser Pilot – automatic steering in the cereals harvest

The *Laser Pilot* system which came a few years later and was awarded a DLG Gold Medal was another breakthrough in productivity. The combine could now be driven along the edge of the cereals crop without the driver having to correct the path of the machine. The full cutting width could be used all the time and accurate yield metering was enhanced, whilst the driver could focus on keeping the speed and throughput close to the limit. A hydraulic reverser for the feed conveyor and intake cleared out any blockages in the unlikely case of a crop jam up front.

The APS threshing drum could now be set precisely from the cab with an electro-hydraulic control. The hydraulics double up as an overload protection so the driver could really work at the limit without worrying about overdoing it. This has a major effect on driver attitudes and directly boosts the daily work rate. The difficulty of finding experienced combine drivers was addressed by including a range of standard settings for different crops, with the intention of helping even inexperienced drivers to get good results. The 3 D cleaning system was taken over from the earlier models and high quality cleaning was ensured by the use of powerful turbine fans. The rotor combines were joined a year later by a full range of straw walker combines to cover the full range of needs for farmers and contractors, and the *Lexion* range was divided into 1,420 and 1,700 mm threshing drum widths – a compact chassis width for contractors who need mobility and a wide body for extra high capacity and large farms.

Not content to rest on their laurels the Claas engineers were soon looking at ways to improve the range and keep ahead of changing customer needs. The upgrade included a shift from a *400* series to a *500* number range, with an array of performance enhancing features. These include the soft start cutter bar engagement to elimi-

122 Lexion 580 rear view with the characteristic tail wagging action of the two funnels which spread the chopped straw evenly across the full cutting width

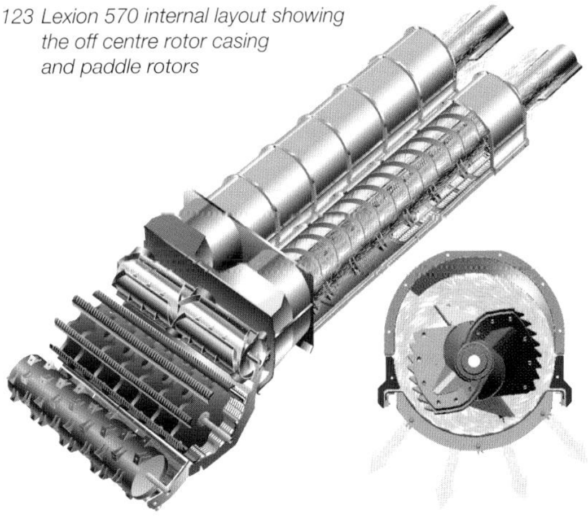

123 Lexion 570 internal layout showing the off centre rotor casing and paddle rotors

125 The Lexion 570 in the harvest

nate peak loadings in the drive and clutches in line with the ever wider cutting widths. A new cutter bar brake stops the header immediately and prevents foreign objects entering, reducing downtime and damage. The *Laser Pilot* automatic steering, previously only available on the left, has been added to the right hand side, since customers sometimes can't always work on the one side.

Inside the newly designed *VISTA CAB* there is more room for a passenger and fully automatic air conditioning. The cutter bar brake button is integrated into the multifunction control lever along with tank discharge and discharge auger swivelling, whilst push button solenoid gear changing has been introduced.

The *Lexion 570* stands out as a compact rotor combine with ideal dimensions for easy mobility and a crop flow designed to handle the straw gently. The paddle type rotors are mounted off centre, a method which loosens up the straw without damaging it. A variator is fitted as standard to match the rotor speed to the crop conditions. Electrically operated rotor flaps under the separation concaves reduce the chaff volume.

The *Lexion 580* became the undisputed king of the harvest with an unrivalled work rate which is powered by engines with 316 KW or 430 net horse power. They produce an extra 50 hp if revs drop, so that temporary overload situations can be bridged. Electronic engine control keeps fuel consumption to a minimum, even in tough surroundings. This amazing performance has made it the first choice for large farms and changed the face of farming irrevocably.

Ludwig Caspers, Heinz König, Jens Möller

124 The Lexion Montana models with Auto Contour control keep the combine level over steep slopes

All round Capability – Maize, Rice and Other Crops

The early export performance of the company made everyone at *CLAAS* aware of the need to engineer products which could handle a wide variety of crops. The rice harvest was a challenge taken on by the team who were attracted by the complexity of working in muddy fields with a highly abrasive crop. The maize harvest lengthened the combine harvesting season and the demands placed on the machines increased. As the area of oil seed rape grew, new answers to prevent cutting losses were expected from the farmers whilst international expansion introduced soy beans to the list. However the harvesting specialist was always in the forefront when it came to finding the appropriate solutions.

Rice is a staple crop for many folk on our planet – In Europe it has a major role to play in the Po Valley in Italy, in the delta regions of Spain and the Camargue region of France. The story began for *Claas* in Italy with the pull type *Super* combine, which had the advantage that it kept in a straight line behind the tractor and didn't leave another set of tracks.

126 A rice combine in the mud ...

The arrival of the self propelled combine soon began to make itself felt and the engineers soon figured out that the drive wheels exerted too much pressure on the field. Steel belt drives were fitted to keep the machines afloat over the irrigated fields. Flotation was only one part of the problem, the other was how to harvest the delicate grains of rice. This was solved with a peg tine drum which rubbed the grain out of the panicle.

Initially this special equipment was developed with the *Claas* importer in Vercelli – *Cantone* – for the well structured fields in the surrounding rice bowl area of Italy. When it came to more difficult conditions in Spain or Morocco, engineering changes had to be resorted to. The machines sank into the ground, despite the tracks, and got stuck in the mud when the lower panels hit the topsoil. The engineers worked on a fix in the Seville region which involved raising the height of the combines for improved ground clearance. Since the Italian specialists were convinced their solution was a good one, they had trouble believing that the tracks and steer axle mount had to be raised. Seeing is believing, so a high level delegation including Luigi Cantone and some *Claas* engineers made its way to Spain to agree on how to get the combines running without trouble.

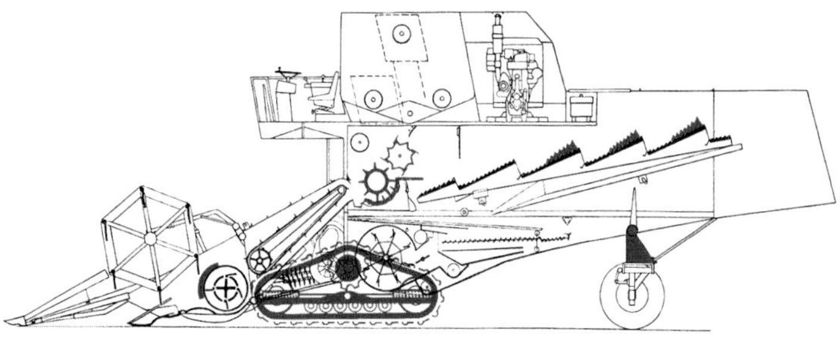

127 ... and the rice equipment in a cross section

128 Claas field staff in the mud – this was co-author Heinrich Roderfeld and Felix Binacchi in Andalusia

Heinrich Roderfeld made a trip report which includes the following: "after the modifications the machines threshed and travelled satisfactorily. This should lead to further sales".

Then the following thoughts: "only *Gigant* and *Mercator* as rice combines for use outside Italy. Does it make sense to have rice only combines, exclusive rice harvesters"?

The reason for this is simple. The rice plant harbours silicate crystals and these cause high wear on feed augers and tables, especially in tropical conditions. This can be limited by applying wear

129 Rice expert Roderfeld, this time with a Cantone employee. The sign proclaims Vercelli to be the European centre for rice

resistant, heat treated coatings to the exposed parts, so a special version could make economic sense. Here's a little tale – several tons of steel for these augers was sent for heat treatment in Cologne. The word "auger" is "snail" in German and so this load of snails ended up being delivered to the company canteen!

Claas then took over the design of the rice equipment internally and made the threshing drum the same diameter so it could be swapped over more readily, a task made much easier with the flange mounting of the drum. Running over muddy fields required special seals to be fitted on the axle drives and wheel bearings on the steer axle. Since the machines are steered mainly by drive brakes the operator needed a position indicator to stay on track.

130 The rice threshing drum, peg tines replace the slats

The cutter bars often have to make their way through laid rice so the knife bar is running close to the ground in wet and rotten stems. In these surroundings the points of the fingers can get clogged and don't work properly, so *Claas* came up with special rice cutter bars. This version employed a moving knife with a fixed knife instead of the fingers. The intake augers, in common with the grain augers, were coated to reduce wear and tear. All the later combine families – the *CS* models, *Mega* and *Lexion* – are suitable for rice harvesting. In fact the APS threshing achieves impressive results in rice.

The *Crop Tiger*

Early in the 1980s the political and economic climate in Asia improved to such an extent that investments, especially in China and India, became feasible. This prompted *Claas* to initiate a development project for a small rice harvester which would also be a multicrop combine. Much as in Europe a few decades previously, farm mechanisation was in its infancy in most Asian countries, and *Claas* felt a commitment to this new world of harvesting. Dr. Breymayer was responsible for the ground research for this ambitious project. His conclusion was that the Asian combine had to have about 60 hp, a 2.10 metre cutting width, full rubber tracks, an axial threshing and separation system with a weight of less than 3.5 tons.

131 Manual rice harvest in India with Claas people power

The great significance attached to this project by the Chinese government was confirmed by the participation of two high level experts from the Beijing Harvest Institute – Professor Dong and Professor Gao – in the joint *Crop Tiger* project as it evolved in Harsewinkel. The full length rubber tracks and the axial threshing unit (called TAF for Tangential Axial Flow) were completely uncharted territory. Under the supervision of Franz Heidjann, a first prototype was built and after successful trials in European cereals and rice, it was air freighted to Shanghai and put through its paces locally by a Chinese test team.

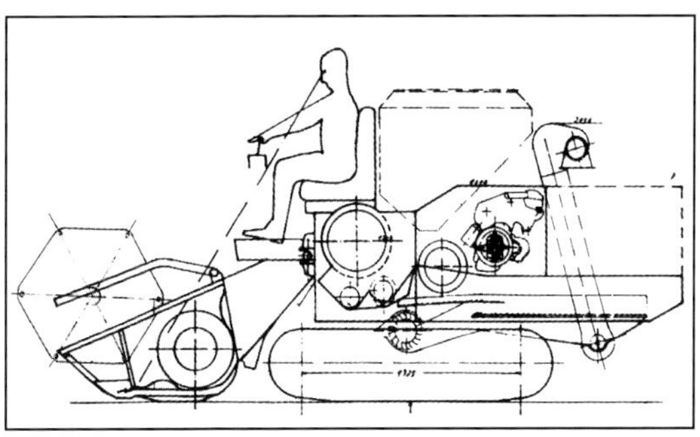

132 The Crop Tiger in section

133 Crop Tiger prototype being tested in Spain with Ludwig Buhne at the controls and Karl Heitmann (right)

The project failed to come off when the designated local production partner ran into financial problems. A new partner was found, this time in India. The new arrangement was with *Escorts* in Faridabad, a company *Claas* had worked well in other fields previously. A new joint company was created – *Escorts Claas*. This time the project progressed to fruition, the *Crop Tiger* has been produced there ever since and exported to a wide range of countries. As expected, this small and low price combine was ideally suited to the needs of farmers and contractors in the initial mechanisation phase of developing Asian economies.

134 Chinese engineering team in front of Crop Tiger prototype with Franz Heidjann (centre) and Anton Buchmann (right)

Maize

With the introduction of new hybrid corn varieties from America in the 1950s and 1960s, maize growing took off in Europe. In the beginning phase manual harvesting was common and mechanisation took place initially with corn pickers which picked the cobs and removed the husks. The cobs were then dried in wire boxes and the grains would then be stripped from the spindles using stationary equipment. The creative minds at *Claas* soon started thinking about how to adapt the combine to this crop, and initially the *Super* was sent into the maize crop soon after the Second World War in overseas regions, for instance in South Africa.

Cutter bars were transformed into maize cutter headers, aligned to cut the evenly spaced rows. Spearing the stalks on the mowing fingers had to be avoided and laid plants were ingested via low profile round tips and covers and transported with the cob to the intake auger via feed chains. The auger itself had blades which were

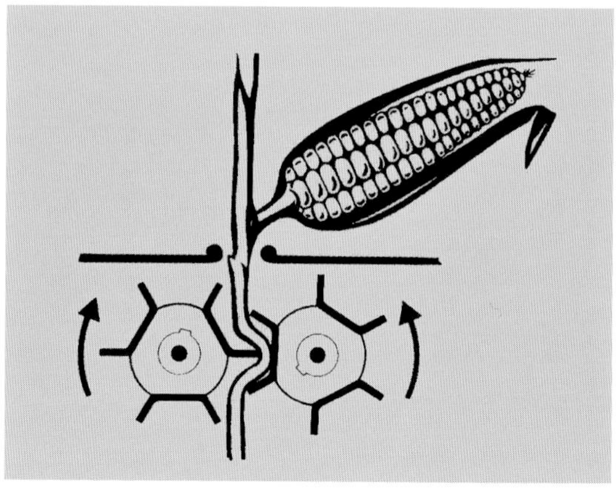

135 Functional diagram of the maize header with snapping rolls and plates

136 An eight row header mounted on a Dominator

supposed to chop or at least snap the stalks so they would pass easier through the combine. Despite the heavy loading on the threshing drum and straw walkers, this method achieved acceptance because it left the field ready for ploughing, at least when the beefed up straw chopper was used.

During the 1960s the modern day maize headers made their debut and took over, thanks to the new principle which involved two counter rotating snapping rollers which pulled down the stem and snapped off the cobs with a snapping plate. The crop feed was by chains whilst the covers were rounded and similar to the early maize cutter bars.

The cobs rolled through the threshing unit and the grains stripped. To stop the spindles falling through, filler plates were added. The concave perforation needed to be made bigger for larger grains and the whole assembly strengthened. These concaves were also suitable for other large grains like beans or sunflower seeds. As mentioned earlier in the *Dominator* story *Claas* had discovered an ideal test bed in Hungary. Norbert Ortkras as test manger and the *Claas* service team all deserve a special mention for their dedication to supporting the machines in the field in conditions which defy description.

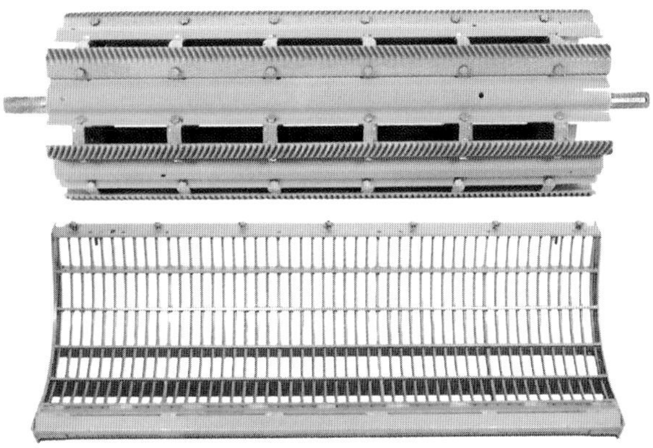

137 Maize threshing set up (drum fillers and concave)

This type of header left the plant lying underneath so an additional operation was needed to chop and destroy the stems outside the combine's crop flow. This problem was solved with the underslung chopper (*HPH*), mounted flexibly and fitted with high speed rotating flail blades

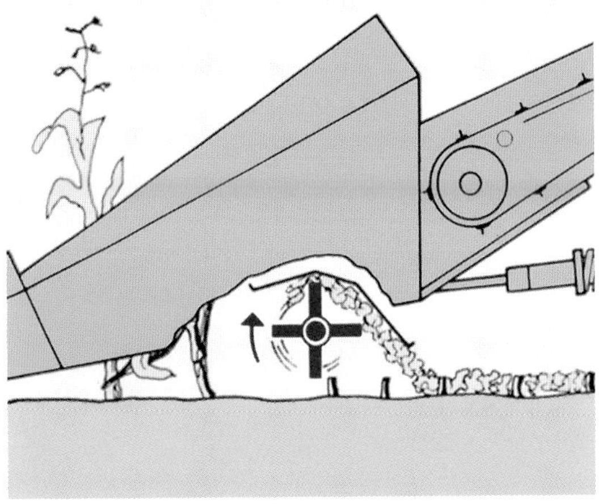

138 Functional diagram of the HPH stalk chopper

on a horizontal full width shaft. This additional task required power and could slow down the work rate, so it could also be taken out of circuit if needed.

The *Multimaster* header range took the process a step further, grouping plucking and chopping into the picking unit. One of the snapping rollers had a lengthways channel with a knife blade intruding into it, whilst the other became a pressure roller to guide the stem. The six row *Mul-*

timaster was made as a folding header. The outer picking units either side were folded to the centre, so that the three metre width limit could be adhered to on the road.

The headers for the current combine range are now developed and manufactured in the *Claas* competence centre and factory in Saulgau. The latest development is the *Conspeed* family featuring conical snapping rollers which add to the stem speed as they pass back and down. Higher work rates are the benefit, aimed at improving the overall return on the high machine investment. A vertical shaft for the chopper can be fitted to each picking unit, whilst smooth plastic tips reduce friction and stop dirt from accumulating.

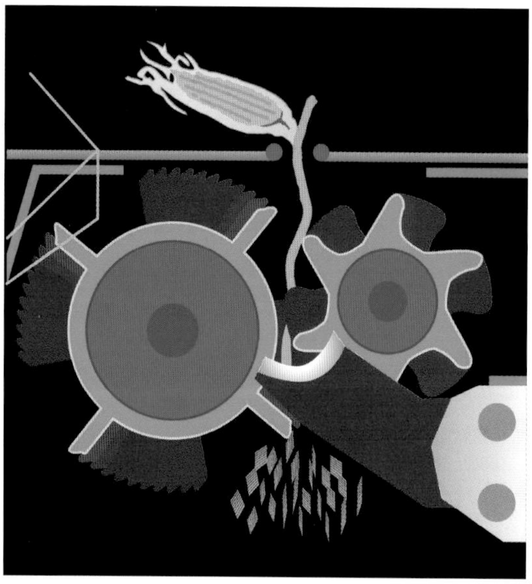

139 Functional diagram of the Multimaster picking unit

Back in 1977 *Claas* introduced another major stress reducing feature with automatic steering through the rows known to this day as the *Autopilot.* A pair of spring mounted sensors feel their way through the rows and deviations are sent to an electronic controller which corrects the path of the combine without delay.

Another maize harvesting process of some note is *Corn Cob Mix* or *CCM.* The threshing unit is tightened up to break virtually all the grain and the spindles. The threshing drum can be fitted with special plates and round bar concaves. The sieves are opened up wide so that the grain and bits of spindle can reach the grain tank. This mixture is then discharged on the field into a portable high power mill where it is ground finely, then placed in a silo for use as forage on pig farms.

Over the years new hybrid plants have been developed which have spread the suitability for maize farming into new climatic regions. Maize types are classified with FAO numbers which show the number of days growth needed. Since early varieties came from climatically better areas, harvest further north often created problems. In the 1960s farmers were often faced with the problem that the crop didn't mature properly, was flattened by gales and the fields were impassable due to rain. Rice half tracks were one way around this, and now climatic influences plus new, high yielding maize varieties have made a combine's maize harvesting capability a central factor in most regions. A trend which *Claas* recognized early and with its systems approach kept a strong lead ever since.

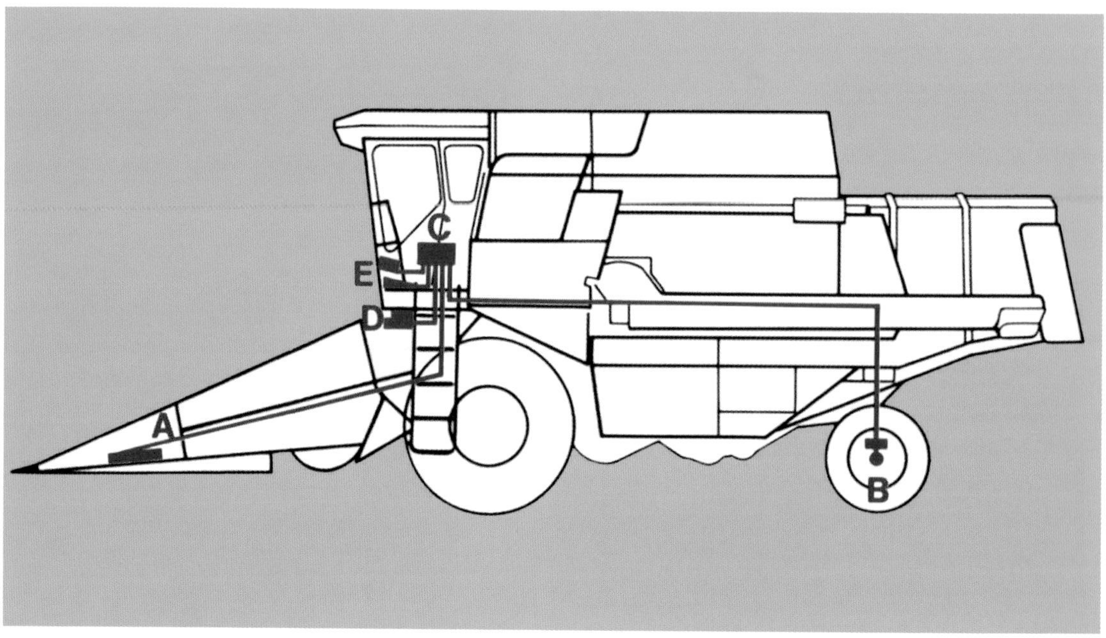

140 Automatic steering layout

141 OSR harvest from the swath with pick-up

Oil seed rape

This crop – abbreviated to OSR and known in North America as Canola – grows in pods which tend to explode as soon as the combine nears, spilling the contents onto the field. In addition the crop knots itself into a thick mat and normal cutter bars inflict heavy losses. Solutions had to be found since OSR is often harvested alongside wheat and other cereals on small and large areas. The first approach was to cut the crop before full maturity and lay it in swaths to ripen. A pick-up was then attached to feed the swath into the combine. Then it was observed that yields went up substantially in the final ripening period and so the combine cutter bar had to be fitted with attachments to catch the seeds up front. Lateral knives cut their way through the mat without tearing and this too reduced losses.

The real breakthrough for OSR farmers came with the *Vario* cutter bar on *Claas* combines, an economic and simple solution for all cereal farming applications. The hydraulic table exten-

142 The Conspeed is the latest maize header innovation from Claas in Saulgau

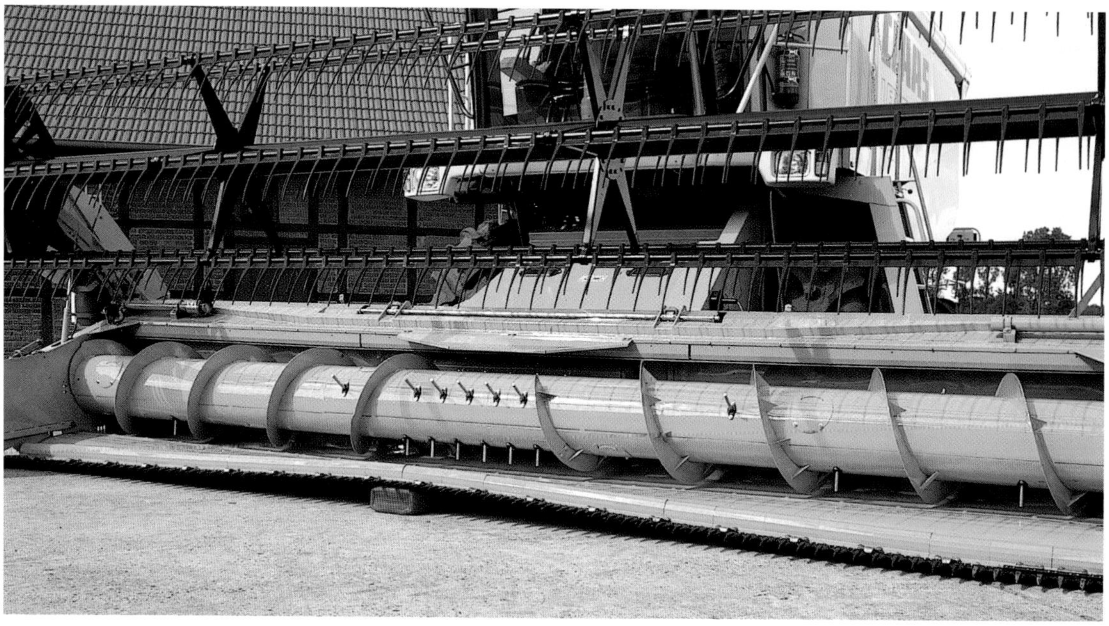

143 Soy bean cutter bar with the flexible knife layout

sion is of universal benefit and filler plates are added to catch the OSR, whilst the lateral knives are fitted in minutes. This explains the immense popularity of this new style cutter bar.

Soya beans

The bean harvest is another interesting application, and extremely important, for instance in North America. The pod is close to the ground so standard cutter bars cause heavy losses. The soya bean cutter bar is fitted with a flexible spring steel knife bar which accurately hugs the ground. The profile of the knife bar is determined by guides on the base of the table. Spring steel sections keep the knives in suspension over the full width, whilst *Claas Contour* guides the whole table close to the ground enabling the knife bar to move freely.

144 Modern style straw chopper

The are numerous other crops, often with mere regional importance. These include sunflowers, grass seed, clover, millet, durum, peas, beans – you name it, *Claas*'ll thresh it. They are all harvested with the standard combine using the machine's wide range of adjustments and settings, plus attachments and locally produced accessories.

Straw chopping

Straw or stems from most of these is of no use in regions where there is little mixed farming and is therefore chopped and spread on the field leaving them ready for tillage

The earliest choppers were fitted with cutter bar blades, which were susceptible to damage, so they were followed by flail knives mounted in pairs on the chopper rotor, where they pass through a bank of fixed knives. The chopped material is expelled by the energy involved and channelled to the ground. Recently straw management has become a vital point for farmers and *Claas* responded as usual with innovative ideas for top rate spreading as cutting widths grew. Above six metres the *Lexion* range had reached the limit for an even distribution with the traditional straw chopper and came up with spreading fans to distribute the straw via swivelling funnels. This now includes the chaff and short straw from the sieves by way of the chaff spreader which works with spreading discs and an air blast from fans.

Ludwig Caspers,
Franz Heidjann, Heinrich Roderfeld

Forage Harvesters and Other Products

145 The Jaguar offloading in the field

The development of the Claas self propelled forage harvesters began in 1973 and was based on the pull type version, which had been providently named Jaguar. Since then countless updates and improvements have been made as the product has dominated the world market. The experience with stationary straw balers led Claas into the production of pick-up balers. The takeover of the Bautz company added hay tools to the Claas range, whilst sugar cane harvesters, drying units and other special machines rounded off the harvesting product line.

Success Story of the *Jaguar*

Mechanical choppers were invented in England and been around from the early 19th century. Trailed forage harvesters made their debut after the late 1940s as tractor power increased. The breakthrough came, however, with the arrival of maize in the 1960s because this made a self propelled forager a viable proposition for the first time. The first versions were mostly one-offs before *CLAAS* took on the task of developing a well designed product.

Why chop up grass and maize? Originally it was to open it up and make it more easily digestible for the recipients. Later reduced exposure to the weather became a feature, so the green harvest was mowed and swathed, then left to dry before being chopped. Silage techniques developed – by compressing the crop in the clamp and sealing it hermetically it was kept fresh. All year round, the daily rations could be sliced off for feeding and by its nature, the chopped crop is easy to handle mechanically.

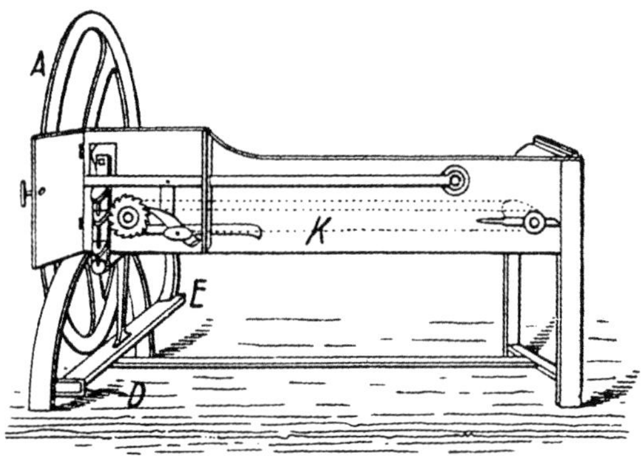

146 The Lester chopping machine ca. 1880 made in England

Chopping in its own right took off as bigger tractors became available for trailed foragers and self propelled foragers opened up new potential as the harvest area grew in importance.

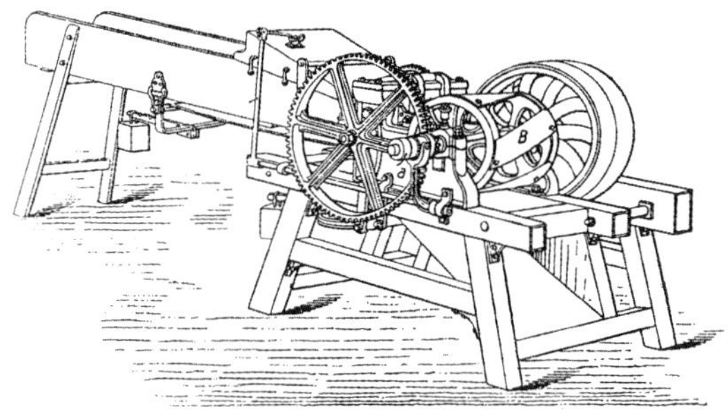

148 The Salmon drum chopper from 1804, also English made

The *Jaguar 60 SF*

With the rapid growth of maize in Europe at the end of the 1960s and early 1970s, customers began demanding equipment suitable for managing the harvest process. Inventive dealers and technically adept contractors built their own self propelled machines by taking the chopping unit from a trailed forager and the engine, drive train, platform and the rest of the bits from an old combine that was being scrapped. The first self propelled foragers in Europe developed much like the earliest inventions in the beginning chapters of this book.

147 The Jaguar SF 60 harvesting combination

149 Jaguar 80 with modular construction

Hanneforth is the name of a dealer close to *Claas* in Steinhagen who did just that. They were a supplier of components to *Claas* and they created a self propelled machine based on combine parts and the workings of a *Jaguar 60*, and gave it the grand name of *Imperator*. They even displayed it at the 1972 DLG exhibition which focussed the company's attention on the lack of a suitable *Claas* product, a subject which the German sales force had been complaining about for some time.

As so often, *Claas* got the message and set out designing a new product within a short space of time. The success story starts from here.

The rapid response was made possible by the availability of the proven components from the *Jaguar 60* which included an 88 KW (120 hp) engine and the full range of combine parts to make it into a prime mover well adapted to tough working conditions in the field. An important design feature was that the parts were all adopted without modification which made for excellent parts interchange.

Thanks to the high engine power the *Jaguar 60 SF* left the trailed foragers standing. Its work rate was higher, it was more manoeuvrable, opening up the field was easier and it could cut a path through the middle of the field. The two row maize header and grass pick-up from the *Jaguar 60* were unchanged.

Just in time for the start of the 1973 green harvest, thirty brand new *Claas Jaguar 60 SF* models were ready for final inspection. Company founder August Claas and his wife Paula came personally with the key employees to assign the first batch of machines their serial numbers.

The *Jaguar 80*

The *Jaguar 60 SF* was just the first step on the long road to success for *Claas* foragers. American products were being bought by contractors looking for higher performance and three row headers. The response from *Claas* was not long in coming and the *Jaguar 80* was soon launched with a wider chopping drum and a remarkable new feature which was the separation of the intake from the chopping housing. This made the access to the knives and the intake rollers much easier. A new ejection fan ensured swift transfer of the chopped crop onto the trailer whilst driver performance was enhanced with the introduction of the *Claas* automatic steering system which used the same sensor principle as described in the combine chapter earlier.

Automatic steering was a major relief for drivers of the forager and provided productivity gains which helped ensure the leading position of the *Jaguar* from early on. *Claas* also sold the automatic steering to competition. The *Jaguar* was

150 More power with the Jaguar 80

originally fitted with a 157 KW (213 hp) engine, three or four row maize headers, a four row maize picker, a 3.3 metre mowing attachment and the pick-up.

The *Jaguar 70*

Without a doubt the Jaguar 80 was so much of a jump that the *Jaguar 60 SF* didn't have a chance in the market place, so development work on the *Jaguar 70* was begun. It was a derivative of the bigger machine, a smaller version designed for silage maize using two or three row headers and this entailed a wider intake. Optional 110 KW (150hp) and 129 KW (175 hp) engines were made available. The splitting of the intake from the drum was also a feature carried over from the *Jaguar 80*. The headers together with the chopping unit swivelled around the centre of the drum to increase ground clearance.

The *Jaguar 675* to *690*

Ten years had passed since the first *Claas* forage harvester had appeared and something completely new was about to be launched. With it the decisive phase of this success story would begin as the market developed. Four new models were announced – they were virtually identical, with engine output going from 127 KW (173 hp) to 220 KW (300 hp). Commonality of design was essential, since volumes were still not enormous and trailed machines were still sold in large numbers. The design was extremely up-to-date and the rear fell away markedly. This design met with the approval of the contractors who were the main purchasers of this type of machine. They also appreciated the numerous new features such as the position of the metal detector in the lower compression roller, the corn cracker located above the chopping cylinder and the high efficiency of the ejector fan with plenty of power to boost the crop on its way to the trailer.

152 New generation Jaguar 690, 6 row maize header

The cab had been taken over from the combine. It was much more spacious than before and mounted on rubber blocks. The drive control lever operated the header, chopping and ejector flap functions in one place. This was a big ergonomic improvement on the previous model range and along with all the other features released all the productivity reserves at a stroke.

151 The Jaguar 70 filled the gap in the first generation range

The separation of the intake from the drum plus swivel mounting on the axis were other features taken over from the predecessor and have kept their place to this day. This was also the first appearance of the six row maize header with folding side units to stay within the three metre road width limits. Later this became a top selling unit on all brands of foragers for many years since there was little economic sense in investing large sums in an alternative product in such a small market. The production of headers and chopping units was concentrated in the *Claas* factory in Saulgau.

153 The Jaguar 695 was the top of the line at the period

The *Jaguar 682 S* to the *695 SL*

The first *600* generation was superseded by the *600 SL* family featuring an even better cab for increased ease of operation. Engine power range now went from 158 KW (215 hp) on the entry level *682 S* and *SL* up to 260 KW (354 hp) on the *695 SL*. This family saw the introduction of the chevron chopping drum, characterised by offset half width knives which evened out the flow of material and reduced the tendency for the accelerator fan to stick. Higher drum speeds and a larger number of knives made ever increasing throughputs possible with an efficient use of engine power. The operating spectrum was

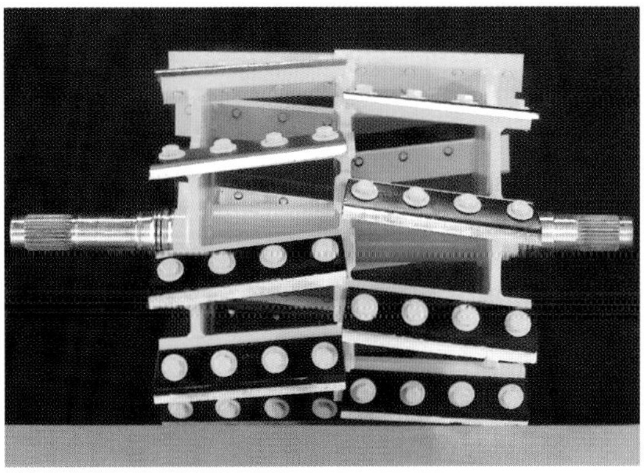
155 The chevron drum

also widened with the introduction of equipment packages for whole crop silage and ground ear maize.

The *Jaguar 820* to *880*

By the early 1990s it was apparent from talking to contractors that another quantum leap would need to be made and the *800* series was the answer. The power range jumped from 228 KW (310 hp) to 354 KW (481 hp), the engine was mounted sideways at the back with a simple drive line, excellent cooling and accessibility to the inside of the machine with a roll out corn cracker design for a quick changeover from maize to grass. This layout is the benchmark for all modern forage harvesters and the good steer axle loading made feasible the fitting of eight row maize headers. A completely new and aggressive design visualised the technical features within the machine. The cab now featured a curved windscreen and sloping roof line, a second seat was fitted, and central lubrication

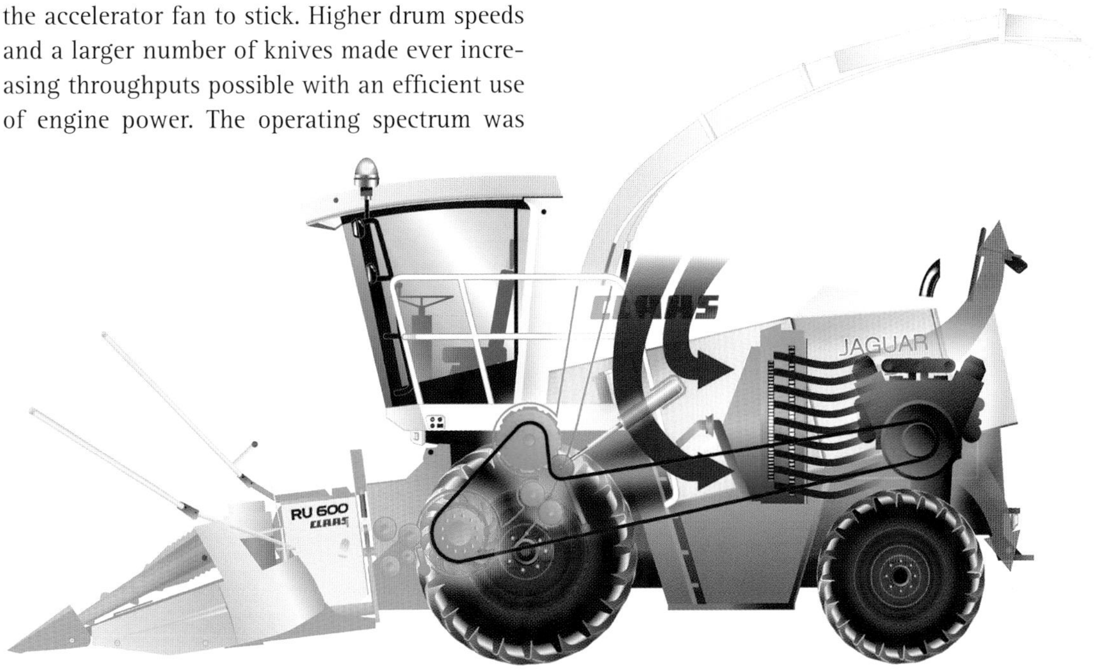

154 Third generation Jaguar 900 highlights the direct drive and innovative air flow

156 The Jaguar 870 is the best selling model today

was made available. The flow of the crop was enhanced by the location of the corn cracker and accelerator fan. The customer response was enthusiastic, and the new range soon showed its superiority and low operating cost.

The *Jaguar 830* to *900*

Over the years, many power barriers had been broken, but with 445 KW (605 hp) the *Jaguar 900* was a major step. The smallest version boasted 236 KW (321 hp), not far off the largest forager of the *600* generation. Whilst the basic design needed little modification, the new *Jaguar* family had benefited from the success of the range in North America.

New features included mud deflectors over the rear wheels and a new style rear panel. The operator compartment was upgraded with the introduction of a single control terminal for all set up and monitoring functions, rather like the combine harvester. Grinding and shear bar settings from the cab were simplified.

Road travel was a major issue for many contractors and so a high speed version called *Speedstar* was developed with a travel speed of 40 km/h (25 mph). The row independent headers had taken over completely from the fixed row versions from the mid 1990s and the *Claas RU 450* and *RU 600* form the modern front equipment for the *Jaguar* range. The versatility has been further enhanced with the *Direct Disc 520* for direct mowing of whole crop silage.

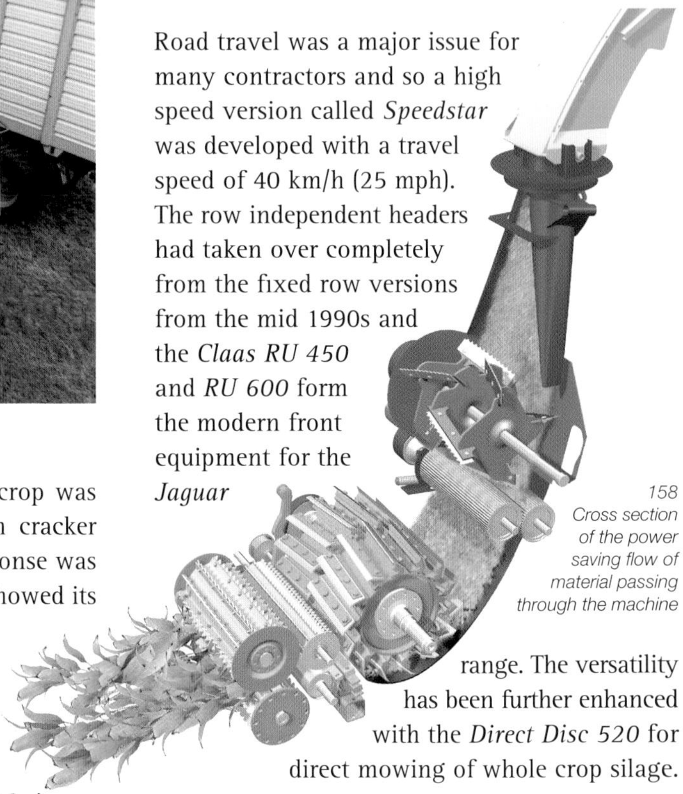

158 Cross section of the power saving flow of material passing through the machine

The *Jaguar* has been a tremendous success story, one that *Claas* pays careful attention to so that it will continue to be the leader for many years to come.

Ernst Klinger

157 The Jaguar range comes with a wide range of headers, such as the RU 600 maize attachment or the Direct Disc 520

Everything for the Forage Harvest

CLAAS moved into forage harvesting in 1969 with the takeover of the *BAUTZ* Company in Saulgau, south Germany. In parallel the chopping technology rights were acquired from the *SPEISER* Company in nearby Göppingen and blended with the Saulgau product line up. Following extensive plant modernisation in recent years Saulgau has been transformed into the competence centre of the *CLAAS* Group, offering a full range of mowers, swathers and tedders as well as loader wagons and chopping technology.

The growth of farm sizes and development of new structures didn't just revolutionise the cereals harvest, the harvest of grass and maize for animal forage has been changed out of all recognition. This process was speeded up when the eastern European and Russian markets opened up after the fall of communism there. Farms were traditionally much bigger, although mechanisation lagged far behind, so machines with high work rates and working widths were much sought after.

159 Top-of-the-line Disco 8500

Mowing

The good old mowing bar had had its day and was replaced by rotating systems in the first half of the 1960s. Unlike the traditional mower, rotating systems chopped the stems at a high speed without the need for a shear bar, speeding up the whole process. This method was protected by patent and *Claas / Bautz* joined the market in 1971 with a rotary mower called the *WM 30* for tractors from 30 hp. This was a two drum mower, each rotor being individually belt driven.

160 Front mower functioning

From 1977 a new drive design was introduced for the *WM 20* and *WM 30* featuring an angle drive built in to the drum housing, a superior layout in all terms. With this step *Claas* introduced freely rotating ground discs to replace the fixed ones which were thought to produce more resistance over the field. From 1992 the product designations were scrapped in favour of brand names, in common with the rest of the *Claas* products. The drum mowers were christened *Corto* and have kept the name to this day.

In 1993 the first *Claas* disc mowers – the *Corto 240 D* and *280 D* – made their debut. There was a big market for this version where farmers were convinced of its superiority – the discs were smaller and turned faster, at 3,000 rpm with a peripheral speed of about 80 m/s. Whereas the drum mowers were driven from above, the disc mowers were driven by a transmission under the discs. A second range was added in 1996, the new range was renamed *Disco* and working widths now went up to 3.40 metres. Both drum and disc mowers came in different tractor fixing versions: front and rear mounted as well as trailed. The trend to larger working widths has

161 The Disco 3000 TC-AS, a modern mower which lays the swath next to the front mower swath for faster field clearance

led to a trend to combine front and rear mounting for greater efficiency.

The entry of multiple mowing combinations was a logical next step and it followed in 1993. The *Corto 8100 F* was a triple drum mower combination, the first machine designed specifically for professional contracting. In the year 2000 the changeover was made to disc mowing for these large units with the *Disco 8500 C*. This featured variable working widths from 8 to 8.30 metres and the ability to split up the combination with one front mower and a pair of foldable outrigger mowers behind the tractor. When the tractor was fitted with a reverse drive it was close to being on a self propelled mower with all the mowing units in visible range. The *Disco 8700 C* was a derivative from this model which was designed for fitting to the *Jaguar* forager to increase its annual utilisation.

From such modest beginnings it's a long way to the *Claas Cougar*. This is the latest addition to the range marking a further enormous jump in performance. It is a self propelled mower with unbeatable work rates thanks to a massive 14 metre working width. Despite this an ingenious folding system keeps it within the 3 metre road transport width.

Over the years the use of conditioners has expanded steadily. They speed up the grass drying process and reduced losses in the silage process by opening up the outer stem mechanically. The production of storable hay means that 10 tons or more of water per hectare have to evaporate first.

162 The Claas Cougar is the biggest mower in the world currently, cutting 14 metres across

163 A tedder with adjustable outer frames

Tedding and swath raking

After being taken over by *Claas*, the *Bautz* range of tedders was kept in production to start with. Then, a couple of years later in 1971 a new four rotor tedder with a working width of 4.30 metres was introduced. Unlike the competitive products it had a bevel gear rotor drive.

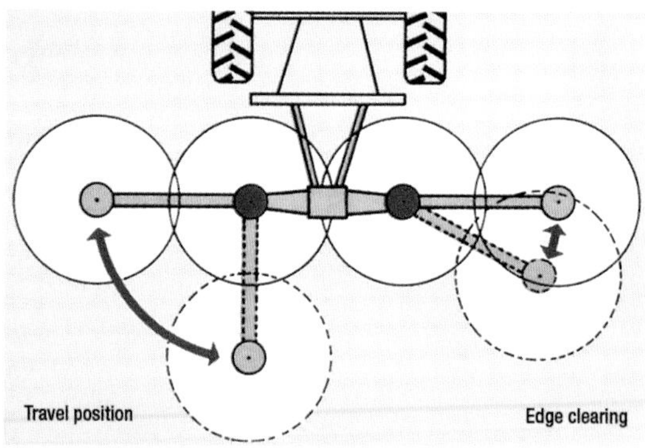

164 This diagram shows how a tedder works

In 1978 a further jump to 5.40 metres was to follow as demand for added width continued to grow. In 1986 the tedder family arrived at 7.80 metres with no end in sight. In the early days the operator changed over from the working position to travel manually. In 1993, this was a thing of a past with all tedders carrying the letter H for hydraulic changeover. The driver no longer had to get off the tractor, saving time and effort, especially as the machines had grown in size and weight over the years. In 1991 and 1992 the rotor tedders became the *Volto* range.

The main constraint to tedding width is the need to fold the machine up for road travel. The *Volto 1050*, introduced in 1996 / 97, was a milestone in this direction. Eight rotors could be folded up using an ingenious folding mechanism, making

165 / 166 *Volto 1050 tedder fully extended and inset in travel position*

this tedder with 9.80 metre working width the most compact machine available in its class. The range was rounded off with the six rotor *Volto 670 / 770* and *870* models with enlarged rotors in 2001, so there's now an ideal product for every type of farming structure.

167 *Single rotor rear swather WS 310 from earlier days*

The first *Claas* brand rotary swathers (or rakes) came in 1974 with the *WSA* tractor mounted models. Prior to this Saulgau had only produced the old fashioned rakes. The new design proved its worth up to 1990 with the *WS 280* and *WS 310* models. In 1989 a new single rotor swather range with widths up to 3.80 metres was introduced. This led to the first twin rotor swather, the *WS 660 Hydro* with hydraulic rotor lift, the *WS 760 Hydro* and *WS 1500*. The new name given to the *WS* range in 1993 was *Liner*.

Swath formation was often the bottleneck in the forage harvesting chain and customers were asking for larger machines, so *Claas* developed

168 *Modern twin rotor Liner 1550 laying two swaths at once*

169 *Working illustration of the Liner 1550 twin function*

double swathers with side swath laying. They could put together 6.50 metres in a single row or 13 metres in a double swath. The *Liner 3000* was a new benchmark in 1999, a four rotor swather with a maximum width of 12.50 metres. Despite this huge clearing performance, the machine is highly manoeuvrable, thanks to the patented chassis design between the front and rear rotors.

The tandem running gear was a small, quite effective feature under the rotors. The running

170 The Liner 3000, large scale four rotor swather for 12.5 metre clearance

wheels absorbed bumps better, enabling faster travel speeds.

Loader wagons

During the 1960s the loader wagon became a key machine for small one man operations. *Bautz* started to engineer these products in 1965. Nowadays the loader wagon still has its place in quite a few regions where this type of silage conservation is popular. The changes in use over the years have changed the specifications out of recognition. The trend to silage led to the introduction of the *Autonom K 25*, *K 30* and *K 40* in 1977 with rake chain feed, profile steel loading bays and rear angled pick-up.

172 Autonom loader wagon with pick-up and swivel intake

Following this start, the *Sprint* range was launched in 1984 and culminated in 1995 with the *Sprint 5000*. Knife design was simplified with a hydraulically folding chopping housing and a complete redesign of the chopping system itself. The pick-up, rotor and housing were grouped together in a single unit that could be taken out

171 Front mower, Ares tractor sandwiched in between, Sprint 320 loader wagon

173 The Quantum 6800 S is the top model in the Claas loader wagon family

in the shortest possible time. In 1998 the *Quantum* loader wagon range took over from the *Sprint 5000* as the top-of-line offering. The largest version was then the *Quantum 6800* weighing in at 20 tons and requiring tractors of over 200 hp to drive it.

Forage chopping

With the takeover of *Speiser*, *Claas* benefited from a vast amount of experience in the field of chopping technology. The company built trailed and mounted forage harvesters and these products were added to the line in Saulgau. The range consisted of machines with 2 and 3 row maize choppers or a 1.75 metre pick-up for tractors of up to 150 hp. The *Jaguar* name came with the products, a fortuitous event since the name has added to the prestige of the *Claas* forager brand.

The single row trailed Maisprinz is worthy of mention as an early example of the systems approach which dominates our modern product development. Together with the loader wagon chopping, loading, transport and discharge was made possible, including for maize.

Günter Schlagenhauf

Source:
Bautz Chronicle, Frankfurt 2004

174 Jaguar 85 trailed forage and maize header

175 The same machine with a 1.75 metre pick-up

176 Today's self propelled Jaguar with 3.80 metre pick-up

The World of Baling

When *CLAAS* began producing pick-up balers in 1934, the company was at the forefront of developments with a new harvest system, one which kept going relatively unchanged for a long while. In 1966 the piston baler superseded the earlier designs, though bale shape was still rectangular. Then the round bales appeared on the scene and wiped out the small square bale, and finally large square bales joined the family, opening up new markets in straw as well as silage.

The familiar stationary baler with one metre channel width formed the basis of the tractor powered version. A tine drum picked up the forage from the swath and an elevator or feed cloth guided it to the baler. The finished bales were then pushed one by one along the bale chute onto the trailer fixed behind. This system enabled three men to bale and load up to six tons of hay an hour.

178 An early swinging piston baler making hay …

The pick-up baler spread fast with several hundred units in service by 1941, a trend accelerated in wartime with the lack of manpower and the need to "make hay whilst the sun shone". Then as now, the climate was unpredictable.

The arrival of the combine harvester boosted the demand for this baler type. Whilst the early combines were fitted with on board baling devices, the straw wasn't usually dry enough for good results. It was progressively laid in a swath and then baled later when it was dry enough.

In the mid 1950s the *Claas* models known as *Pick-Up 1* and *2* were replaced step by step by a number of new models. The intermediate elevator disappeared, making the new balers more compact and the sales volume grew rapidly. Let's put it into figures: in the 1965 / 66 production year over 8,500 balers were produced. The range consisted of the low (*LD*) and medium pressure (*Medium*) with 80 and 100 cm channel widths and up to 8 t/h work rate.

The small *Magnum* baler and the more powerful *Maximum* with 36 x 50 cm bale size and a work rate of up to 14 t/h rounded off this first generation baler range with the swinging piston arrangement. Their era came to a close in 1972 / 73 with a final run of 300 *Maximum* balers.

Ram type square balers

Whilst the bale size stayed small and square, farmers wanted more density, well shaped bales and wider pick-ups. In response *Claas* designed the *Markant* family. The baling channel was 36 x 46 cm and their popularity was immedi-

177 … and the big Maximum version

179 The Markant, the big selling square baler of the 1970s

ate. The extra wide pick-up was now alongside the baling channel and a controlled rake forced the crop sideways into the channel. The ram was mounted on roller bearings. It was fitted with a vertical knife which chopped the crop as it was fed in with each stroke and this improved the uniformity of the bale shape. The Markant came with twin twine knotters as standard.

The bales were either dropped onto the field or could be pushed onto trailers attached behind via a bale slide or similar contraption. Then *Claas* made single handed operation possible in 1973 with the introduction of the hydraulic bale thrower. Gradually a whole new baler family took shape with the entry model *Trabant* and the top model called *Dominant* with a benchmark work rate of 18 t/h, three times the original output of the first balers. Individual needs were catered for. For instance, there are countries where rodents have a habit of chewing their way through the twine and for these customers, *Claas* offered an optional wire tying system.

Between 1966 and 2000 some 133,740 ram type square balers left the production lines at *Claas*. The peak was in 1974 with over 11,000 units, followed by a rapid decline in the years after. This had two reasons: firstly the market for balers with the smaller bale dimensions of 0.36 x 0.46 x 1 metre was saturated and secondly round balers were taking over steadily. By 1982 *Claas* was building as many round balers as square as the classic square baler which began it all made its final bow, at least in Europe.

Round balers

The first round baler series from *Claas* was the *Rollant 85* which saw the light of day in 1977. This model had a fixed chamber with 1.80 metre diameter and 1.50 metre width and could bale 400 kg of straw, the equivalent of 20 square bales. Round bales could be handled with a front mounted loader on the tractor and proved to be more weather resistant.

With the *Rollant* design, *Claas* had broken with tradition and adopted a new style steel baling chamber to replace the conventional belt chamber. This was the basis for the enormous success of this product range which in due course became the market leader in Europe. In 1984 production reached 5,400 units and they required a total of 84,700 steel rollers, a production volume of mass proportions. There were by then five models with different bales sizes from 0.9 to 1.8 metres. The standard bale width of 1.2 metres was agreed on, a dimension based on the approved transport width for bales.

The pace of innovation at *Claas* continued unabated as documented by the *Rollatex* net wrapping introduction in 1983. Wrapping bales in net was a new idea and made the bale package much more stable so it stayed in shape properly. *Claas* was able to have a

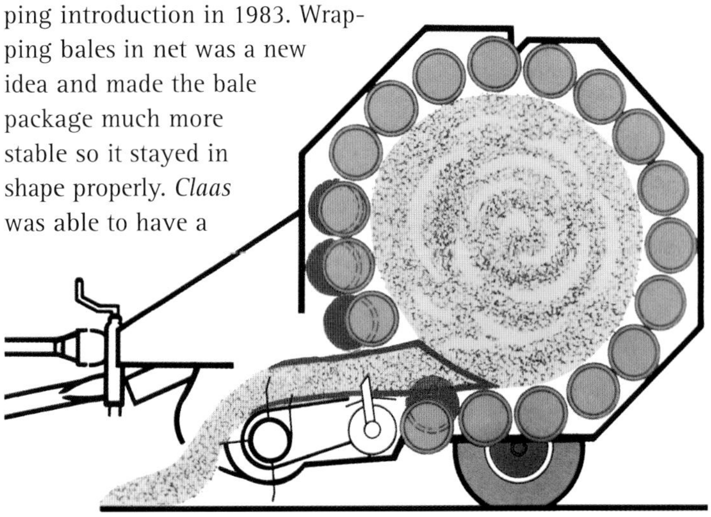

180 The Rollant design principle marked the start of a new era

181 Rollant 250 RC with the integrated bale wrapper – efficient round bale silage

patent issued on this invention. Prior to this date the bale had to be held together by twine wrapped around it as much as 20 times. *Rollatex* took just two turns with a net which had been created especially for this application. The big advantage was increased work rates, up to 50 % faster than before. To cap it all, *Claas* went another step further with the presentation in 1985 of the world's first non-stop round baler, the *Rollant Rapid*. A pre-chamber had been incorporated to store the crop and build up a buffer whilst the bale was being wrapped. No more stopping during baling was a great idea, but unfortunately the high extra cost couldn't be translated into better operating economics, so the product never caught on.

Meanwhile the smaller *Rollant* models with 1.20 m bale diameter had established themselves firmly in the growing silage baling market. To serve this segment better, *Claas* introduced a chopping system in 1992 with the *Rollant 46 RC*. The bales could be more easily broken up in the stables and were also more densely packed.

The *Rollant Uniwrap* was the next development milestone in the bale silage process. The *Rollant 250 RC* had been built in combination with the trial *Uniwrap* bale wrapper from 2002. After the silage bale had been pressed and tied, the tailgate opens automatically and the bale drops into a recess which lifts it onto the wrapping table. Once in the tailgate is closed again the *Uniwrap* device begins to seal the bale hermetically. The *Rollant* family has been immensely successful, with over 76.000 machines built up to 2003.

The *Variant* variable chamber baler joined the fixed chamber *Rollant* line up in 1994. It produced bales from 0.9 to 1.8 metres diameter in a variable belt chamber. The *Variant* soon developed a reputation as the highest performing round baler in the *Claas* product range. It can make bales weighing up to 350 kg with an hourly throughput of 20 tons. The bale is formed by counter-rotation, a specific feature not found on competitive products, as is the rotor position close to the bale chamber. This ensures that bale rotation starts early in all conditions. The *Variant 180* became a firm favourite amongst contractors, so it was only natural to produce a smaller version for bales up to 1.6 metre diameter, aimed additionally at the farming community. Together the two *Variant* models have been produced in significant numbers. By 2003 a total of 6,220 units had been produced in the *Metz* factory.

Large square balers

The *Quadrant 1200* was the first large square baler produced by *Claas* and made its debut in 1987. This baler was designed for large farm estates and contractors and initially used primarily for straw baling. The bale dimensions of 1.20 m width, 0.70 m height and a length of up to 2.50 metres made the bales ideal for transport, since the road truck could be loaded fully up to the limit with bales weighing up to 360 kg each. As a result the *Quadrant 1200* soon became a highly popular choice for contractors and straw dealers in areas like the Champagne district or the Rhine Valley who transported the straw to customers in the Benelux countries, for mushroom cultivation or animal use. The *Quadrant* bale size became so popular that it was copied by competitors, but the quality of the original article has enabled it to defend its strong position in the market place. Nowadays grass silage is chopped and baled with it, in addition to hay and straw. For this application the *Quadrant Roto Cut* was introduced with an extra chopping rotor.

The *Quadrant* functions in a straight line behind the tractor which needs a minimum of 100 kW for good results. Power flows through the PTO to the large main drive gear unit which in turn drives the baling ram with a force of up to 400 kN. The rake, feed and auger drive also branch off from here, along with the chopper and knotter drives. Bale formation takes place in an extra length baling channel with hydraulically adjustable compression plates. The high density bales are tied with six lengths of plastic twine with up to 3.5 kN strength.

The proven *Claas knotters* were beefed up to meet the increased loadings inherent in the use of thicker twine. The basic design of the *Quadrant* has not been radically changed in the course of its development. Over the years, however, tremendous advances have been made in terms of operator comfort allied to the use of electronics. The driver can stay informed on all of the important operating parameters such as baling pressure, the baling process, bale filling right / left and crop moisture with an on board monitoring and adjusting terminal. Contractors are catered for with a job specific summary of bale numbers and total baled length for easier invoicing. Baling pressure and length settings can be carried out from the tractor cab.

A variety of new features has been incorporated over the years. Maintenance of these high production balers has been simplified by the addition of automatic lubrication and knotter cleaning fans. A tandem axle was added for faster road travel. The *Fine Cut* chopping system with 25 mm chop length was introduced for specific customer applications such as turkey farms, which require short chopped straw. Other products were developed by *Claas* such as the *Quadropac* bale stacker. It was trailed behind the baler, capable of stacking four big bales on top of one another and then laying them on the field.

The current *Quadrant* product line consists of:

Quadrant 2200 – the successor to the *Quadrant 1200*. This is the most productive baler in the *Claas* product range. The combination of extra length baling channel, increased bale density and higher work rates produces bales of 1.2 x 0.7 m section and a length of 3 m, each weighing up to 450 kg in straw at a rate of just 45 seconds per bale.

Quadrant 2100 – a derivative of the *Quadrant 2200* with similar functional design. The main difference is a smaller baling channel section with 0.8 m width and 0.7 m height to make smaller bales which are particularly in demand with independent farmers and for bale silage.

Quadrant 1150 – the successor to the *Quadrant 1100* is the smallest model with 0.8 metre wide and 0.5 high baling channel. This machine is offered with a trailed *Duopack* bale accumulator which stacks two bales on top of one another before depositing them on the field, enabling these fairly small bales to be handled efficiently.

A total of 7,390 *Quadrant* balers had been produced at the end of 2003.

Gerhard Clostermeyer

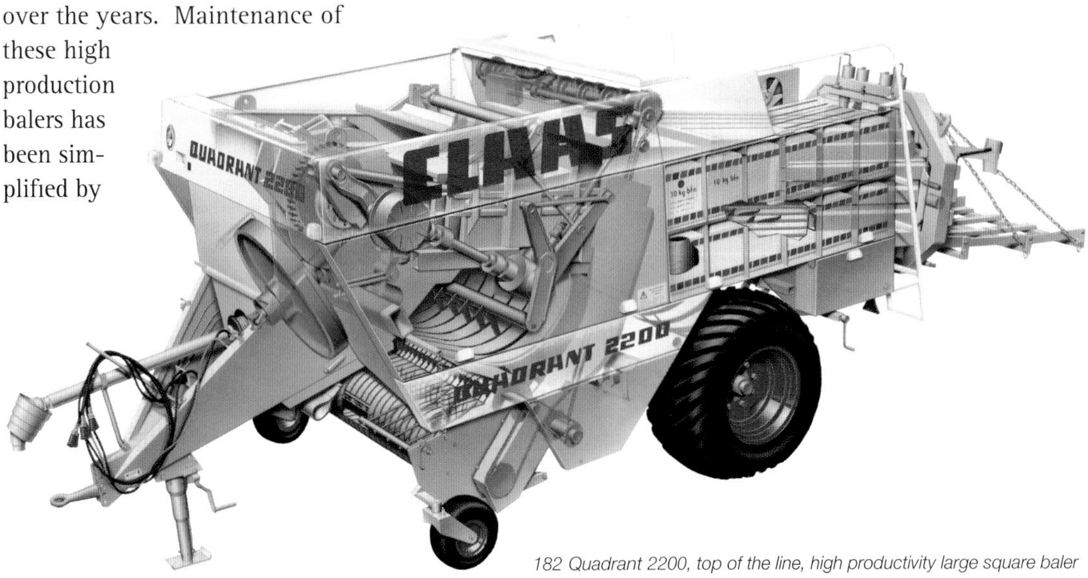

182 Quadrant 2200, top of the line, high productivity large square baler

Other Products

Apart from its well-known products *CLAAS* frequently tried to discover other niche markets in its history and sometimes it had no choice. For example, the production of seed drills in 1946 was a result of an order by the occupying forces, whilst the sugar cane harvester was an in-house development during the 1970s. The *Apollo* forage drier was a remarkable technical achievement which came to a premature end due to the oil crisis.

The fact that *Claas* got involved with seed drills is directly attributable to the food shortages following the end of the war. A certificate emanating by the *Agriculture Bureau* (*LWA*) in Münster dated June 22nd 1945 was issued in German and English. (Illustration 183). The original translation varies a bit from the original, so here is a closer translation:

The Gebrüder Claas farm machinery factory in Harsewinkel is to be employed jointly with the Westphalian farmers' collective to produce machines to sustain food production. Within this project seed drills (Saxonia Siedersleben 2 m) and potato harvesting machines (Schatzgräber) are urgently required.

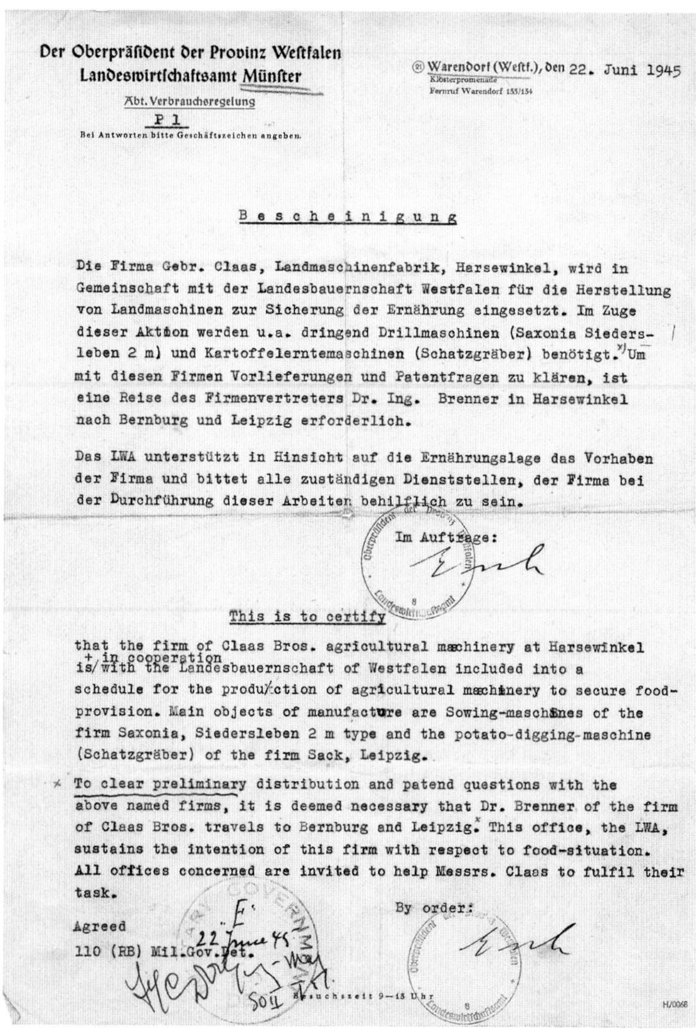

Der Oberpräsident der Provinz Westfalen
Landeswirtschaftsamt Münster
Abt. Verbraucherregelung
P 1
Bei Antworten bitte Geschäftszeichen angeben.

Warendorf (Westf.), den 22. Juni 1945
Klosterpromenade
Fernruf Warendorf 153/154

B e s c h e i n i g u n g

Die Firma Gebr. Claas, Landmaschinenfabrik, Harsewinkel, wird in Gemeinschaft mit der Landesbauernschaft Westfalen für die Herstellung von Landmaschinen zur Sicherung der Ernährung eingesetzt. Im Zuge dieser Aktion werden u.a. dringend Drillmaschinen (Saxonia Siedersleben 2 m) und Kartoffelerntemaschinen (Schatzgräber) benötigt.x) Um mit diesen Firmen Vorlieferungen und Patentfragen zu klären, ist eine Reise des Firmenvertreters Dr. Ing. Brenner in Harsewinkel nach Bernburg und Leipzig erforderlich.

Das LWA unterstützt in Hinsicht auf die Ernährungslage das Vorhaben der Firma und bittet alle zuständigen Dienststellen, der Firma bei der Durchführung dieser Arbeiten behilflich zu sein.

Im Auftrage:

This is to certify

that the firm of Claas Bros. agricultural machinery at Harsewinkel is + in cooperation with the Landesbauernschaft of Westfalen included into a schedule for the production of agricultural machinery to secure food-provision. Main objects of manufacture are Sowing-maschines of the firm Saxonia, Siedersleben 2 m type and the potato-digging-maschine (Schatzgräber) of the firm Sack, Leipzig.

x To clear preliminary distribution and patend questions with the above named firms, it is deemed necessary that Dr. Brenner of the firm of Claas Bros. travels to Bernburg and Leipzig.x This office, the LWA, sustains the intention of this firm with respect to food-situation. All offices concerned are invited to help Messrs. Claas to fulfil their task.

By order:

Agreed
110 (RB) Mil.Gov.Det.
22 June 45

Besuchszeit 9—13 Uhr

H/0068

183 The original certificate issued by the Agricultural Bureau (LWA) in Münster, June 1945

UNIVERSAL-DRILLMASCHINE
BAUART = SAXONIA

Um einem dringenden Bedürfnis für die Westzonen abzuhelfen, haben wir den Bau von Drillmaschinen aufgenommen.

Lieferbar ist: 2-m-Drillmaschine mit 13 oder 17 Reihen, 2,5-m-Maschine mit 17 oder 21 Reihen. Parzellen-Drillmaschine 1 m breit, mit 7 Reihen.

Für die 2-m-Maschine ist 13 Reihen, für die 2,5-m-Maschine 17 Reihen **Normalausführung.**

Maschinen mit der größeren Reihenzahl von 17 oder 21 werden nur von besonderen landwirtschaftlichen Gebieten benötigt.

Aus den obigen Reihenzahlen sind sämtliche größeren Reihenabstände, also weniger Reihen, herstellbar.

Technische Einzelheiten:

Hölzerne **Laufräder** Ø 1,16 m (3 Umdrehungen = 10 m) Breite 55 mm (60 mm)

*

Vorderräder Ø 56 cm, Breite 45 mm

Spiralrohrsaatleitungen

Zusatzeinrichtungen für Grob- und Feinsaat auf besonderen Wunsch, s. Rückseite.

Gewicht: 2 m: ca. 475 kg; 2,5 m: ca. 520 kg

Preise:
2 m 13 Rh.:
17 Rh.:
2,5 m 17 Rh.:
21 Rh.:
Parzellendrillmasch.: ......

Die Maschinen sind mit einem langsamen Gang, normalen Gang und groben Gang, sowie mit einem Kleinstmengengang (letzterer auf besonderen Wunsch) ausgerüstet. Die Umstellung erfolgt durch einfaches Wechseln von Vorsteckzahnrädern. Ferner besitzen die Maschinen Wechselgetriebe mit 24 Einstellmöglichkeiten, so daß sich im ganzen 3 (bzw. 4) mal 24 Einstellmöglichkeiten ergeben. Die 24 Einstellmöglichkeiten der Getriebe werden mit nur 2 Schalthebeln bedient.

Die Maschinen werden serienmäßig mit **Autosteuerung** und kombiniertem Hinten- und Seitensteuer geliefert, ferner mit einer Moment-Entleervorrichtung, Pferdeschoner, Abdrehvorrichtung und Einstellsaattabelle. Die Säschare sind aus Hartguß.

Die Einzelteile der Maschine entsprechen der Saxonia-Bauart, so daß der **Ersatzteildienst** von Original-Saxonia-Maschinen obiger Abmessungen durchgeführt werden kann.

W. Girardet, Druckerei, AL/61, Essen — 7635/10000, Juli 47, Klasse B

184 First Claas pamphlet for seed drills dated July 1947

In order to clarify initial supplies and patent questions, a journey will have to be made by the company's representative Dr. Brenner from Harsewinkel to Bernburg and Leipzig. In view of the food situation the LWA supports the company's project and requests all officials concerned to be helpful to the company in carrying out this work.

The production authorisation number 18, dated October 18, 1945 ordered *Claas* to begin the production of seed drills. Then the Westphalian farmers' collective issued the certificate to show that *Claas* was actively involved in the production of seed drills and was to commence with the manufacture of an initial series of 3,000 units.

In 1946 a trial run of 100 machines was produced and allocated to farmers in the area surrounding Harsewinkel. This led to resentment in the neighbouring region of Münster, because they felt they had been ignored. In theory at least the machines were sold with a supply authorisation, but despite strict allocation rules it was common

Comparative field measurements across Germany						
Baden Morgen	Bavaria Tagewerk	Hanover Morgen	Hectare 100 Ar	Prussia Morgen	Saxony Acker	Württemberg Morgen
=	=	=	=	=	=	=
400 □ rods	400 □ rods	120 □ rods	10.000 □ m^2	180 □ rods	300 □ rods	348 □ rods
			Equivalent (m^2)			
2,7778	2,9349	3,8153	1	3,9166	1,8069	3,1729
			Ha. conversion rate			
3.600	3.407	2.621	10.000	2.553	5.534	3.152

185 The table shows the differences in existence after world War two as regards area measurement

practice to supply machines in order to barter for materials which were in short supply.

The factory workers at *Claas* didn't have enough wages to live off, especially the refugees who had come with nothing left but what they stood up in. As a result the workers' committee tried to organise sales of seed drills internally. This was against the law and August and Theo Claas were prosecuted along with the chairman of the workers committee, Theodor Haase. Fortunately the prosecution was dropped because this type of barter arrangement was common and normally it was tolerated. In the course of time it was finally legalised anyway.

A *Claas* pamphlet dated July 1947 proclaims: "we have started producing seed drills to help alleviate shortages in the Western zones".

Another interesting detail is the description of the standard "horse saver". This enabled the operator to fine tune the seed drill without disturbing the rhythm and pace of the horses. The table at the top of this page gives a summary of the different area measurements in Germany at that time. A totally confusing tradition and sometimes the same term meant something different, depending on which part of Germany it was!

By September 1952 the name of *Saxonia* had disappeared from the seed drill brochure in Germany, although it was still mentioned in foreign language versions. By 1955 the range had disappeared completely, after cumulative production of 16,246 units.

Ludwig Caspers

The Sugar Cane harvester

Sugar cane, also known by its Latin name of *Saccharum offitarum*, belongs to the grass family. Its cultivation spread from Asia to most tropical and some sub-tropical regions some 400 years ago. The plant grows a knotted stem of two to 5 cm with reed like leaves and reaches a height of 7 m. Growth and maturity until the next harvest takes about one year, during which a more moist and warm summer climate is extremely important in the early phase of growth. The sugar content which accounts for up to 15 % is concentrated in the stems, increasing in strength from top to bottom. In contrast with sugar beet, sugar cane

186 By 1954 sales literature was more attractive and in colour

187 One of the first sugar cane harvesters in Cuba, 1974

has to be replanted in rows every three to ten years, the frequency depending on the yield (60 to 120 t/ha).

Harvesting takes place during the drier winter period. Sugar cane used to be harvested manually, an arduous process requiring a large number of labourers using machetes. Nowadays modern harvesting equipment is increasingly replacing manual methods, and can achieve up to 200 tonnes per hour throughput. Currently many fields are still burned before harvesting, because this makes the mechanical or manual harvest that much easier. However, the drawback is that the cane has to be processed in the plant within 24 hours.

In addition, increased environmental awareness has led to severe restrictions on burning fields, which in turn makes it necessary to have machines capable of separating the chopped cane from the leaves and plant tops. There is still a long way to go with some 70 % of the cane harvest still being harvested manually, at least partially. Nonetheless the trend to increased mechanisation is irreversible.

Back in 1970 engineers from Cuba convinced *Claas* of the necessity to mechanise the sugar cane harvest and concluded a development agreement aimed at creating a system for low loss, clean harvesting of both burnt and green sugar cane. *Claa*s manufacturing knowledge combined

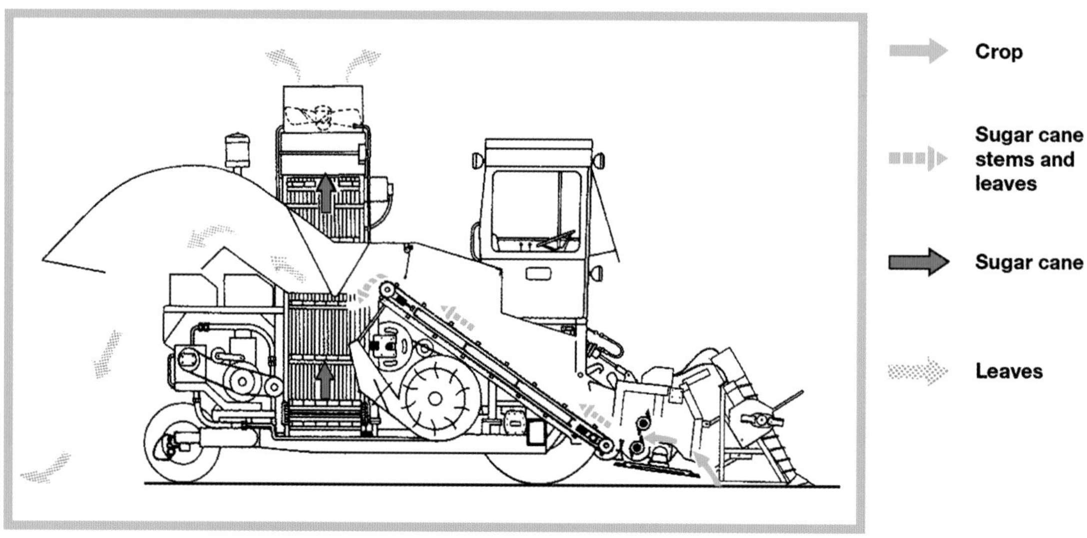

188 Cross section of the sugar cane harvester

CLAAS Service:
always at
your service
We know from our many years of experience in producing and supplying agricultural equipment just how much the profitability of the farm and the performance of the machine depends upon a 100% spares availability. Every working hour should be fully utilized. The service and spares backing that has been built up over many years is also behind every CLAAS CC 1400 sugar cane harvester. We not only build and supply machines that can be relied upon, we also back this up with a service that is second to none in the industry. Operating world-wide, CLAAS back up not just with service in the field but also training engineers and operators, carried out by experienced CLAAS field specialists. We operate a 24 hour spare parts service, which is always available when you want it.
Strength in the harvest with CLAAS reliability
CLAAS OHG · POSTFACH 1140 · D-4834 HARSEWINKEL 1
9.80 (Vogel) engl. 30 / 189.327.1 Printed in West Germany

189 International sales promotion with this 1980s publication

with Cuban expertise regarding field conditions ensured good results from the very beginning. The first prototypes were already running in 1971, followed by the delivery of the first production machines called *Libertadora* to Cuba a year later. In 1975 machines were shipped to Mexico and South Africa, this time labelled *CC1400*. Following this *Claas* exported these machines to South America, Africa, Asia and Australia. The product continued to be developed, as the *CC 2000* and *CC 3000* joined the range.

The big sugar refineries, cooperatives and the States in the USA (Florida) and Brazil who had pioneered mechanisation in the first place were now looking for sugar cane harvesters with more output. When it came to putting new ideas into effect, the company's worldwide experience of harvesting in the most diverse conditions turned out to be a major asset. New products such as the *Gladiator* and *Ventor* models followed in 1991 and 1997.

190 The CC 3000 in South America, about 1975

Without a doubt sugar cane will substitute sugar beet production and this will accelerate the mechanisation trend in the producing countries. Manual harvesting is tough, dirty work and not without risk, so investments in equipment are set to expand. The producing countries are keen on making machinery themselves, so it can be expected that local assembly and manufacturing will play a major role in the development of this product line.

Hillrich Otten

The *Apollo* crop drier

This is one of the few examples of well thought through and thoroughly calculated engineering going from production release to museum status in a short space of time, with only a few sales in between. This was the case with the *Claas* crop drier called *Apollo*. The early disappearance of the product was not due to technical shortcomings, that was a direct result of the oil crisis

191 The Claas Apollo drier being towed behind a tractor

in the 1970s. Oil prices rose 500 %, making this equipment economically unviable

The combine harvester for forage

What was the basic idea behind this product? Quite simply, if the cereals harvest could be done in one operation with the combine harvester, why not mechanise the forage harvest the same way? There was no system available for the forage harvest, with each step from mowing to silage or hay production carried out separately. This was a long way from the single operation in the cereals harvest, and the losses in the process were much larger.

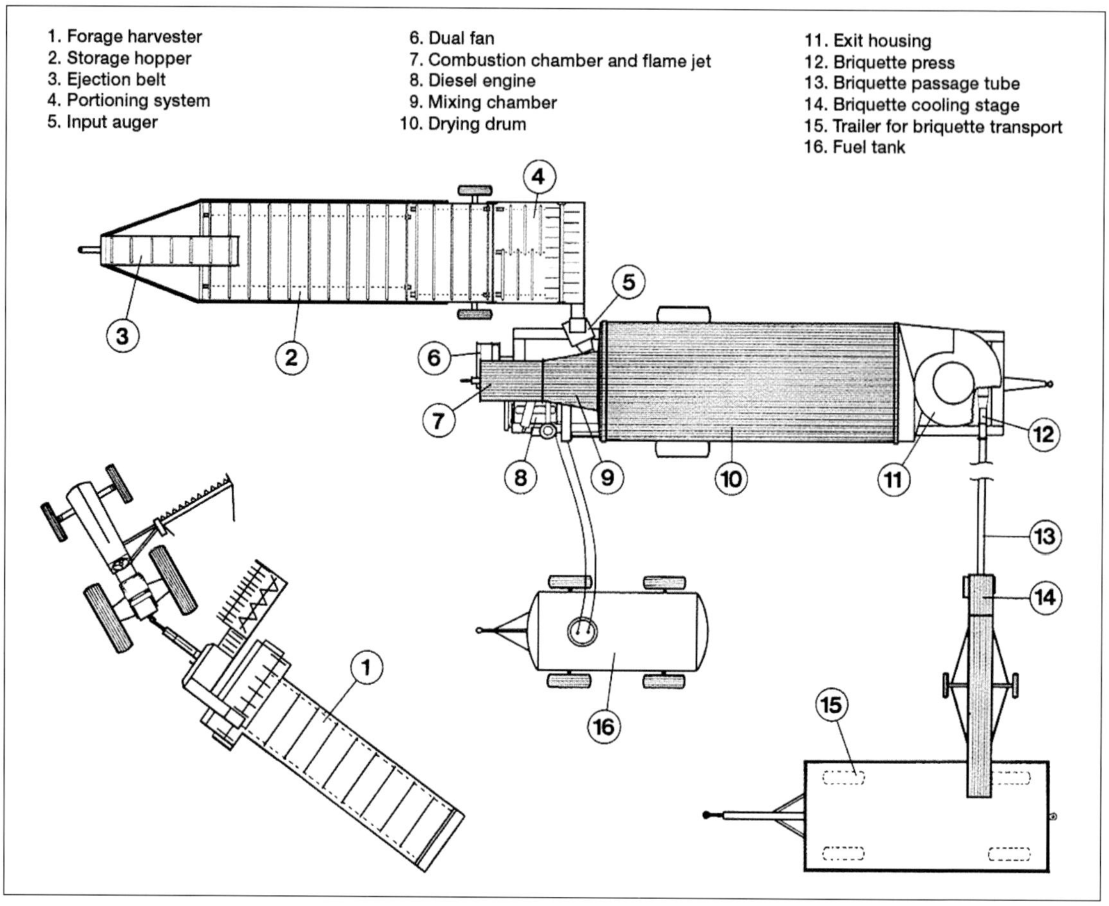

192 Layout of the complete system for the forage harvest

Early in the 1960s the number of farm equipment producers started developing new forage harvesting systems. These producers included *Claas*, *Fahr* and *Taarup*.

The basic idea was to use a mobile drier fitted behind the tractor, set it up at the edge of the field where it would work automatically. The supply hopper for the drier was filled by one man and a tractor, a mounted forage harvester and loader wagon, such as the *Claas Rapido*, which was a combined mower / forage wagon.

This driver also looked after the drier. Up to 5 t of damp, green crop was turned into 1 t of dry matter per hour and turned into briquettes using a packing device. The basic forage structure of the hay stayed intact, a vital factor for cattle forage. The briquettes were extremely dense, so that the 5 ton trailers of that period were fully laden and the 10 hour working day would fill just two of these trailers and taken back to the farm.

This highly concentrated forage saved plenty of storage space. Customers were fascinated by the

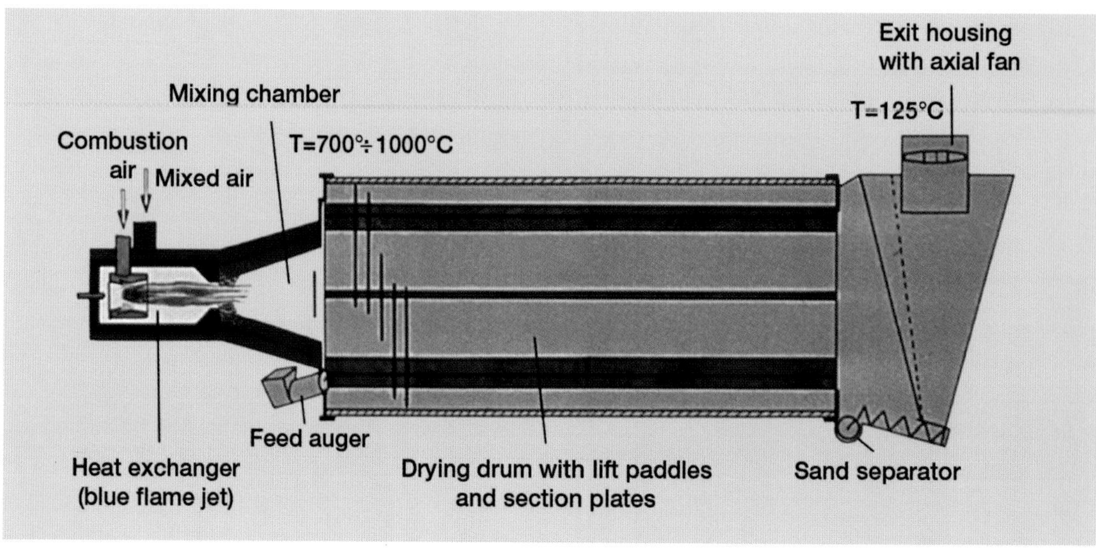

193 Functional diagram of the Claas Apollo forage drier

194 Claas Apollo system at full steam

idea of storing forage like they stored potatoes, a completely revolutionary innovation! Every activity became much easier-storage, retrieval, portioning were greatly improved. In addition it became feasible to market the forage, its high density making transport economic.

Apollo, the *Claas* forage harvest system

The *Claas* crop drier acquired its name from the rocket of that day *Apollo*, which it certainly resembled. The team in the advanced research department under Dr. Friedrich Feldmann looked at different ways to improve forage conservation, in particular reduction of losses. Extensive feasibility tests were carried out at the *Claas-LVS* agricultural trial station in Bielefeld, following which first prototypes were built and tried out. Parallel to this project, other trials were carried out into things like forage value, energy input, labour requirements and operating economics.

The green light to go ahead with production planning was given after Dr. Feldmann had presented a comprehensive research paper on the "*economics of new style green forage drying*". He summarised as follows: *the traditional disadvantages are overcome and highest possible return on investment is achieved with this system. The technological benefits are described in detail: modern design, elimination of the need for fixed structures, plenty of distance from residential areas, minimum labour requirement, simple organisation (harvest, transfer and drying in one hand). Consistent full capacity utilisation thanks to fully automatic processes, despite constantly varying crop humidity. Very low forage losses both in quantity and quality by avoidance of climatic risks. (Report appeared in Miterlebte Landtechnik, Volume II, Max Eyth Gesellschaft für Agrartechnik).*

195 The Rapido combined mower and forage wagon

196 The Claas Apollo produced easy to handle, compact briquettes ...

The system made it possible to reduce forage costs per litre of milk. The quality and digestibility of this "high energy" hay would also cut the demand for expensive, unstructured forage substitutes to a minimum.

Once detailed trials had been completed in the locality and further afield the first production models were assembled. Their first appearance was at the *DLG* exhibition in 1972 in Hanover. The presentation was at the *DEULA* school site in Hildesheim. The drier was demonstrated every day to the public. The first units went to the *Institute for Grassland Research* in Brunswick, to the *Hessische Staatsdomäne* (*Hesse State Domain*) in Niederbeisheim and the machinery ring in Laufen. The new *Claas* forage harvesting system featured in a large number of publications and speeches, both in Germany and abroad. Before long the first export orders were being processed.

Not unexpectedly the new forage harvesting method was discussed intensively by the experts. In actual operation in the targeted annual utilisation of 1,000 hours could be achieved in practice. Reliability and labour requirements also came up to expectations, once the initial hurdles had been overcome. The critics concentrated on the lack of system output. In reality even if 75 ha of pasture could be conserved each year, it could be argued that the work rate was not high enough, particularly in the first cut. These critics did however often overlook the fact that just one man was needed for the whole process. Observation of the process in action revealed that best results could only be achieved if traditional processes were reviewed and both crop planning and organisation were carried out professionally.

197 ... full of concentrated nutrition ...

198 ... making cost effective mechanised cattle feeding possible

Premature termination following the oil crisis

The cost of oil obviously had a major influence on the overall operating economics of the system. These costs were very low when the project was initiated and experts projected an unimaginable maximum of 50 % increase in the foreseeable future. Dr. Feldmann went as far as to base his projections on a doubling of the oil price. In reality the oil price went through the roof, and even Dr. Feldmann had to come to terms with the fact that nothing more could be done. In the *Miterlebte Landtechik* journal, he concluded that this is a "classic example of the risks inherent in the business environment, without which no technical progress can be made".

HASSO BERTRAM

Sources:

Feldmann, Friedrich: the brief story of the Claas Apollo forage drier in German. Miterlebte Landtechnik, Volume II, page 81 Max Eyth Gesellschaft für Agrartechnik

Wandel, Herrmann: "Hot air from Apollo" – hot air driers in the field, published in German: der Goldene Pflug, German Agriculture Museum Hohenheim Volume 16, page 22

Tractors lead into a New Dimension

199 A modern CLAAS tractor and a vintage Renault side by side

Renault is primarily known as a French car maker with a long tradition. In farming too, since the company built its first tractors in 1919 for the French market only. A new tractor factory was then put up in Le Mans in 1938. The production process was modernised in 1969 and Renault started to get itself established in other markets. A worldwide distribution system has become available for the tractor range from France following the takeover by Claas in 2003. The tractor product range is rounded off with the Xerion, a top end system vehicle. Together these products turned Claas into a long liner virtually overnight.

Renault Agriculture – a long Tractor Tradition

The roots of this traditional French company go back to 1898 when Louis Renault started making machines and vehicles under the simplest of conditions. The first steel belt tractors were derived from tanks employed in the First World War. As part of the state's decentralisation policy a separate company was formed in 1938 and then nationalised after the Second World War. Production of tractors and engines in the dedicated Le Mans plant was initiated in 1942. The factory grew steadily from then on and was modernised on a regular basis.

The story begins in a simple shed at the bottom of the family garden in Billancourt, just outside Paris. It's here that the young Louis Renault built the first *Renault* vehicle, a small car. The project was highly successful and by 1913 over ten thousand had been produced.

200 Louis Renault aged 20 in his workshop, end of 1889

Renault was heavily involved in national defence during the Great War and the FT attack tank is particularly noteworthy for its part in the 1918 French offensive which helped end that dreadful war. Farming in France had suffered seriously from the lack of manpower and confiscation of horses by the military during the long period of warfare. Thus Louis' attention turned to mechanisation of farming as early as 1917.

201 FT 17 tank assembly, 1918

Immediately after hostilities had ceased, the D14 department which made the *FT17* tank and was called "Artillery" started series production of the *GP* type tractor. The commitment to the farm equipment business was strengthened by the transformation of the company farm in Herqueville, Normandy, to a test centre.

202 A first prototype farm tractor

Louis Renault also decided to create a new production site on December 4th 1918. This project included social amenities such as workers' accommodation and leisure facilities.

On July 27th 1924 approval was given for a link to the rail network but there were other administrative hurdles which wasted a lot of time. As a result the contract creating the *Société Anonyme des Usines de Pontlieue* – the Le Mans factory – wasn't signed until December 14th 1938. Production of tractors was kept going in Billancourt until 1942.

The German occupation was accompanied by numerous acts of confiscation and the factory which was designed for production of heavy equipment soon fell under the control of the invaders who installed *Junkers* within the *Renault* facility in 1940 and tractor production was forbidden. Opposition to this was however so intense that permission had to be granted to produce 300 tractors as well as truck compon-

203 This picture from 1942 shows the main gate and rail link

ents so the *Junkers* people had to pack their bags in 1941. Machine and assembly line tools for the tractors were then shipped from Billancourt to Le Mans.

The tractor assembly area and machining line for gears were housed in the area where previously truck gearboxes, front and rear axles were produced. The priority given to the production of trucks and armoured vehicles for the army left enough capacity spare for the manufacturing of just 141 tractors between 1940 and 1945. The war wasn't over of course and the factory was bombed three times in a row. In the night of the 13th March 1944, serious damage was inflicted on the works.

When the war finally did come to an end, the pioneer Louis Renault was denounced and interned as a "bad Frenchman". He died shortly afterwards in a French prison, and the circumstances surrounding his death are still unclear to this day. His empire, the Usines *Renault* was nationalised on the 16th of January 1945 and the assets transferred to the state. The former company *S.A.U.R.*[1] was replaced by the *Régie Nationale des Usines Renault*, indicating its new

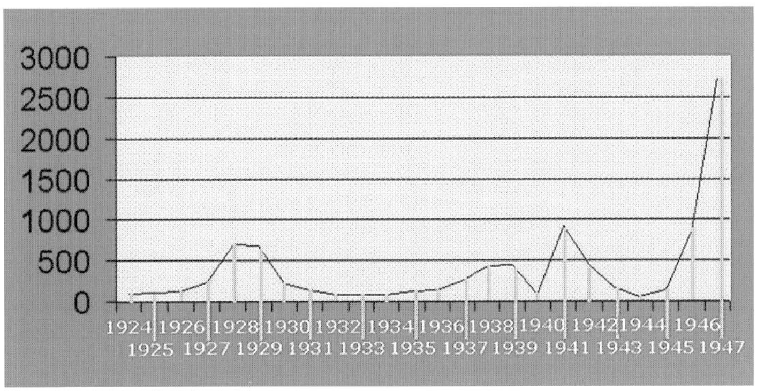

205 Tractor production between 1924 and 1947

status with Pierre Lefaucheux as the first Managing Director. The Le Mans facilities were taken over by public declaration on the 15th of November 1945.

204 Following 1944 bombardment

206 Assembly line around 1950 / 1952. Several Renault 3042 in the foreground ...

From 1947 / 48 *Renault* tractors were no longer just simple traction vehicles, since the *3042* series had hydraulic lifting with a position indicator and variable track widths.

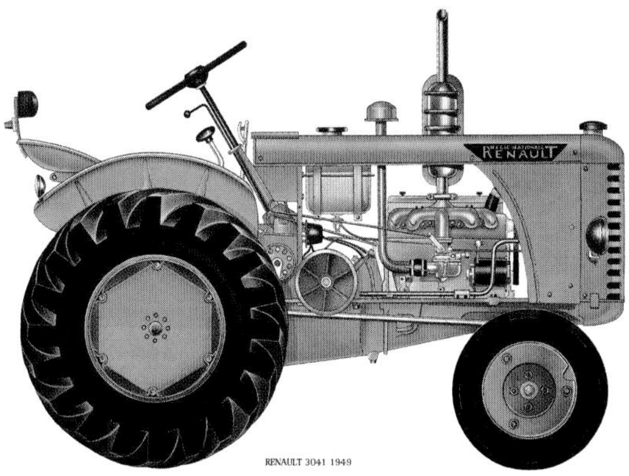

207 .... and the Renault 3042 in a contemporary ad

At the end of 1955 *Renault* introduced two new ranges of tractors, the *D* series and the *E* series

209 The D 22 tractor

derivative. No less than 72,000 of these models were built between 1956 and 1960. Drawing 209 shows the series *D* prototype which was launched in 1955 with its internal code being *ET5*. This was also the beginning of the long partnership with *MWM*, the German engine producer.

210 The Renault 385 fitted with central hydraulics controlling mounted implements

The *ET5* turned out to be a big seller with almost 200,000 sales and *Renault* continued its development up till 1968. The *Renault* brand became closely identified with the *D 22* me-

208 Aerial view of the Le Mans plant in 1959 after installation of a new assembly line

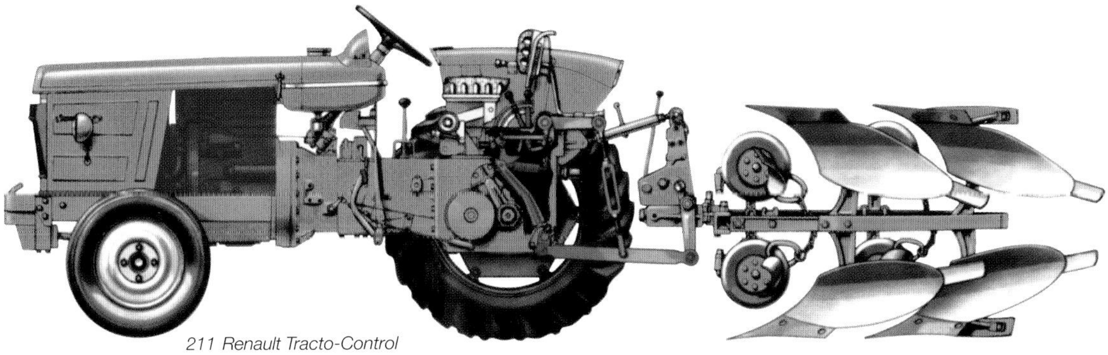
211 Renault Tracto-Control

dium power models. In 1959, the R & D department plus sales, service, parts and general administration were regrouped at Billancourt.

With the birth of the *Renault 385* in 1963 *Renault* moved into the higher power category which then was 50 hp and above: this was an innovative tractor featuring central hydraulics and disc brakes inherited from the successful *Renault 8*.

The *Tracto-Control* hydraulic lift was the outstanding new feature which made its debut at the 1966 *SIMA*[2] exhibition. Whilst the majority of competitors used the upper link for power control, *Renault* used the lower linkage to enhance operating performance.

212 A new tractor generation displayed in 1968

Porsche-Diesel and *Renault*

In 1950 the *Allgeier* company acquired a licence from *Porsche* and started tractor production in the former *Dornier* factory in Friedrichshafen. Six years later the *Allgeier* tractor manufacturing operation was taken over by *Mannesmann* who then created *Porsche-Diesel.* On the 1st of June 1963 they signed a contract with the nationalised *Renault* Company which involved selling *Renault* tractors in Germany and closing down their own tractor manufacturing. The new company was able to sell 3,300 *Renault* tractors and dispose of the inventory left by the last production run of *Porsche-Diesel.*

Whilst *Renault* tractor sales in Germany were virtually non-existent in 1963, the company had reached 3 % market share one year later due principally to the existing *Porsche-Diesel* distribution network with 350 dealers and 1,200 sales people.

In 1968 a new range was presented which took over from the *Master* models. Another range based on the same design, but with 35 and 46 hp engines, followed on its heels and replaced the "valiant" *ET5* range.

A new company structure was under review and put into effect in 1969 enabling *Renault* to run its tractor activities independently.

During this period the tractor market had been moving up steadily in terms of power. This led *Renault* to bring out the *94* and *96* models in 1969, with 77 and 88 hp. Four wheel drive was also gaining in popularity and since *Renault* didn't make driven front axles a deal was signed

213 The Renault 1181-4

214 Evreux training centre

with Carraro in Italy for supply of front axles and this agreement is still valid today. Following on the light and medium ranges, 75 to 140 hp was added in 1974 with a turbocharged *MWM* diesel on board.

Training centre in Evreux

1974 was also marked by other changes:

- The *DMA*[3] organisation moved from Pont de Sèvres to Vélizy, a suburb of Paris.
- The service function moved to Le Mans.
- The training centre moved from Sonchamp to Evreux.

215 1979 procession on the Champs Elysées

The market was crying out for more power and *Renault* responded by procuring transmissions and front axles from *ZF*.

In 1976 the registrations of *Renault* tractors had increased by 9 % whilst the total market had declined by 4.2 %. (1976 = 74,559 units). *Renault* market share went up to 17.9 % versus 15.8 % in 1975 giving *Renault* the market leadership in France. This result stemmed from sustained efforts to update and improve the tractors combined with strong retail promotion. Daily production in Le Mans reached 71 units in 1976.

The engineers focussed on improving operator comfort. Front hydraulics and PTO made their first appearance and the cab was designed for control of implements used in reverse.

The *Carraro* axles were fitted with limited slip differentials called Blocamatic. At the end of 1978 *Renault* once again topped the league in terms of registrations and this success was celebrated with a procession on the Champs Elysées on the 7th of March 1979.

The Le Mans factory – 1977 onward

During 1978 and 1979 the assembly of components such as transmissions was turned into a modular process, instead of taking place on the main assembly line. This led to a substantial productivity improvement in the plant, which employed 1,965 people.

Starting in 1980, a new corporate identity programme was put into effect, with the various activities of the state company being colour coded. Agriculture was coded green.

The new *TX*[4] and *S* models were launched in 1981 with two tone paintwork, accompanied by a massive advertising campaign. Despite the soft market conditions *Renault* managed to surprise everybody at the *SIMA* with a number of new features including:

- Adjustable rotating seat
- Adjustable steering column
- Synchronised mechanical reverser
- Front lift and PTO
- Hinged cab mounting making it easier to get to the main tractor assemblies
- Improved comfort with air conditioning.

1
Rear lift hydraulic assembly line

2
Main assembly line

3
Cab assembly

4
The finished product rolls off the line

216 Collation of photos showing the new TX series assembly line in 1981

The market rewarded this wave of innovation with no delay and as a result *Renault* reached a market share of 19 % in France in 1981. The new subsidiary *Renault Agriculture* was founded on the 2nd of September 1985 following a decision taken by the general assembly.

With the introduction of the top end range of products *Renault* had already started investigating the increased use of on board electronics in 1981. Five years later the *TX 16* and *TS 16* were equipped with *TCE electronic traction control* and *ACET* for improved driver efficiency.

Also in 1986 the vine and orchard (V & O) tractor range was completely reviewed and the new *Deutz* powered models were designed jointly and then produced solely by *Carraro* in Rovigo, Italy.

The whole tractor range was then updated in between 1986 and 1988 with special emphasis being placed on the small and medium sized machines plus the V & O models. This update led to significant improvements in appearance, comfort, safety and the introduction of wet disc brakes.

The introduction of the so called "white" range is another noteworthy event – this was a special range which impacted positively on the sales figures. Encouraged by this success *Renault* then

217 Ad campaign in Autumn 1986 for the TX 16 and TS 16 launch

NOUVELLES GAMMES VIGNES ET FRUITIERS 7 novembre 1986
RENAULT

218 The new V & O range

added the Tracfor range on an attractive value for money ticket.

The *M* and *P* ranges were the next additions to the *Renault Agriculture* product line up in 1989 featuring a new design which was then adopted across the upper range.

Between the end of 1989 and early 1990 *Tracto-Radar* made its appearance with improved operating efficiency thanks to monitoring of the travel speed via a drive wheel slip control.

Powershift transmissions made their debut in *Renault* tractors in the early nineties as *Renault Agriculture* continued to add economic value and features to the product range.

As electronics became more and more prevalent on board the tractors, the need for sophisticated diagnostic tools arose. Both the R & D and service teams joined ranks to come up with the answer which was introduced as *Metadiag* after several years of intensive labour.

The portable computer system made trouble-shooting more reliable for the workshop mechanic. It was presented for the first time at the 1993 *SIMA* and introduced across the whole network during the same year.

Le seuil de fatigue, mesuré par la norme OCDE 2631, passe de 4h pour un tracteur classique, à 7h pour un tracteur TZ équipé d'une cabine hydrostable.
MEDAILLE D'OR SIMA 87
RENAULT TZ
Renault 145.14 Turbo
HYDROSTABLE
100% 69% 59% 59% 38% 34%
Une cabine classique équipée d'un siège sans suspension transmet 100% des vibrations au conducteur; avec un siège à suspension mécanique ou hydraulique, 69% et 59%.
La cabine hydrostable, dans les mêmes conditions, en transmet 59%, 38% et seulement 34% avec le siège à suspension hydraulique monté en série.

219 TZ suspended cab with "Hydrostable" (Poster)

220 Renault Agriculture launched the Ceres range in 1993

Metadiag is a part of the *META* programme (*Maintenance Evolutive du Tracteur Agricole or Flexible tractor maintenance*) instigated in 1991 and comprised *Metadoc* which opened the door to automatic parts searching. This system was introduced to the service network in 1998.

In 1993 *Renault Agriculture* introduced the *Ceres* tractor range. This was a landmark event – the introduction of a medium power tractor combining new technical features with a new look. The importance stems from the fact that this size of tractor is the heart of the line in the French market.

When *Deutz* decided to give up production of the *MWM* engines fitted to the *Ceres Renault Agriculture* was forced to react swiftly. On the 17th of January 1994 a press release was issued announcing an industrial partnership with *John Deere* to include *DPS* engines made in France. In return *Renault Agriculture* was to build tractors in Le Mans in *John Deere* livery.

The high power segment remained an important strategic area, but *Renault Agriculture* didn't have a transmission suitable for the 150 hp + tractor market. Not far away *Massey Ferguson* were struggling to make a profit from its transmission facility in Beauvais. Dominique Chauvin (MD of *Massey Ferguson* in France) and Bruno Morange (MD of *Renault Agriculture*) got together and eventually signed an agreement on the 7th of April 1994 to create the *GIMA*[2], a 50:50 holding located in the *Massey Ferguson* Beauvais plant.

The new company had 630 employees (in R & D and production) and the deal maintained the separate brand identities with a clearly defined product offering and marketing through the separate distribution channels.

In 1997 the Ares range was introduced to replace the *T* top of the line class and equipped with a new *GBA* type transmission.

221 Machining centre from Mandelli

222 The 2001 Renault Agriculture product line up

Bruno Morange also signed another important agreement a short time later. This time it was on the 17th of November 1995 and the deal was made with *JCB Europe* granting exclusive distribution rights to *Renault Agriculture* for *JCB* products in mainland France.

Meanwhile the Le Mans plant continued to develop as the old transfer lines made way for machining centres.

Renault Agriculture had been investigating automatic guidance systems for tractors for some time before announcing in a press release dated the 28th of October 1999 that "after two years of joint research with *CEMAGREF*[6] and *LASMEA*[7] institutes *Renault Agriculture* is pleased to announce the first guidance system for tractors using GPS technology, opening the door to new faming services."

The *Temis* range finally replaces the *T* series in 2000 and following 45 years of partnership, the *MWM* diesels were replaced by Iveco engines. At the same time the first *Renault Atles* tractors left the assembly line in Le Mans.

So that's the long history of *Renault* during the 20th century in a nutshell. In total some 680,000 tractors have been built and some major obstacles overcome. The most difficult years were 1946, 1970 and 1985 but these tough times have always been mastered thanks to a continued belief in innovation and customer value.

More recently the *Ceres* which was launched in 1993 has been superseded by the *Celtis* range in 2002. This all round tractor contains all the experience of *Renault Agriculture* and is available in four basic models from 72 to 100 hp. It has already achieved the position as the best selling tractor in France.

Jacques Gouet

If you'd like to learn more about the history of *Renault Agriculture* there is a two volume encyclopaedia in French by the author of this chapter (*Encyclopédie du Tracteur Renault*) published by *ETAI* Paris. (www.etai.fr)

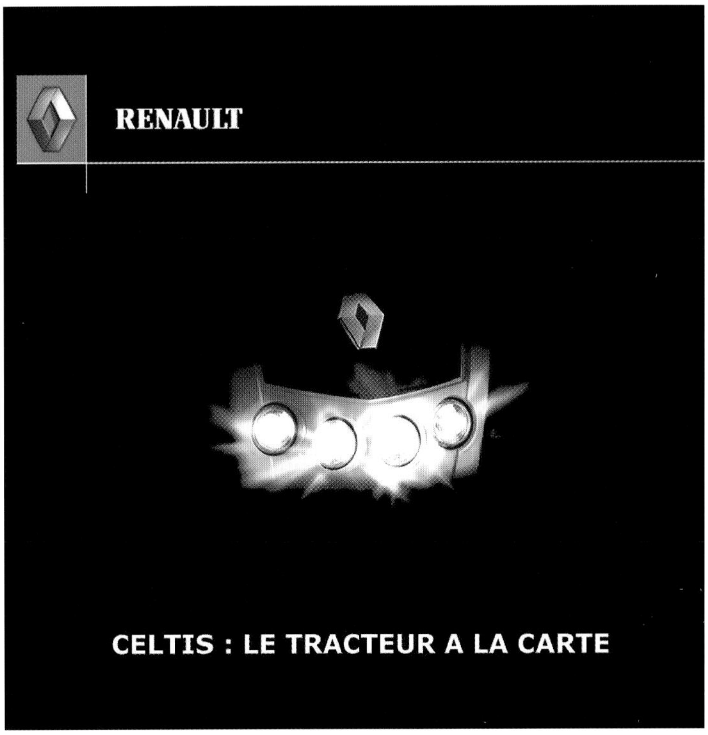

224 Celtis launch promotion in 2002

Notes:

[1] Société Anonyme des Usines Renault (= Renault Corporation)

[2] Salon International de la Machine Agricole (= International Farm Equipment Show)

[3] Division du Matériel Agricole (= Farm Equipment Division)

[4] The design of the Renault TX was awarded the IFEI trophy (IFEI = French Institute of Industrial Design)

[5] GIMA = International Agricultural Mechanical Group

[6] CEMAGREF = Test Centre for farm equipment, rural, water and forest engineering

[7] LASMEA = Scientific and Material Laboratory for electronics and automation at Blaise Pascal University in Clermont-Ferrand

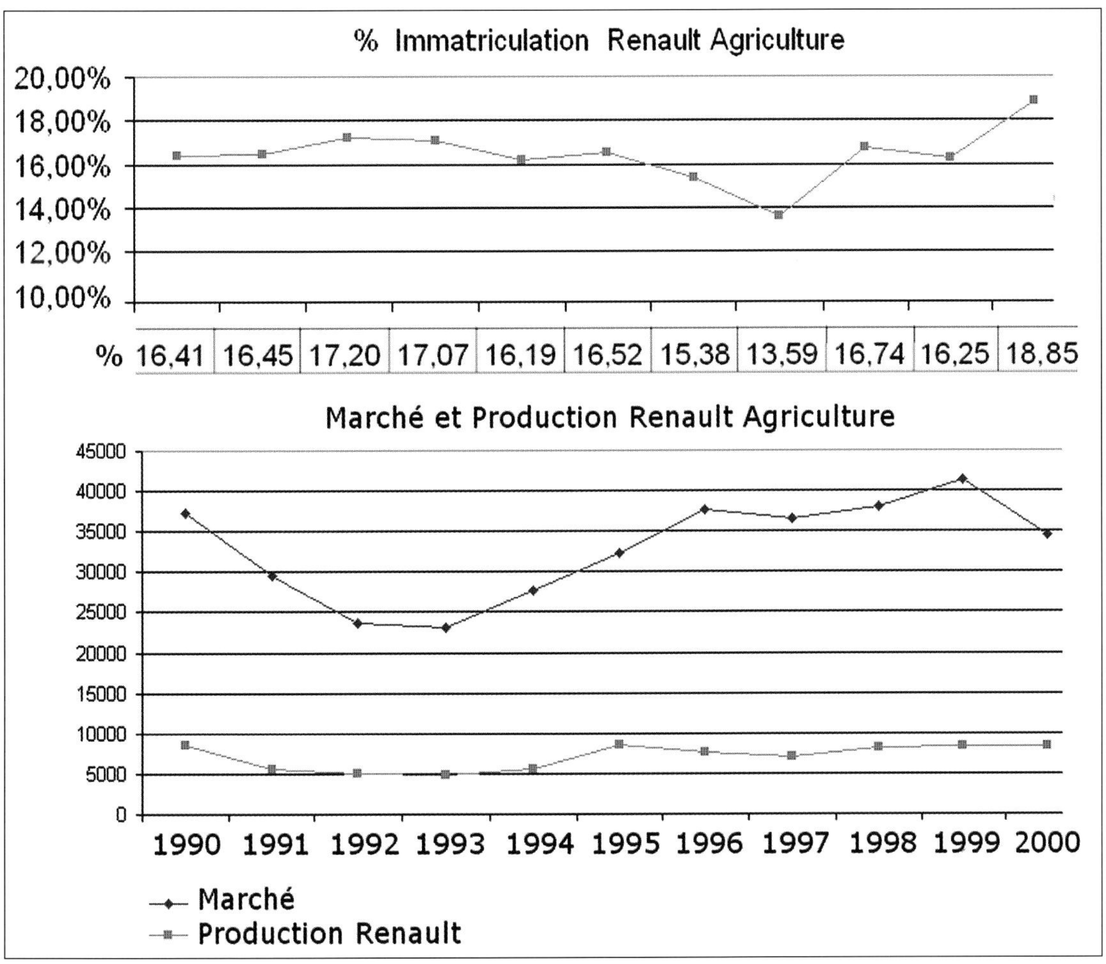

223 Upper graph – Renault Agriculture market shares in France. Lower graph – total market in France, Renault Agriculture production

Tractors in the *CLAAS* group

The cooperation agreement between *Renault Agriculture* and *CLAAS* was signed during the *SIMA* show in Paris in February 2003. This agreement marked a turning point in the history of the two companies. The introduction phase for the green tractors from Le Mans had already begun on October 1st, 2003 and they were received enthusiastically in the market place. For *CLAAS* this also meant a change in philosophy from being a harvesting specialist to a long liner. At the same time the tractors were about to be made available to a much broader market.

Renault Agriculture was, up till then, the agricultural equipment division of the international *Renault* automotive group, and manufactured tractors from 50 to 250 hp. In 2002 the turnover amounted to approximately 636 million € and a total of 9,480 tractors were sold. The company employed around 2,000 people, principally in Velizy, the company headquarters and product development centre and in Le Mans, the main factory.

In the year 2002 some 7,800 tractors were manufactured in the Le Mans facility by about 700 employees. In addition, transmissions in the range from 67 to 154 hp were built here. The plant covers an area of 21 ha, of which 7.5 ha are under roof. The production activities encompass transmissions, cabs, tractor assembly, after sales and also include the international parts centre. A customer visit facility is in the planning stages, based on the Harsewinkel model since a lot more visitors are to be expected from abroad in future.

Alongside this dedicated production facility, *Renault Agriculture* (*RA*) also has interests in other companies in the business. For instance, *RA* has a 50 % holding in the *GIMA*, a joint company manufacturing transmissions in Beauvais. These transmissions, which are also fitted to *Claas* tractors cover in the range between 90 and 260 hp.

In addition, *Renault Agriculture* has a holding of about 10 per cent in *Agritalia.* Around 5,000 vine and orchard tractors a year leave the Rovigo plant in the north of Italy, of which some 1,500 are destined for the *Claas / Renault Agriculture* organisation. There is also the 20 % share in, in an Indian tractor plant in Hoshiampur, where a total of 18,000 tractors in the 30 to 60 hp range are built annually.

225 Main gate at the Renault tractor plant at Le Mans

Cooperation deal with *Claas*

The takeover of *Renault Agriculture* gave *Claas* the opportunity to add a range of tractors to the product line up. This decision was encouraged by the need to secure the company's position on the world market and the demands by distributors outside France to have a consistent brand image plus a full product offering for the widest possible range of customers. In addition, it was obvious that the product lines of the two companies matched each other perfectly. Customers benefit additionally from a new and independent force in the equipment supply area.

226 A handshake concludes the alliance between Claas and Renault Agriculture: on behalf of Renault, board member Patrick Faure and on the right Helmut Claas

The links between the two companies have been developed over many years, with particularly strong bonds to the dealer network in France. In addition to the strong home base, the new deal opens up plenty of potential in central and eastern Europe. A major investment programme has been launched into improved technology and raising quality standards for the tractors from Le Mans. The *Claas* success factors such as innovation plus first rate service and parts

228 A historical moment as the first green tractor nears completion in August 2003

supply will be grafted onto the *Claas* tractor product range in the foreseeable future. This is only possible thanks to the market leadership of *RA* in France, allied with the potential offered by the *Claas* distribution strength elsewhere. In these markets outside France, *Claas* already has a strong sales and service network, most of whom had to compromise as regards tractor brands in the past. In future customers can look to one supplier for high-performance tractors, combine harvesters and forage harvesting equipment. The response by most distributors has been enthusiastic, whilst others have gone their separate ways. In general, the network has been strengthened and enhanced by the deal.

Stronger synergy effects

The alliance between *Renault Agriculture* and *Claas* has already paid off with a 10 per cent increase in tractor sales in the first year. The green tractors were given a strong launch at the

227 The new tractor generation on the line in Claas livery

229 New models take shape with the latest CAD technology

230 Celtis is the all rounder for smaller mixed farms

Agritechnica show in 2003, during which Helmut Claas promised that changing the logo to *Claas* meant much more in terms of quality, image, service and parts supply. The challenge has been taken up by the *Claas* distributors, for instance in Germany, where over 1,000 *Claas* tractors were sold in the first year of joint activity.

Four ranges cover the bulk of the market

The product range has been switched over to the familiar *Claas* green. The *Celtis* is the entry model, typically used in mixed farming, the *Ares* covers the medium to high output range with the *Atles* range extending above that for large arable farms. In addition there is the top of the range *Xerion*, an internal *Claas* development, engineered and manufactured in Harsewinkel.

The *Claas Celtis* fits into the market for tractors up to 100 hp, where it carries out a wide range of tasks on traditional structured farms. The range includes four models from 75 to 102 HP (55 to 75 KW).

The *Celtis* features a new cab with a large roof panel, which provides exceptional comfort for

231 Ares is currently the biggest selling Claas tractor

232 Atles is the top of the line tractor for large scale arable farms

this tractor category and excellent all-round visibility. The cab is offered in two versions, either with the higher comfort roof or low profile roof. The latter has an overall height of less than 2.5 metres, so it can work in low buildings and stables. The doors open up fully and can be locked in the 180° position for moving through narrow stable passages.

The *Ares* tractor range is the upper end of the power scale for discerning, high intensity users. It combines modern technological features with excellent operating economics and high comfort levels. This family is divided into three models: the *Ares 500* with four cylinder engines, the *Ares 600* with entry level 6 cylinder power and the *Ares 800* with a larger six cylinder engine. The range covers the spectrum from 96 hp (71 kW) to 205 hp (151 kW). The complete range is fitted with powershift transmissions plus an additional creeper gear optionally.

The *Claas Atles* is designed for the over 200 hp clientele. The two models in this family are aimed at large farms and contractors and are highly reliable, top performing machines. Excellent tractive force is supplied by 232 hp (171 kW) and 253 hp (178 kW) heavy duty engines.

The *Claas Xerion* is of a difference parentage and with power in excess of 300 hp, it is worthy of a special chapter in the *Claas* history.

Horst Biere, Horst-Dieter Görg

Sources:

Claas annual report 2003, page 29 ff
Claas Intern No. 122, 123 and 124, 2003 / 2004
Claas Intern Special 2003
Claas Vision No. 19, 2003

233 The latest V & O models in Claas livery, introduced in November 2004

Xerion – an in-house Development

Way back in the 1970s first efforts were made at *CLAAS* to construct a multipurpose machine for farming. Quite a few ideas were borrowed from the *Huckepack* design generated in the 1950s. The first prototype was developed and produced in 1979. With so many pioneering features there were plenty of hurdles to be overcome in the field. The result was that this meant returning to the drawing board more often than was really good and many years went by before the first machines were ready for the market. The new style *Xerion* has achieved new importance with the *Renault* tractor agreement.

The arrival of self-propelled technology is in one of the main driving forces behind progress in farming techniques. Each self-propelled machine is designed for a specific function and they have gained ground or completely substituted earlier equipment as farm specialisation has progressed. This has occurred naturally on the basis of their improved performance and operating economics. The downside is of course the limited annual utilisation, since farming and in particular harvesting is highly seasonal. Consequently these expensive specialised machines spend most of the year sitting around and tying up capital.

The alternative approach to this in a number of fields has been the development of multipurpose machinery. In the case of farming this inspired engineers to look at a new approach which was to develop a prime mover as the core element to which adaptable implements and tools for individual applications could be added. Then only one set of drive components, a single steering and cab would be needed. The implements would be less expensive than specialised self-propelled machines, whilst the basic prime mover could be used more efficiently during the whole year.

This basic philosophy had led *Claas* to the development of the *Huckepack* in the 1950s and the so-called *HSG* project, the first *Claas* designed tractor which was axed during a cost reduction program in the early 1970s. At about this time *Mercedes* were introducing a similar type of machine in Germany, the *MB Trac*.

Project 207

This project team was instigated by Helmut Claas on the 19th of September 1978, following feasibility studies which centred on the new style *Dual Mode Responder* (*DMT*) transmission from Sundstrand in America, a stepless, power splitting unit which broke completely with previous technology.

The project was given the task of developing a multipurpose prime mover which finally saw the light of day as the *Xerion*. Initially the suitability of the *DMT* transmission for off road applications was to be investigated, since it had only been used in buses and trucks in the USA. As a result the vehicle was given the uninspiring name of the "*DMT* test vehicle". The project was kept highly secret and was managed by Nils Fredriksen.

234 The HSG was the first Claas tractor project from 1968 to 1972

It is a sign of the persistence of the company that, despite the many setbacks, market changes and new approaches, the *Xerion* project was not called into question. It continued for 18 years before the definitive market introduction could occur.

The multifunction concept

One of the basic design parameters which set this project apart was that the basic machine should emulate the characteristics of a tractor. This was quite a break in tradition for Claas, the harvesting specialist. The requirement to transmit power efficiently onto the ground had a major effect on the overall development of the multifunction system. There were plenty of other important design objectives such as:

- Suitability for high-performance fieldwork. The total system consisting of the prime mover and the specific implement were to have the same output, ease of handling, visibility, manoeuvrability and comfort as the comparable self-propelled machine. The objective was to achieve the same standards as a self propelled unit with no compromises, a tough target to meet.

- Straightforward and rapid changeover from one application to another. The target was for two people to carry out the transformation in 15 minutes or so, which meant that the implement had to be fixed with quick connectors and only a minimum of bolts could be used. Quite a challenge with heavy, complex structures, as you can see on the following pages.

- The interfaces with the implements should be specific to *Claas* where possible and the specially designed implements only usable on the *Project 207* prime mover. This entailed close cooperation with the specialised manufacturers of implements for the various functions.

The *Project 207* team was set the task of defining the layout of the prime mover with typical tractor characteristics plus a range of specific implements and attachments. All of these would provide the same performance as a dedicated self-propelled machine.

Initial feasibility studies showed that the overall investment in a *Project 207* mechanisation package would cost 40 % less than a dedicated self-propelled solution. The annual operating costs could be reduced by up to 30 %, which made this idea potentially a very attractive proposition for customers in the future.

The working modules

The first self-propelled applications which were developed in depth were a forage harvester, combine harvester, a sugar beet lifter. During the project a seed drilling combination and a mower were added. This was no overnight operation, in fact it took 15 years from the inception in 1978 until the first customer presentation in 1993.

The project team looked first at familiar areas of harvesting technology such as forage and cereals. In the autumn of 1979 successful tests were carried out with a four row maize header and an outfit based on the *SF 80* forage harvester. In the course of the following years two other adaptations were made, but it was becoming difficult to keep up with the pace of self-propelled forage harvester development. The corn cracker became a feature, whilst chopping drums grew both in diameter and width. Gradually the 250 hp fitted to the *Project 207* began to look a little bit on the small side, whilst the weight and dimensions of the working modules grew beyond the planned dimensions. At the same time it was realised that the *Claas* self-propelled foragers were very successful in their own right and paid their way for the contractor, so that this project was finally abandoned.

It is easy to imagine that the combine harvester adaptation was a very controversial chapter in the company's history. During the 1980s two totally different prototype combines were built and tested. In 1980 and 1981 trials were carried out with what became known as the side saddle combine. This rig was attached to the prime mover with special couplings down one side, so that the driver had good visibility from the cab. The combine harvester drive was provided by a special transverse PTO shaft. This combination was good enough to be called a self-propelled combine harvester. It was also a much better solution than the pull type combines which were still popular in many countries, such as Canada. The trouble was that there were such serious problems driving and handling this trial machine that the engineers agreed to try again with a different approach. This time they quickly came to the conclusion that a drop down version in separate modules would work better. It took until early in 1988 before a prototype could be put together and tested, first in the cereals harvest and then in maize. Unfortunately the results were such that this project was also put to rest.

With the realisation that the traditional areas of company strength were not that suitable for multifunctional machinery, all that was left of

235 The first prototype with a forage harvester pack in autumn 1969. August Claas pays a visit to the team. (Third from left)

236 The forerunner of the Xerion with the combine pack ...

the *Claas* specific applications by 1993 was the triple mowing combination, the *Corto 8100* with 7.8 metres working width. Just fitting a mower was never enough to justify this project, but another limiting factor was strategic. It was just unattractive to pour in reserves and pursue alternatives to existing successful product ranges. Attention therefore turned to making development contracts with implement manufacturers.

An immense amount of time and energy went in to the development of a sugar beet lifter. Sugar beet harvesting looked fairly standardised, focused on the six row method. The project team decided to concentrate on a six row, single phase method which also allowed opening up of the field.

Between 1982 and 1996 six different models were developed, together with implement partners such as *Kleine, Bleinroth* and *Holmer* in Germany. The final choice was a bunker machine with 8 m^3 capacity produced by *Holmer*. A number of these were sold to Russia following the market introduction in 1996.

In 1993 a very promising self propelled seeding combination was designed together with *Rabe*. It featured a working width of 6 m and was composed of a front packer, discs, seed drill and a 3 m^3 seed hopper. This was a big step forward since the contemporary tractor mounted systems had only half this hopper capacity. On this occasion *Claas* had at last managed to overtake the self-propelled movement with the *207* Project.

237 ... and set up as a fully functional combine

The *Claas* multifunctional system was first shown to the public during the *International Claas Forum* in 1993. Following this came a flood of ideas and suggestions from customers for new modules that could be fitted. The implement manufacturers also came forward with their ideas which resulted in spectacular combinations such as the 13 m^3 slurry spreader with injector technology from *Kaweco* in the Netherlands, the *Amazone* spreader, the *Jenz* wood chopper, the four row potato harvester from *Herder* and the *Bisang* bunker forager, to mention just a few interesting applications.

The prime mover

One of the most fascinating stages of this project was to define how the prime mover should be designed to work together with all these different application modules, whilst being able to carry out the work expected of a tractor in its own right. It was essential to do the groundwork thoroughly if the project was to be successful.

The beauty of dedicated self-propelled machines is that the functional components and cab can be matched perfectly to the job in hand. The travel function is a subsidiary operation.

With multifunctional equipment the basic machine stays virtually unchanged in all the different applications. That means that the working modules have to be adapted to the unchanging layout of the prime mover, and that leads inevitably to compromises in terms of their operation. The engineers then have the task of reducing the effect of these compromises to a minimum.

The *Claas* design team sought to soften up the rigid structure of the basic vehicle so that the working modules could be adapted with a certain amount of leeway. In order to reach the self-propelled performance targets special attention had to be paid to a large number of criteria. Crop intake and flow for one, the provision of drives to a high performance harvesting attachments working close to the ground and large scale hoppers on top of the machine on the other. Not to forget ergonomic requirements such as unimpeded driver visibility onto the whole working process. For tractor operation basic requirements included a powerful three-point linkage at the rear and a cab located close to the centreline. This position would however get in the way of large hoppers, so a flexible approach was needed all round the prime mover.

238 Application study with new design, 1993

239 A Xerion sugar beet lifter

This was all unknown territory, of course, and the key solution was to swivel the whole cab through 180° and add a side position as well. This provided following solutions at a stroke:

1. Room to top mount large crop containers and hoppers
2. Use of the existing three point linkage from the tractor for locating implements in reverse direction and
3. Best possible driver visibility during the working process.

This was a highly innovative approach and from then on it would be possible to adapt the working modules whilst reducing their functionality and performance limitations. Once this idea had come to fruition it was going to be possible to achieve comparable work rates to self-propelled units. At the same time, however, increased demands would have to be placed on the prime mover. The transmission had to be capable of operating in both directions and reach a high top speed, both forward and reverse. The cab required a special device so it could be raised and swivelled. Then it was going to take a robust locking device to fix it positively to the chassis. If that wasn't enough all of the operating func-

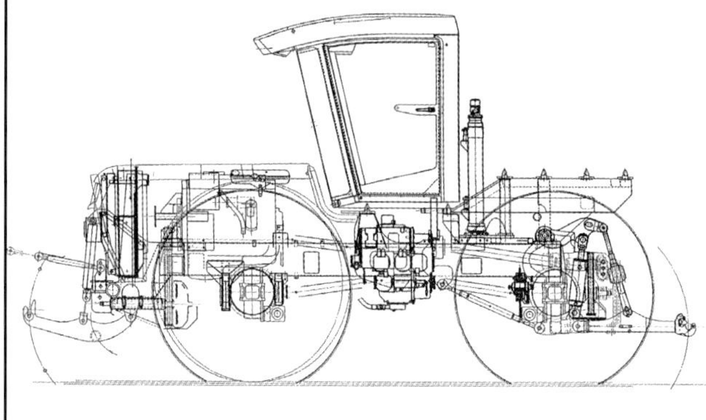

240 Functional diagram of the Xerion prime mover in 1993

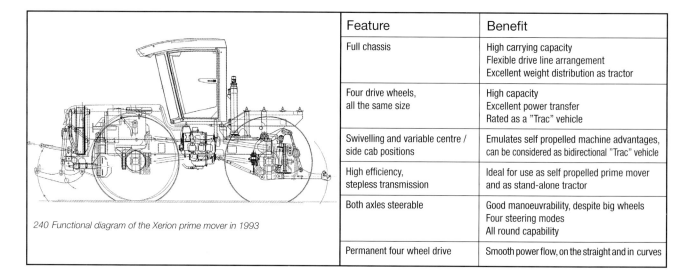

Feature	Benefit
Full chassis	High carrying capacity Flexible drive line arrangement Excellent weight distribution as tractor
Four drive wheels, all the same size	High capacity Excellent power transfer Rated as a "Trac" vehicle
Swivelling and variable centre / side cab positions	Emulates self propelled machine advantages, can be considered as bidirectional "Trac" vehicle
High efficiency, stepless transmission	Ideal for use as self propelled prime mover and as stand-alone tractor
Both axles steerable	Good manoeuvrability, despite big wheels Four steering modes All round capability
Permanent four wheel drive	Smooth power flow, on the straight and in curves

tions had to take account of the cab swivelling, so a flexible approach to the electrical system, hydraulics and pneumatics was called for. In all a daunting list of requirements, however where there is a will there's a way.

This unprecedented catalogue of technical requirements led finally to the creation of a machine with unique specifications, unrivalled to this day in terms of its engineering excellence.

The transmission

Such an advanced machine would be worthless without a stepless transmission. A good tractor must be able to transmit the engine power onto the ground efficiently. The prime mover simply had to have a high efficiency stepless transmission, which – then as now – is a complicated issue. A year after the project had been initiated in 1978, the first test machines were running with the stepless, power splitting *DMT* transmission. It was designed with the *207* in mind along with other multifunction vehicles.

Unfortunately the *DMT* project was axed by *Sundstrand* in the autumn of 1979, leaving the *Claas* team in a state of shock with no transmission. They scoured the market for an alternative and also sketched their own designs for the transmission, either a power splitting one or a powershift. The *207* system was tried out with a *Twin Disc* 12 range transmission in 1982 / 83 and later with an 18 range power shift transmission engineers in house. Neither of these was really suitable and so they were dropped.

As luck would have it, contact was made to Professor Friedrich Jarchow of the Ruhr University in Bochum, Germany during a transmission conference early in 1986. His work on patent development was already well known within *Claas.* For instance he had presented an *Audi 80* car with a stepless, hydrostatic-mechanical or power splitting transmission named after his design – the Jarchow principle. It was a pleasure to drive and had high mechanical efficiency. The company signed an exclusive contract with him and then worked on transmission concepts suitable for use in tractors. The desire to develop a *CVT* or continuously variable transmission internally was quickly accepted within the company. The decision to produce the *HM 8* hydraulic-mechanical transmission for up to 200 hp was made in 1987.

The crux with regard to the overall suitability of the *HM 8* transmission was its mechanical efficiency. If this could be proved, the Project *314* – the continuation of the *HM 8* development project – would get the go ahead. Helmut Claas set the 30th of June 1989 as the deadline. A test bed was set up in collaboration with Professor Jar-

241 Swivelling the cab, 1987 style ...

242 ... with the Project 207 prototype number 3

243 First tillage trials in 1979 included ...

244 ... working with a reversible plough

chow at the University in Bochum for the initial testing phase and the author was able to phone Helmut Claas on the deadline date to inform him about the promising measurements and efficiency results.

Project *314* was given the thumbs up immediately, so further prototype transmissions were organised and in January 1991 the first practical tests with the *HM 8* transmission were launched with a converted *MB Trac 1500.* Simultaneously the *Schlüter Eurotrac*, a large tractor built by a specialist manufacturer in Bavaria, was converted for first driving trials in April 1992.

The discussions with *Schlüter* were terminated since this producer lacked the stamina to continue. Following this, interest was revived in developing the *Claas* prime mover. Since the *HM 8* project was well advanced, it was decided to use it in the new batch of 207 machines. In the summer of 1993 two new *Claas* machines were built in the framework of the Project *407* and the marketing team christened the *Xerion* for the first time just ahead of its first public showing in November 1993.

Understandably there was considerable pressure to finally get going with the *Xerion* self-propelled system in the marketplace. By then substantial resources had been allocated to the development project and there was no certainty of success, with ambiguous economic feasibility studies plus a mixed reception to demonstrations in France, Hungary and England. Market research also shed no light on the acceptance of the scheme. The only way forward was to jump in the deep end with customers who would try it out in real working conditions.

Prior to the cautious introduction with five units, all of which were covered by a godfather programme, the machines were thoroughly redesigned. *Raba* in Hungary was given the order to produce beefed up steer axles. A *Perkins Navistar* engine was fitted, the frame was welded instead of bolted together, the *HM 8* transmission was enclosed in a cast housing, an output limiter was fitted to it as a result of the higher PTO power requirement and a new design was created by an external design office.

The jury was still out regarding the acceptance of this new self-propelled system. The introduction phase with the five machines was continued from 1996 and 1997 to early 1999. Initial production runs were repeated in order to widen the practical trial phase and by 1999 some 80 *Xerion* machines were in operation. Gradually acceptance of this approach began to increase and the overall concept began to look increasingly viable.

Transition to production in series

With the benefit of all this information the period between 2000 and 2003 was used to consolidate the project and redefine the parameters. During this phase no new machines were sold.

Claas decided in May 2000 to design a new *Xerion* model with a higher engine output, while still retaining the basic features of the earlier

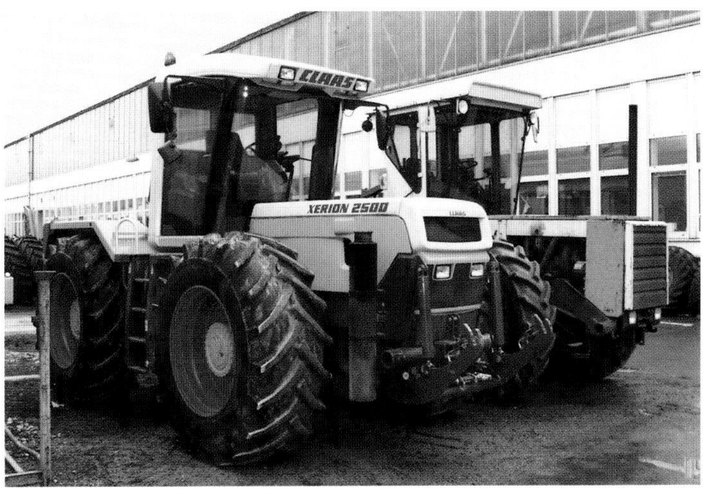

245 The Xerion is instantly recognisable with its modern styling. Behind it a prototype, 1996

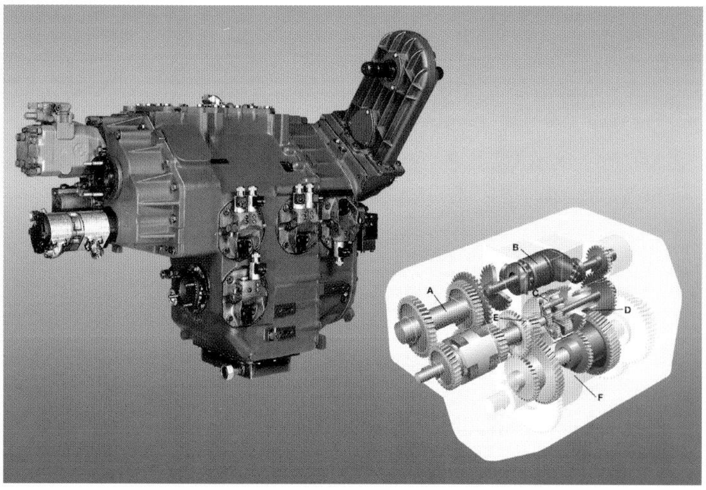

246 Photos and functional diagram of the HM 8 transmission

vehicle. This new development under the auspices of Andreas Stelzer and Foreman Heinz Hartmeier included following specifications:

- Maximum engine output of 335 hp
- Longer wheelbase
- Use of the newly developed *Claas HM II* transmission by *CIT* since 1998
- Modular design.

Previously there was just one *Xerion* model to cope with several different application areas. In the new modular approach different basic machine types could be offered, with only the cab position differing.

To broaden the utilisation as a carrier, a fixed front central cab option over the engine compartment was added. This version opened up a large surface area for fitting units such as tanks, hoppers and the like on top and even made it possible to turn it into an articulating unit.

In 2001 two of these new units were built for functional testing. Before long the *Claas* experts realised that the *HM II* transmission designed by the *Claas Industrial Engineering Division* couldn't meet the increasing power demands. Instead a new transmission was incorporated based on a joint development of the *Eccom 3.9* transmission from *ZF*.

This new layout was quickly recognised as an excellent basis for the top of the line *Xerion* customer needs and the first series production was carried out in autumn 2004.

Persistence has paid off. After all these trials and tribulations *Claas* now owns a remarkably versatile high end tractor and multipurpose unit which complements the new tractor range ideally. Without a doubt it will be at home in the most demanding farming and contracting applications in east and west.

NILS FREDRIKSEN

247 New dimensions are now possible – the Xerion combined with an articulated slurry injector in 2004

The growth of a Family Company

248 Bird's eye view of the Claas plant in Harsewinkel today

When the original company - Gebrüder Claas - was founded, it was from very modest beginnings. Nonetheless it had something special which made it into such a significant player in the worldwide market. In the process many wide-ranging decisions were made. New products were created, diversification was carried out, unusual marketing approaches adopted. Factories were added away from Harsewinkel - an axle and transmission plant in Paderborn, a baler factory in Metz, a component factory in Schloss Holte plus several foundries. The takeover of Bautz in Saulgau added green harvest equipment to the Claas product range in 1969. Production of small combine harvesters for rice was developed in Faridabad, India, cutter bars sourced from Hungary and production technology based in Beelen, some 10 km from Harsewinkel. A new combine facility is taking shape in Omaha, Nebraska whilst a radical modernisation programme has transformed the main plant in Harsewinkel and made it fit for the challenges of sophisticated combine production for the years ahead. Finally investments are being made in Krasnodar in Russia to underpin the developments in the expanding markets in this region.

From Gebrüder Claas to today's Company

As we read earlier *CLAAS* originated with production of straw trussers in 1919 and got into the combine business in 1930 by instigating research into a completely new product. In those days it was a machine factory with a strong artisanal flavour. It has gradually transformed itself into a respected farm equipment company with a global presence. The *CLAAS* Group has gone from strength to strength in the last years. *CLAAS* is well represented around the world with an international production and distribution network, a workforce of some 8,000 employees and over 80 national importers.

How long can a company be classified as a glorified workshop, when does it become a medium-sized company, at what point does the transition take place to being a major corporation, or even a world class entity? Is business development governed solely by the laws of natural selection and survival of the fittest, or is there an element of luck as well? This sort of question is often asked inside corporations which have reached the status of global players. We would like to investigate a little further whether we can define the major steps in the way that *Claas* developed. Maybe we'll find that it was a succession of intuitive steps and smaller decisions in the early years which finally paved the way for today's success.

It would seem that the incessant drive for innovation and product superiority are common threads throughout the decades and these have always been rewarded by customers investing in the products and generating steady growth. Within this there are milestones, both large and small, on the long journey from the early years to the global corporation of today. However, the company has never forgotten where it comes from and the customer is still the be all and end all.

In the beginning the first products were straw trussers, built by August Claas and a total of three staff when he set up in business in 1913. This was similar to the beginnings of many other farm equipment businesses of that period. For many of these the outbreak of war meant the end of their business, but the *Claas brothers* got together shortly before the tragic events which blighted Europe and possibly this gave them the will to continue later. It was fortuitous that all of them returned safe and sound from the front.

The brickworks – a first milestone

After hostilities had ceased the brothers were resolved to carry on their business in the brickworks which later became corporate headquarters. The purchase of the site in 1919 demonstrates a remarkable entrepreneurial attitude, which definitely contributed to the success of the company in the decades to come.

The search for new ideas which is closely linked to the name of August Claas was demonstrated for the first time with the landmark patent for the improved knotter. It takes a very special sort of skill to keep looking carefully at ways to improve things which others take for granted. The company was rewarded for his keen powers of observation with a good order book which made them the envy of many of the competitors.

249 The knotter was the earliest Claas trademark, invented and patented in 1921. It made the company famous around the world

This too is repeated frequently in the company's history.

Diversification has always been a popular way to increase turnover. It was tried out early with the addition of spreaders during the 1920s, followed by the new straw balers.

The world economic crisis was the next event which killed off many a young company, but August Claas managed to steer through the crisis and the small company survived. He never lost his flair for designing new machines and despite the extremely difficult environment, the combine harvester was taking shape and would change the world of farming for ever.

The birth of the combine harvester

This decisive phase of the company's development sheds light on the subject in hand. The idea to develop a combine harvester originated with the joining of minds between the ambitious entrepreneur August Claas, the academic Professor Karl Vormfelde and his assistant, the engineer Walter Brenner. When they faced the combined resistance of the farming experts, the academic world and farm equipment producers, they didn't just give up. August Claas had made up his mind and was prepared to see it through, come what may.

Whilst the world's attention was focused on the 1936 Olympics in Berlin, a little bit of history was being made just 150 km away on a field in a little place called Zschernitz. The first *Claas MDB* combine described in detail earlier in this book had reached maturity, it had managed to achieve acceptable results and that proved all the sceptics to be in the wrong. In retrospect the management had shown vision and had remained steadfast in the face of apparently insurmountable obstacles.

An open attitude to building up international business relationships was an early feature of the company's development. The company was fortunate that Paula Claas, who was August's wife, had studied business and spoke several foreign languages. She was put in charge of the export business, an early example of equality, and would frequently accompany her husband on trips abroad, visiting customers and exhibitions.

This unique mixture of entrepreneurial skill, risk taking and intuition with just a bit of luck thrown in was a winning combination. The labour force in Harsewinkel had reached 500 by the year 1939, just two decades after the brothers had come back from the First World War and bought up the brickworks. Even during the turbulent war years up to 1945, the management never lost sight of their prime business and were busy developing the next generation of combines. Nowadays this would be considered an excellent example of strategic focus.

All that was left after this period was to pick up the pieces and start again. They were not discouraged; in fact this total mess around them seems to have spurred them on. It meant working with the hundred people left and try to start

251 Paula and August Claas in 1967

production of the range of trussers, balers and combine harvesters again. Demand was enormous, only there were no resources available to either manufacture, purchase or distribute the machinery. Despite this, the company managed to recover very rapidly and, sure enough, their enthusiasm was rewarded.

Whilst manufacturing was reinforced with the construction of a foundry, they had realised very quickly the importance of establishing a brand identity. They worked hard on establishing an international presence, taking part in international farm equipment exhibitions in Paris, Brussels and even the prestigious *Royal Show* in England. The *Claas* combine had soon become a well known and highly successful product.

First mover

Every business has its leaders and *Claas* developed a philosophy of innovation very early on and has never lost it. The first European combine 1936 was followed by the first European

250 The new head office building in 1953, just after completion

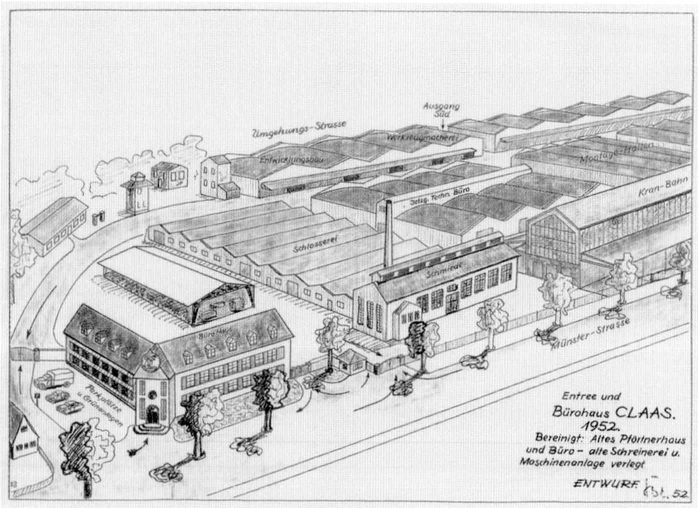

252 Walter Brenner sketched the extension to the Harsewinkel factory in 1952 with the head office building in the foreground

self-propelled combine in 1953. Once again the company moved ahead of competition with a pioneering product to reinforce its core business. The *Hercules* combine or *SF* as it was later known was an important strategic move.

Manufacturing capacity was extended progressively as demand for mechanisation on farms continued to boom with no end in sight. Whilst Harsewinkel grew and grew, the company had the foresight to invest in new plants elsewhere. In the post-war period of political uncertainty, it made sense to spread the risks. In 1956 a new transmission and axle plant was set up in Paderborn, some 60 km from the HQ. Baler production was relocated to a new facility in Metz, north eastern France. This decision to go outside Germany for the first time made sense, since France was the biggest market for balers. In 1960 the production of hydraulic components was centralised in a factory between Paderborn and Harsewinkel, at a place called Schloss Holte. By this time *Claas* had become a large employer with a payroll of around 3,300 staff.

From a customer point of view *Claas* was an acknowledged leader in cereals harvesting, but not really present in the grass and forage business. In 1969 that all changed with the takeover

253 Claas products were frequently awarded medals of excellence by the DLG

of *Bautz* in southern Germany, which added a full range of reputable forage harvesting equipment and filled the gaps in the harvesting specialist line up.

The specialisation and focus on harvest technology had established a clear differentiation advantage for *Claas* against its competition. This positioning was given another boost with the acquisition of the rights to the *Speiser* forage chopping technology. This also included the use of the *Jaguar* brand name, which turned out to be very fortuitous. The *Jaguar* brand covered trailed forage harvesters, the market for these products still being its infancy. The transition to self-propelled technology began in early 1970s and *Claas* moved quickly to establish technological leadership, a lead which it has never relinquished. The *Jaguar* range of forage harvesters is the world market leader, with a market share of around 50 %. Production is concentrated in the Harsewinkel plant.

By the 1970s *Claas* had established a position of some strength in many countries around the world. During this expansion into new markets, the company had added to its product portfolio and developed specific machines for these markets such as the sugar cane harvester. *Ford* who were a significant tractor producer at the time forged a strategic alliance with *Claas* to market the combine range in the USA. The broad range of high-quality innovative harvesting technology provided the foundations for durable market success in the Western European farming community.

Engineering for growth

Periods of market decline were used to consolidate and be ready for the next upturn with inevitable increases in customer demands for performance and operator features. Products would be upgraded and made ready for the next phase of expansion, engineered literally for growth. Following the recession in Europe in the early 1990s the company benefited from an unparalleled period of unbroken growth, adding an average of 10 % to the turnover each year. In fact turnover quadrupled from 1993 to 2004 at which point it was close to 2,000 million euros.

The original core product is still the combine harvester, and above all it is this product which has underpinned corporate growth. The combine has changed out of all recognition whilst market structures, whether dealers, farmers or contractors, have also gone through several phases of rapid development. *Claas* has managed to fore-

254 The Claas Super featured on the 50 Franc bill in Luxembourg, issued in the Grand Duchy in 1961. Three million of these banknotes were in circulation until 1976

cast future demands accurately and provide the right machines at the right time. Staying close to the customer, listening carefully to their needs and adapting technology from all over are vital elements in this process.

Diversification took the company out of harvesting, as testified by the *Manufacturing Engineering Division* (*CFT*), which was spun off in the early 1990s based on the company's expertise in manufacturing. This division supplies precision tooling and automation systems to the automobile, aviation and other sectors and has contributed strongly to growth.

The move away from pure product investments to a full service corporation is underlined by the *AGROCOM* division, whose objective is to come up with specific software solutions for farming. The spectrum of products includes decision making tools for farmers, improved fleet management and improved economics of equipment.

The most significant strategic decision in recent years came about in 2003, after many years of speculation. *Claas* definitely needed a tractor partner in one form or the other but various alliances had not produced the desired results. A complete acquisition was necessary to secure the distribution network and *Renault Agriculture* was the ideal candidate. They provided a full range of marketable tractors, added 600 million euros and 2,000 employees to the company portfolio. The majority takeover meant that *Claas* had joined the ranks of the major players with a full line up for every farmer and contractor and an exclusive product range for dealers.

During the last few years the company has been at the forefront of investment in the former eastern European states. A factory in Hungary was given the task of producing cutter bars for the group. Currently work is in progress on building a plant in Russia for the production of combine harvesters in this vast agricultural region which can only be served by raising local content.

From the very beginning to today, the company has been managed by members of the *Claas* family. They have shaped its development and will continue to do so in future. Despite a workforce of 8,000 people, the company has not lost its family touch.

The founding fathers, August Claas and his brothers, were able to hand over the business to the next generation, with the eldest son, Helmut Claas, becoming the most well-known of them. Following in the footsteps of his grandfather and father, he took a mechanic's apprenticeship. After this he studied mechanical engineering at the Technical High School in Hanover and specialised in machine tools and manufacturing techniques. A further year was spent studying agriculture in Paris following which his

255 A Matador being slung on board ship in 1963

256 Helmut and Erika Claas at home in their garden, 2001

first business assignment was the formation of the French daughter company, the forerunner of today's subsidiary, *Claas France SAS.*

In 1956 Helmut Claas returned to Harsewinkel and worked in the technical area which covered development and production. Even at this early stage of his career he had understood the importance of close connections between customers, engineering and production. He quickly realised that the interplay between these three elements is the key for innovative product strategies, short development cycles and competitive production costs.

Helmut Claas was designated as Technical Director in 1962. When the legal entity changed from being a limited company into an open trading company (oHG) in 1978, Helmut Claas took over unlimited liability and became Managing Director. It was under his leadership that the *Dominator* family evolved to become Europe's most successful combine. As his responsibilities continued to grow along with the company, he still kept a close eye on what was happening in the R & D department. Revolutionary developments such as the *APS* threshing system, the *hybrid system* and the hydrostatic-mechanical power splitting transmission were strongly initiated by his technical expertise and unfailing intuitive skills.

In 1996 the company was changed into a share owning partnership, a structure which matched the family-oriented management style. At this point Helmut Claas left the board of directors, staying on as Chairman of the Supervisory Board and Partners' Committee, from which he controls the strategic direction of the group.

In reality nothing much has changed after this reorganisation. He still works closely with the board of directors and feels a strong duty in regard to corporate governance. To keep a handle on the diverse developments within the group, he has set up a number of expert committees, which each contain members of the partners' committee and directors according to their sphere of responsibility. Helmut Claas participates in most of the committee meetings and focuses in particular on the themes of "Product and Market Strategy" and "Personnel" with the support of his daughter Cathrina.

257 Celebration for the 400,000th Claas combine, a Lexion

In his spare time Helmut Claas likes to keep in touch with what's going on in the world of farming. He is a cereals and sugar beet farmer in his own right and has a farm in England, where he likes to spend as much time as possible. He also runs his own *Xerion* and a *Lexion 480* on this farm. The machinery and labour are also contracted out to a neighbouring estate producing cereals. In this manner Helmut Claas is carrying on the traditions of his forefathers: he is a farmer, contractor and industrialist. The education of the up and coming generation is also close to his heart, so he set up the *Claas Foundation* in 1999 to promote pursuit of science, research and training in the agricultural and allied fields.

259 Ground breaking ceremony to mark the start of the multi million factory overhaul in Harsewinkel, summer of 2001.From left to right: Reinhold, Günther, Cathrina and Helmut Claas

The shareholdings were reorganised in 1972. The new owners were August Claas, Helmut Claas with a majority shareholding and his cousin Günther Claas. Reinhold Claas, his brother, joined the partners later on.

Reinhold Claas is the younger brother of Helmut Claas, and he joined the company in 1957 where he was assigned to baler development. In this capacity he was responsible for planning and installation of the baler factory in Metz. Additionally he was also on the board of two manufacturers of special roller bearings. Reinhold Claas is active today in various committees of the *Claas Group* and in the Partners' Committee, together with numerous other public engagements.

258 Early sales campaigns have become a regular feature of the year

Günther Claas is the son of Franz Claas and joined the company after studying in Göttingen, Hamburg and Innsbruck. He made a large contribution to the development of the Spanish daughter company in the 1950s, predecessor of the modern day *Claas Ibérica SA*, of which he is Honorary Chairman of the Supervisory Board. After successfully accomplishing the mission in Spain, he carried out a number of different management functions within the *Claas Group*, the last of which was in the purchasing division. Following retirement he continues to carry out his family responsibilities and is a member of the Partners' Committee and Supervisory Board.

The next generation which will take over the reins is already assuming responsibility for the future. For instance Cathrina Claas, daughter of Helmut and Erika Claas has completed her commercial training and has graduated in Business Studies from the University of St. Gallen, Switzerland. Following that she spent some years with a large international corporation abroad. During this period she was nominated to the Partners' Committee. In 2004 she was made Deputy Chairman and has since begun to focus on her tasks within the company. The other partners have also begun to transfer responsibility to the next generation. For instance Günther Claas has passed on his seat in the Supervisory Board and Partners' Committee to his son Oliver.

Volker Claas, oldest son of Reinhold Claas, has taken over his father's role on the Supervisory Board with effect from 2001.

Horst Biere, Astrid Enge

Sources:

Manuscripts by Helmut Claas on the occasion of being awarded honorary doctorships at Silsoe in July 1998 and Hohenheim in September 2000, address to the VDI Agricultural Congress in Münster, November 2000 and the opening ceremony for the new exhibition centre in Hohenheim, June 2004

The *CLAAS* Factories and Subsidiaries

Alongside the main factory in Harsewinkel production capacity grew along with the expansion of the product line. Whilst the impetus for new plants came initially from labour considerations, later decisions were often based more on market factors reflecting globalisation and addition of new activities to the company's portfolio.

Initially the need to set up new facilities was triggered by the boom in combine production. It was no longer possible to employ everyone needed at one spot since the labour market around the Harsewinkel had been swept clean. The abundance of labour in the post-war years had all but dried up. The search for new locations began in earnest.

Industrial components from Paderborn

The first location for a new facility was found on a former air base some 60 km from Harsewinkel. It was not too far away and labour was available. Ground clearing began in 1955, workers were hired and given initial training in Harsewinkel before production was started, relieving some of the pressure on the main plant.

The first building was 3,500 m² in area and was finished in the summer of 1956. The production tooling for gearboxes, drive axles and hydraulic components was moved from Harsewinkel and the staff could get to work. The main gate, offices, washing and changing facilities were located in an old barracks building.

Production was instigated on October 1, 1956. The plant director of the time addressed his workers with a clear message to the team: "Gentlemen, *Claas* has put up the first part of these buildings for you. Up to you now to earn the rest".

The factory was expanded steadily as the number of components grew. Within just 10 years the labour force had reached 1,000 employees and it had become very competent in its own right, helping to develop improved products for the whole group.

261 A robot painting a combine drive axle

The introduction of the *Dominator* combine range in the 1970s put added pressure on the Paderborn factory. Component diameters increased and tolerances became tighter in line with improved technology within the group. Computer controlled cost management was introduced and the factory turned into a profit centre. Hydraulic components began to be marketed to other OEMs in 1975 using the *Claas* brand (*CIT*).

Social facilities were added to improve the workers' well-being. In addition investments were made into training of mechanical skills and over 300 young people completed their engineering apprenticeships in the factory.

260 The first 60 employees in Paderborn with plant manager and co-author Meinolf Reiher on the left and Walter Claas (centre right with jacket and tie)

The machinery was also regularly updated and investments carried out to keep standards at the highest level. The management is particularly proud of the new control pulley production and machining centres. The demand for a high-quality finish and different types of painting required by customers necessitated further investments so the quality of the paint finish was brought up to standard thanks to a new painting centre with two robots. This centre produces no pollution thanks to an emissions-killing post combustion system.

The production area was expanded step-by-step and nowadays 25,000 m^2 are under cover on the 100,000 m^2 site. The company has developed an enviable reputation for quality, both within the *Claas* Group and with external customers. It has innovated in gear manufacturing with, for instance, a method to eliminate distortion due to heat treatment of hardened steel gear sprockets.

The company today is an independent subsidiary, both manufacturing and marketing the products and called *Claas Industrietechnik* (*CIT*), a respected supplier of heavy duty axles, transmissions, hydraulic cylinders and valves to manufacturers of construction equipment, vehicles for municipal use, materials handling equipment, machinery and related product categories.

Hydraulic components from Schoss Holte

The company also set up a facility in Schloss Holte, close to Bielefeld about 30 km from Harsewinkel. The buildings were initially used to make components and assemblies for the combine harvester production. Then *Claas* acquired a 37,000 m^2 plot of land adjacent to it and built up a 14,000 m^2 factory in three stages between 1965 and 1971.

In the process a tool and jig department was created, along with an apprentice training centre

262 Bird's eye view of the Schloss Holte plant

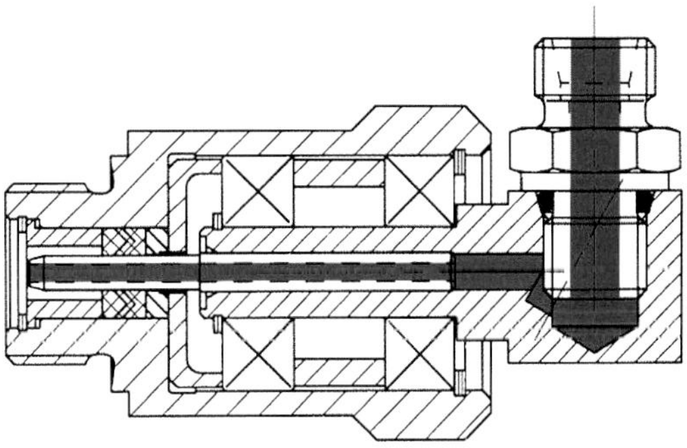

263 This single channel right angle junction was designed as a low-cost component for use in clutches and rotating adjusters

for 15 apprentices. The new equipment made it possible to produce larger components such as maize headers and combine feed housings. In its heyday the labour force reached a peak of 500 and a pre-series of 75 *Markant* balers was manufactured here. This plant was also given the responsibility for supplying all the machine tools and jigs to the new baler factory in Metz.

The moment of glory for the Schloss Holte plant was when it was given the task of producing the *Claas Apollo* system featured from page 97 of this book. In total the factory produced ten of these forage drying systems before the axe fell on the project. At about the same time the decision was made to concentrate the hydraulic manufacturing along with the electronic components which went with it, such as the automatic steering systems for the maize headers on combines and forage harvesters.

Faced by a severe downturn following the first reform of the European agricultural policy (CAP) the management was forced to rationalise manufacturing and on April 1, 1993 the board decided that the Schloss Holte plant had to close and the entire production would be moved to Paderborn.

Wolfgang Hornberger, Meinolf Reiher

AGROCOM

The group came to terms early with the need to develop new software solutions and embed information and communication technology into the farming product lines. *GPS* technology was one of the first systems which offered potential for improved farming practices. The ability to locate accurately the position of the machine as it crosses the field could be matched to the yield and enable yield maps to be created with the combine harvester. The stored information would then be retrieved by the farmer who could build up a file of data with which to adapt inputs to yield potential. This was the original background to the set up of the new *AGROCOM* division in 1994.

AGROCOM products were originally designed to achieve three objectives: improved decision making in the field, fleet management and equipment operating economics for arable farmers. New hardware was developed to go with this, for instance the on board *AGROCOM Computer Terminal* or *ACT*.

Claas decided to take over shares in the *Klöpper & Wiege* software company which was based in the nearby town of Lemgo in 1997. This takeover opened up several new fields of activity outside of the arable farming area. Following the takeover with 87.5 % *Claas* majority, the company was turned into the *AGROCOM GmbH Co. Agrarsystem KG.*

Klöpper & Wiege had specialised in software for management of areas such as animal production, field data banks and geographic information systems (*GIS*) which complemented the existing product range of *AGROCOM* perfectly.

The new company moved to Bielefeld with a complement of 40 staff and distribution of the products was carried out by specialised outlets. A separate sales company was set up in the eastern part of Germany as a 60 % subsidiary of *AGROCOM*. This markets auxiliary components and systems in conjunction with the local *Claas* dealer.

Stefan Böttinger

Forage harvesting systems from Saulgau

As recorded earlier in the takeover of the *Bautz* Company in 1969 turned out to be a major strategic acquisition for *Claas*. Josef Bautz had taken over a small workshop in 1909, from which he was able to build up a significant reputation as a producer of forage harvesting equipment. After World War Two he diversified into combine harvesters and tractors and then concentrated on the combine and green harvest equipment business areas.

When *Claas* took over *Bautz* they acquired the broadest range of forest harvesting equipment on the German market. The *Bautz* brand name was kept going until 1980, and phased out gradually since the new products were predominantly branded *Claas* and the old brand name faded away. Finally the Saulgau facility was integrated fully into the *Claas* Group and renamed *Claas Saulgau GmbH*, and has stayed so until this day.

For 15 years the subsidiary was controlled by the corporate headquarters in Harsewinkel, some 600 km away and in 1986 Saulgau was given its independence for production and marketing. This was a major step forward since the newly styled profit centre could decide faster, respond more rapidly to customer demands and provide better service in a rapidly changing market.

Today the factory in the Saulgau employs 550 people. They work in a modern environment, the production process has been updated and made more flexible in line with the increased expectations of the market. Wide-ranging investments

264 The Saulgau plant from the air

have focused on the need to stay a few steps ahead in the highly competitive global market environment in which the company operates.

The success of the Saulgau operation has led to increased responsibility for the coordination of the forage harvesting activities of the *Claas* group. This approach takes in the whole harvesting chain which includes balers from the Metz facility and self-propelled forage harvesters from Harsewinkel. The forage harvester business has become a vital business aera for *Claas* and Saulgau is at the heart of the future corporate strategy for the forage business.

Rolf Meuther

Claas Fertigungstechnik – CFT

CFT is the specialist *Claas* division for manufacture of machine tools and plant. It was set up in 1968 in the main factory to produce tooling for the company's own manufacturing facilities plus taking on work from outside to even out the capacity utilisation. From the beginning the automobile and component industry were targeted and many became faithful customers.

CFT was spun off as a separate entity in 1988. As the factory in Harsewinkel was reaching its capacity limits once again and demand for *CFT* products continued to grow, a new location was needed. A suitable site was found not far from Harsewinkel, in a place called Beelen. Everything fell into place quickly and within just seven months the brand new production facility was in place. It was inaugurated in October 1992. The objective was to create a plant which would be cost competitive and open for future expansion. The production area covered 9,000 m^2 initially and has since been extended to 14,000 m^2. The customer list is full of household names like *BMW, Daimler Chrysler, Ford, Opel, Porsche* and *VW*. They get high precision machine tools to exacting specifications to make anything from protective steel panels to high tensile windscreen A and B pillars and the like. The Beelen plant also produces high-quality machines and equipment used in joining, welding and partially mechanised pressing production procedures.

The division's activity was boosted by the takeover of *S.I.S.* in Coventry and *Burkhardt Systemtechnik* in Nordlingen, Bavaria in 1998, primarily to strengthen the materials handling area. Little by little the number of employees in Beelen has gone up, from 200 to 340.

A further important acquisition in 2001 was the takeover of *Brötje Automation*, world market leader in joining and assembly technology, a purchase which also opened the door to the aircraft industry. This company based in Oldenburg makes assembly cells for aircraft fuselage and wing sections and had 220 employees in 2003. This takes up the number of people employed in this business within the *Claas* Group to a total of 620. *CFT* has become a consistent growth segment which helps reduce dependency on the cyclical farm equipment business, while supplying *Claas* and other manufacturers with firstrate manufacturing technology.

Hans Budde, Ludger Wiemann

265 Beelen – Claas Fertigungstechnik, home of sophisticated machinery and equipment

266 This plaque was issued at the topping out in Gütersloh in 1948

Claas Guss

We move on to the foundry division centred on the *Claas Guss GmbH* in Bielefeld, which is also the location of the *Ravensberg Foundry*. Then there is the *Christophorus Foundry* in Gütersloh, the *Saulgau* and *Nortorf Foundries*. Each of these has its own individual history.

Claas got involved in castings since many cast parts are used a lot in farm machinery because they are particularly robust. The *Ravensberg Foundry* was founded in 1890 in Bielefeld manufacturing ovens and stoves. It kept going through the ups and downs of the first half of the 20th century. After production was resumed following the Second World War the company moved to a new location in 1964. However they overstretched their resources to such an extent that the company collapsed. August and Franz Claas took over the defunct company in 1965 since there were quite close contacts in existence already and they managed to keep the labour force together.

267 Temperature check at a heat induction oven

The *Christophorus Foundry* was registered in 1948 and was the first new factory that *Claas* set up after the Second World War. The project was instigated by August Claas with the foundry engineer Heinrich Rosenberg. The simple logic was that there was an urgent need to overcome the shortage of castings for the production line in Harsewinkel, so it made sense to become self-reliant. The St. Christopher logo was adopted and figured on various medals and other cast objects. The saint was supposed to protect everyone from the dangers of working in this somewhat hazardous environment. The topping out ceremony took place on September 17, 1948 and that very same day the first trial castings were made for the memorial plaque shown on the left.

The foundry in Saulgau was erected by Josef Bautz in 1922. The motivation to get into castings was similar to the Gütersloh foundry, and was to provide a reliable source for high-quality castings. This foundry, along with the others, has moved with the times and substantial investments have been made to ensure cost-effective, environmentally friendly and safe production.

One major development worth mentioning was the takeover in 1982 of the Gütersloh and Saulgau foundries by the *Ravensberger Foundry*. The acquisition of the *Nortorf Foundry* took place on November 1, 2000. It had been founded in 1933 with just eight employees specialising in castings for electric motors and farm equipment. During the Second World War production was kept going with a total of 45 employees. Obviously there were close links to the war effort because the plant was shut down for a while and resumed production in 1946 with just six employees. Foundries are dangerous places and the *Nortorf foundry* burnt down in February 2003 with the loss of about one third of the production tooling. Thanks to the great effort made by everyone, steel began flowing again after just 4 ½ months break.

The foundry operations were managed for many years by Günther Claas and Winfried Hespers. Günther Claas ended his directorship after 30 years at the end of 1997. Winfried Heespers retired in the autumn of 2004, having spent 42 years with the company, of which 22 were as managing director. He is still on the advisory board of the company where he can continue to remind everyone of his motto: "We want to be one of the best!"

268 Putting the heat on in one of the foundries

Claas Guss has established a leading reputation in the world of castings, employs about 450 employees and turns over some 50 million Euros per annum. The renown of the company stems from the high technical standards of the foundries, highly qualified and motivated staff plus a forward looking service philosophy in regard to development of new products for customers. The customers come from all types of businesses and appreciate the company's expertise in forming this complicated material. The majority of customers are manufacturers of machine tools and automotive producers. The company has worked hard at diversifying the customer base, so the agricultural equipment share is only 20 % of total turnover.

Günther Schenkel

Sources:

Wir Giesser, (We foundry people), Claas Guss employee journal

The Metz baler factory

The factory in Metz was the first major investment by *Claas* outside of Germany. It was spurred by the lack of capacity in Harsewinkel and the need to relocate some of the production. The site at Woippy near Metz was purchased in 1958 and the first production building was erected. The choice was made on the basis of the good infrastructure and the market opportunities in France. On this occasion the company showed foresight in locating a factory close to the main market.

Construction of the plant commenced in 1959 and the first machines were built with a labour force of 20 people plus a foreman. Before production began the new colleagues were thoroughly trained in Harsewinkel. It wasn't until 1962 that the first French built balers came off the assembly line. A railhead was added in 1965, which was important for efficient shipment of these machines, following which the factory was given the production go-ahead for the new range of *Claas Markant* balers. As business grew the company was turned into a share company in 1969 and from then on has been known as Usines *Claas France* or *UCF* for short.

Another landmark was the production of the 100,000th baler in 1978. The introduction of the *Rollant* round baler family in 1979 brought about a major change in manufacturing procedures and two years later the production of

269 The early days at the Metz factory ...

270 … a long way from today's plant

knotters was transferred from Harsewinkel, a sign that the Metz plant had come of age. After all the knotter was dear to the hearts of the founding fathers. The 200,000th baler left the plant in 1985, a reflection of the enormous growth in the baler market and the major role played by *Claas*.

In the years that followed the structural changes in the farming environment led to the introduction of new types of baler. The first of these was the *Quadrant* in 1988, followed in 1995 by the Variant round baler, and once again this entailed a complete redesign of the production flows. The total volume was dropping, individual machine size was growing. Following this factory restructuring, the balers were produced on parallel assembly lines which provides a maximum of flexibility to dealers and customers.

UCF was given its independence in 1996, R & D were transferred from Harsewinkel and a new marketing team was built up. This had a decisive impact on the development of the business and strengthened links to the customers, especially with the creation of a customer centre at the plant. Manufacturing methods were thoroughly reviewed and based on a team philosophy. Small work groups manage the whole production process. Employee training is strongly pushed and the company invests much more than the 1.5 % of the payroll costs demanded by the French government.

271 Modern baler production in Metz

The *Uniwrap* baler / wrapper combination was added in 2000. By now total production had passed the quarter million mark. Today the labour force is made up of 410 employees plus 17 apprentices and about 75 % of the machines produced in Metz end up outside France. The first major investment by *Claas* outside Germany turned out to be the first of many. Many other international manufacturing decisions have since been made by the company, as the next examples show.

Wilhelm Strothmann

272 The main gate at Törökszentmiklos

Törökszentmiklos in Hungary

Claas has traditionally maintained close links with Hungary and when the opportunity came to manufacture in the country, the decision was not long in coming. *Claas Hungaria KFT* is a 100 % subsidiary of the *Claas* Group, acquired in 1997. A workforce of around 330 people manufactures components such as the cutter bars for *Claas* combines. The plant also produces drum mowers and the bale wrapper which is then completed in Metz. Substantial investments have been made in buildings and machine tools to ensure that *Claas* quality standards can be met consistently. This includes a new power supply centre, laser cutters, CNC bending machines and welding equipment. In addition a 4,000 m² building has been erected for the painting activity. The factory has become an important integral part of the company's production network.

Big combines from Nebraska

The American market is big and *Claas* decided to set up a combine production facility in Omaha, Nebraska in 1999. Manufacturing was to be focused on the *Lexion* combine range, the product line that most closely meets the demands of big farmers in North America. The factory is located in one of the main grain producing areas and the site is 65 ha in size. The facility consists of a production area, an office tract, an exhibition centre and a machine test track for hands on trials by customers. The *Lexion* family is marketed throughout North America with *CAT* branding and the familiar yellow livery. Sales and service are the responsibility of the *Caterpillar* dealer network.

274 / 275 Omaha factory, Cat Lexion at a U.S farm show (inset)

Small combines from India

The development of the *Crop Tiger* was described on page 73 and this product is manufactured in Faridabad, not far from Delhi. Originally founded as a joint-venture with the Indian *Escorts Corporation*, *Claas* took over full control in 2002. This plant now employs around 200 staff. The main markets for the combine which is at home on the small, moist paddy fields is in India, South Korea, Taiwan and Japan. Population growth, increased mechanisation and India's large farming area make this the ideal factory location. *Claas* expects to see considerable growth in its Asian commitments in the future.

276 The Crop Tiger, made in India for the whole of Asia

Mid range combines from Russia

The latest *Claas* factory is going up in Russia, at Krasnodar. The company is committed to investing 20 million € over the next few years in this new facility which will produce the *Mega* combine range, the ideal product for the local markets which require high-performance with straightforward technology.

277 Groundbreaking ceremony in Krasnodar witnessed by Helmut Claas in person

Claas is closely involved in the development of modern farming technology in Russia and its neighbours. The investments in local production are designed to strengthen the company's position in the market and open up new business opportunities in the region.

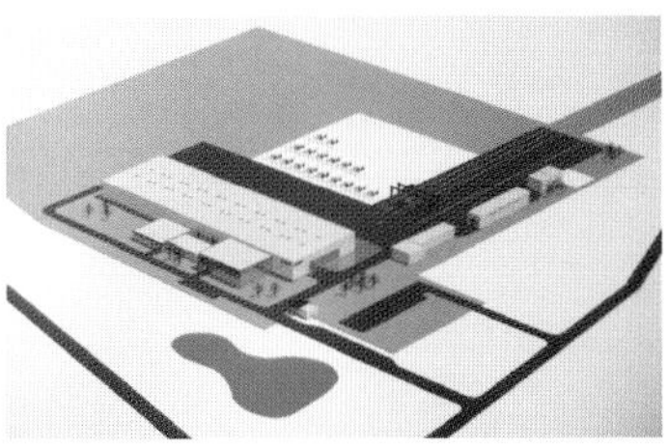

273 Computer layout of the Krasnodar plant

278 Claas machines on show at the ceremony

From "Made by hand" to Quality Mass Production

In the beginning the products were simple, things were done manually, volumes were small and everyone knew each other personally. That's a long way away from the vast product range and the complex interdependent manufacturing structures of today. How did *CLAAS* managed to keep the company's manufacturing skills ahead of the game and stay competitive, particularly in the recent years which have seen an enormous acceleration in the rate of change? This chapter looks at the development of manufacturing within the group.

The story really begins in 1920 when the company had moved from Clarholz and set up in Harsewinkel making straw trussers in quite small numbers. These weren't just any straw trussers, the owners were proud of the quality standards of what they made. In addition attention was paid to keeping the production costs competitive and these values really haven't changed since then. Back then *Claas* workers were as a rule good craftsman who had very simple tooling at their disposal. Blacksmiths were still in high demand because there was a lot of metal bashing and most of the components were either riveted or bolted together. Gradually the transition to higher volumes took place as the production of spreaders was added to the trusser production and the factory was expanded. By 1930 the labour force had grown to 250.

The next new product to be added was the straw baler family which reached its production peak in the years from 1934 and 1940 and contributed to a major boom for the young company. Manufacturing was improved steadily and mass production methods were adopted for the first time. The availability of steam power enabled the company to drive the forging hammers by steam.

280 The Harsewinkel factory in August 1941

As the production volume continued to grow the Harsewinkel factory began to burst at the seams and further buildings were added. Mostly these were simple constructions and still made of wood. The company didn't like to spend a lot of money on fancy buildings when simple design would do. By 1937 there were over 400 people employed in this complex of sheds.

279 Bird's eye view of the factory with its eight sheds, the very small village of Harsewinkel in the background

281 The scene outside the sheds in 1950

The instigation of combine harvester production in serious numbers was a new challenge for the production team. These machines were technically more complex and this meant the staff had to be better qualified. All of a sudden there were new requirements for machining, sheet steel had to be cut and bent, castings formed, machined and fitted. Joining up of components also became more sophisticated. The metallic silver paint finish was still applied by dipping and paint brush, but the area to be painted and the complexity of the pieces had now increased. All this required a more disciplined manufacturing process and marks the transition from a craftsman's workshop to an industrial company.

Fortunately the location of the plant in Harsewinkel well away from strategic targets left it unscathed after the end of hostilities in 1945. Farm machinery production was resumed very quickly when the occupying forces realised that nothing sinister had been going on here and there was the urgent need to get machinery out to feed the population.

You will have read earlier that the company had been working discreetly on the *Super* combine design throughout the war years and production restarted in 1946. After this start it increased rapidly year by year. In total 9,905 combines were built in the following ten years. The addition of self-propelled combine harvesters started the trend to higher value, more demanding manufacturing which has continued ever since. To cater for this increased volume and complexity, new assembly lines were installed to ensure that the production in series was both efficient and economic. Parallel to this, investments were made in new machine tools and assembly jigs to feed the lines. Steam power had had its day and as energy requirements were expanding rapidly, it became necessary to hook up the factory to high-voltage electrical power lines. The production planning function was introduced in 1954. Shortly after that the assembly lines which ran across the plant had to be turned around to run lengthways. This made it possible to lengthen the assembly line to accommodate more individual assembly steps. A statistical quality system was brought in for the first time in 1961 and coupled to a quality incentive programme for the production staff.

282 Historic picture of a parts store in August 1941

Qualität
ist der
beste
Verkäufer
Kontroll-
stelle
Fließbandmontage schleppergezogener Mähdrescher
im CLAAS-Werk Harsewinkel
Diese Aufnahme entstand 1962

283 Assembly of pull type combines in Harsewinkel, 1962

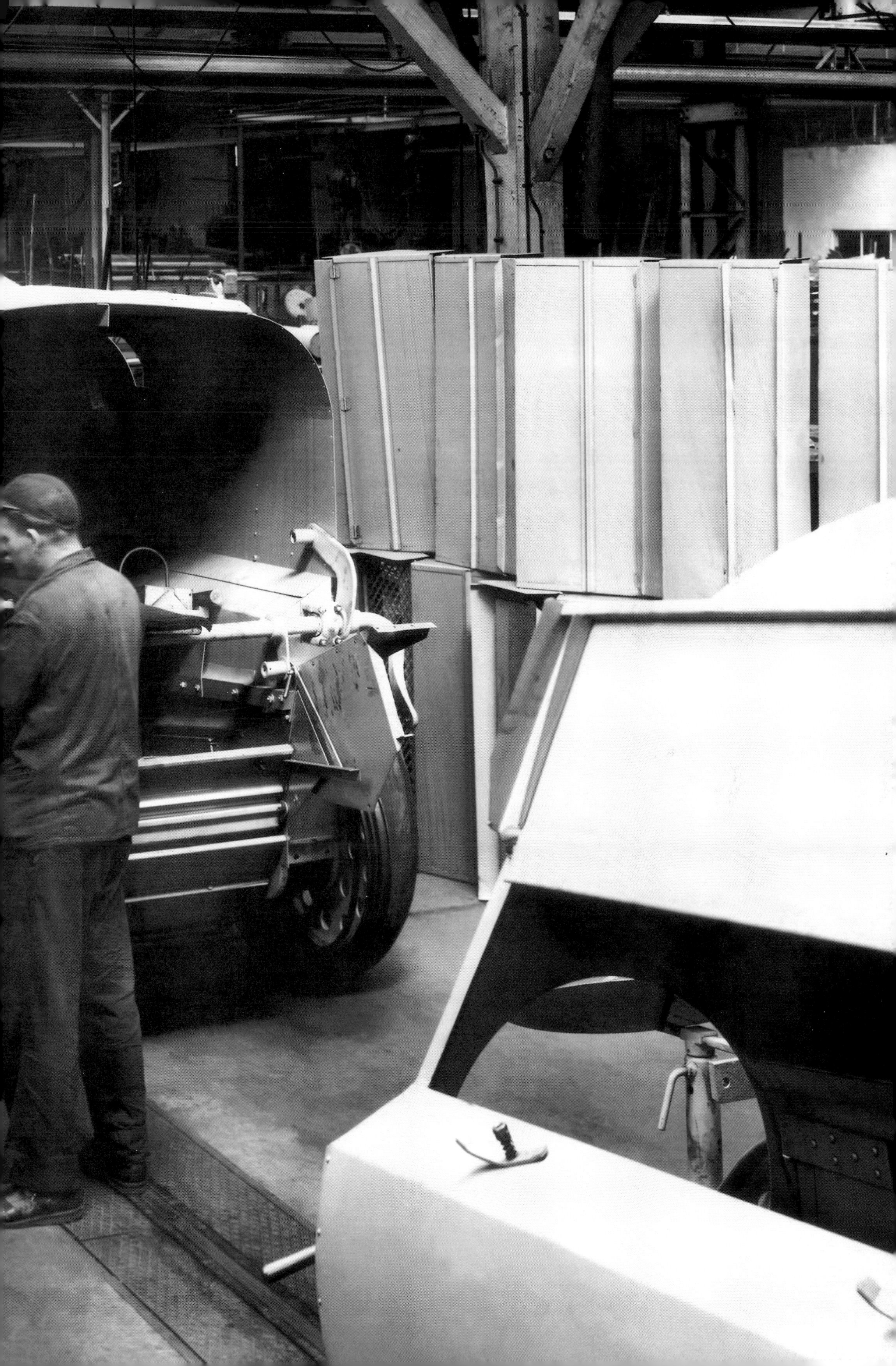

The combine harvester was assuming major importance for the Harsewinkel plant and the machines were becoming bigger and bigger, with the proportion of self-propelled combines increasing apace. This put considerable pressure on the available space under roof. In 1962 the 100,000th combine came off the assembly line. Everything was still being done more or less by hand and the arrival of EDP and work organisation procedures was a welcome relief to the whole factory personnel.

It's hard to imagine that combine production in 1965 exceeded 23,000 units, a figure which is not far off the total combine market worldwide in recent years. At its peak the factory turned out 140 combines a day. This was only possible thanks to the close teamwork which had evolved in the production crew, allied to a high level of flexibility and the fact that everyone felt they were part of a big family unit. Each individual was proud of the quality of work they did and the success of the operation. All around them the factory was expanding month by month as sales continued to grow above all expectations. The production team was always faced with new challenges as the demand came to produce more with the ever present constraints of getting everything out before the harvest began – the challenge which has never ceased to be a major feat every year!

The production volumes were impressive and many innovations were made to make the production line more efficient. This included time and motion analysis and continuous assembly-line production. Underneath line 1, two parallel moving steel belts were fitted to move the combines steadily down the line. An under floor conveyor was built in-house and installed at the end of line 1 and line 2 as a control and quality inspection line.

It is no exaggeration to say that the factory was bursting at the seams yet again. Lack of space meant that many activities had been located away from the main assembly-line. For instance final combine assembly took place on the other side of the main road which went through the plant. (The famous "East-West Highway"). Before assembly took place the basic combines were painted, the paint finish was allowed to dry and then they were personalised before being released for dispatch along four shipment lines. Large assemblies were painted separately in a paint booth. The engine unit was assembled on a separate flow line and grain tank assembly was concentrated in another building, which was previously the carpenter's shop. Cutter bars were manufactured in yet another shop where grain tanks were painted, cutter bar reels assembled and also painted. In addition the factory was producing all of the balers on a 150 metre long assembly line.

284 By 1955 the plant had assumed new proportions

285 Production on line 1 in 1963

The basic assemblies were primer painted in three solvent paint baths. The largest parts were treated in a shop with a paint content of 50 tonnes, whilst smaller parts were painted in a different location and very small components were dipped in paint in transit. A remarkable feat of coordination, teamwork and skill was required every day to get everything moving in sync. The fact is that the amazing growth showed up weaknesses in logistics processes and materials flow. There were bits and pieces everywhere, they would get lost somewhere in the plant and assembly was often interrupted by missing components.

Another amusing phenomenon at the time – up until 1966 a combine armada had to be driven every day across town to the railway stations in Harsewinkel and Gütersloh where they were shipped to their final destinations. The local railway company finally extended the line into the factory and set up a railhead. This was a major step forward in the dispatch area and prevented traffic jams in the local area. To this day rail shipment has continued to play an important part in the combine dispatch area, and the machines have always been engineered so that they can be carried within the gauge of tunnels within most of Europe.

At this time there were 1,180 people working in the Harsewinkel factory and *Claas* employed 3,500 people in total. The pre-production was produced in two shifts and assembly in one shift. It says a lot for the simplicity of the machines that 140 units a day could be built. There was no buffer between pre-assembly, painting and assembly so these parts made overnight were parked outside, regardless of the weather. When the assembly shift turned up for work in the morning, they had to move all this stuff back into the assembly area which created big traffic jams on the East-West Highway. With all this to and fro going on, it's no surprise that the paint finish wasn't good enough and certainly wouldn't meet today's requirements.

By 1967 / 68 production had to be completely revamped in order to sort out the traffic jams and materials flow problems. There were plenty of good ideas on the table before the total redesign was gone into and put into action. Everyone knew that production would have to be kept going whilst the plant was being remodelled, so disturbance had to be limited to a minimum.

At this point a major change was made which made a huge difference to the finish quality. The machines were no longer to be finish painted after assembly. Instead each component would be finished painted prior to assembly, providing much better protection and quality. Of course this transformed the whole painting system and the materials flow.

As a result a state-of-the-art painting facility was installed for large components. Prime painting was done from now on in an electrophoretic bath, which at that time was the largest of its type in the whole of Germany and the first in the agricultural equipment business. The new painting layout included cleaning and surface pre-treatment, a prime paint drier with cooling zone and a paint line for the topcoat. A large part of the equipment was produced within the company and the buildings had to be extended

286 Large combine assembly in 1964 with sideways flow

287 A good view of the overhead conveyor and the "East-West Highway"

in order to house the large-scale painting facilities.

Painting of the smaller parts also needed to be expanded. The new pre-treatment centre was installed along with two lines for the topcoat. The prime painting dip system was later changed over from solvent based paints to electrophoretic prime coating.

The introduction of individual parts painting made it much easier to handle the machines at the end of the line. They could now continue without a break from the quality control area to the end of the factory.

Chassis construction was changed over to an assembly line process with under floor conveyors. The component groups were assembled at right angles to the main number 1 assembly line and this too had a positive effect on the materials handling in the plant.

288 The assembly-line had been turned around and the machines now flow lengthways

Free capacity after this reorganisation meant that cutter bar and reel production could be brought together under one roof. The assembly process was switched over from stationary assembly to a proper assembly-line. The welding shop was also reorganised at the same time.

One of the most striking changes was the handling system for large parts, particularly those which were produced overnight and were only needed next morning for the single shift assembly procedure. A new conveyor system was designed which took the large panel sections from the body shop production area to the painting centre and on to the assembly line. This so-called "Power and Free Transport System" consisted of a chain driven handling system with a length of 3,200 m and a free running 800 m system. The whole handling system was produced by *Claas*. From then on it was no longer necessary to move the production parts in and out, so after all this was done working conditions and efficiency in the plant changed out of all recognition.

Let's summarise the other main features of this factory remodelling:

- Introduction of inert gas welding
- Provision of paint supply via a ring circuit
- Erection of two oil storage tanks, each with 1,000 m^3 capacity and an oil supply ring circuit
- New central heating system with boiler house and heat supply network
- Redesign and reinforcement of the electrical system
- Flexible and rotating welding jigs
- Supply network for welding and other gases
- Increased use of air tools.

With the production of the *Consul* range in 1967/68 a new manufacturing challenge was taken on with the single piece chassis. The fixing points of all jigs and tools were now identified clearly by means of a new system of scale drawings. The chassis production was concentrated on a special body shop line called the "Side Frame System."

Whilst all this was taking place in 1967 a total of 13,059 combines was produced. It was a dif-

289 Fit for the 21st century. The new buildings are ...

ficult time for the labour force, because they not only had to come to terms with daily changes in their surroundings and procedures, they also were asked to produce three new model lines: *Comet, Cosmos* and *Senator.* If that wasn't enough, production of various components was being transferred to other plants at the same time. Inevitably there were frequent interruptions in the manufacturing and materials flow process which were frequently overcome by the ever present team spirit on the factory floor.

Manufacturing of self-propelled forage harvesters was added in 1973. Assembly line 2 was modified to make it possible to produce both the forage harvester line and combines. Preceding this in 1970, component assembly of the *Dominator 80* had been introduced on line number one. This method of assembly was the major innovation which accompanied the *Dominator* family and it entailed major changes in the chassis and body shops as well as the pre-assembly areas. This period also marked a major increase in the depth of production and a broadening of the number of models and options with major implications for the manufacturing process.

In 1978 another round of changes took place with the extension of the finishing line, introduction of the *SAP R/2* computer management system and the erection of the first high-rise storage facility in the plant. Technological change also affected the panel making functions with sheet steel machining centres being expanded as the importance of individual stamping, cutting and pressing operations dwindled. In 1987 / 88 the first robots made their appearance in the production process.

The machines increased in size continually, and when the *Lexion* range was introduced into the plant in 1995 it was quickly realised that the limits had been reached yet again in terms of the overall size of the individual panels, components and the finished machines themselves. As a result there were bottlenecks in many of the production areas with a lack of space that couldn't be resolved without major changes. The first of these was the remodelling of assembly-line number 1. Previously the machines had been assembled sideways on the line, but the new models were just too long and the assembly process had to be turned around by 90°. The frame and chassis components caused major headaches too and parts of this manufacturing process had to be moved elsewhere, with a negative effect on component flow and the plant. The painting facility had also reached its limits in terms of size and capacity once again. Rather than play around with unsatisfactory individual solutions it was decided to bring the factory up-to-date with a bang.

Fit for the 21st century – the *Synpro 10* project

All of the main factory structures and manufacturing processes had been left more or less unchanged following the earlier major restructuring in 1968. This was true of the flow of large assemblies between the body shop, painting area and assembly lines. It applied equally as well to the painting location and the type of paints used, the roof mounted materials handling system, the positioning of storage areas, steel cutting, processing and welding of small

290 ... erected over the old ones whilst production continues

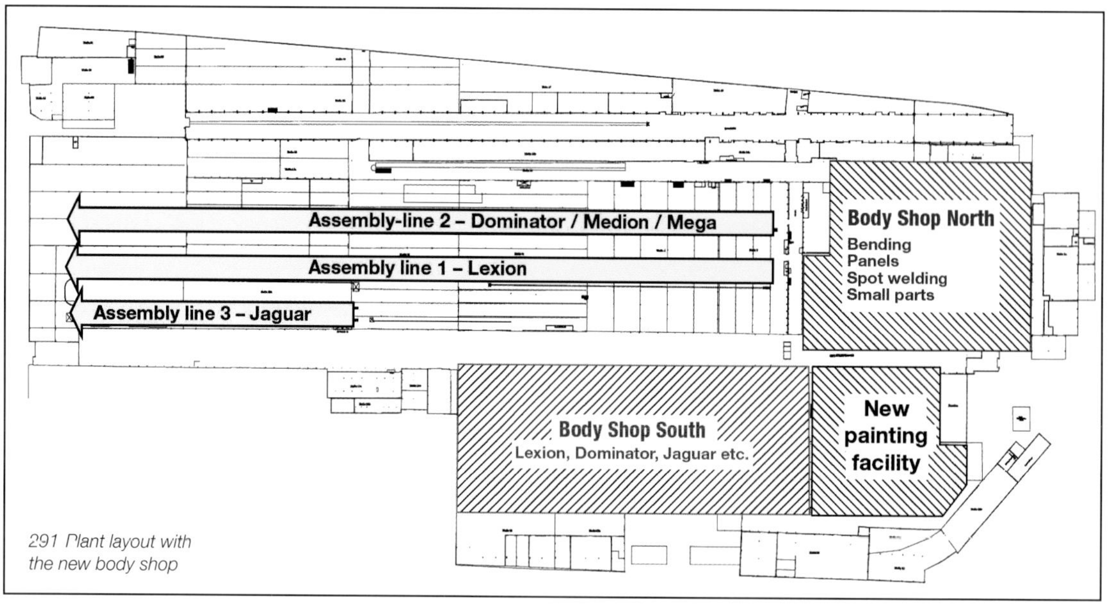

291 Plant layout with the new body shop

parts. By the year 2000, it was obvious that the factory had to be brought up to date to stay competitive in the future. In addition the plant had become the hub for worldwide manufacturing activities. There would inevitably be the need for the production of key components or partial manufacture of machines as new markets for the company developed.

Once the decision to do the job properly had been taken, attention was focused on the painting area. This had to be done first in order to free up enough space for the remodelling of the body shop and assembly areas. It was agreed that there would be just one central painting facility instead of the separate paint lines for small and large parts. An existing building which was ripe for demolition was selected as the new location for both the painting facility and part of the body shop which badly needed the space on the ground floor. As a result the painting facility moved up a floor which in fact improved the materials flow and the final result is an impressive three-storey production centre known as Hall 5.

The designers looked closely at the ways to improve the flow of large panel sections as they made their way from the body shop through the painting area and on to the assembly lines. In future they would not get in the way on the ground floor and whilst this opened up lots of room downstairs, it meant that the roof over the main East-West Highway had to be raised.

Customers have come to expect a very high quality paint finish commensurate with the premium *Claas* brand. In addition environmental considerations are paramount since outdated painting procedures can cause serious health and pollution problems. With this in mind, there was no alternative but to adopt the latest technologies and maybe develop a few new ones.

The new process is ahead of its time in all senses: panels are pre-treated with zinc phosphate, after which they are subjected to an electrophoretic prime dipping, followed by a powder top coat. Only about 10 % of the area is painted with traditional liquid paint. The process takes place over three stories, with pre-treatment and priming on

292 The new surface treatment centre in 2003

the ground floor, topcoat application on the first floor and the buffer storage on the second floor.

The gigantic new hall was erected with no interruption of the production flow and this phase became fondly known as open-heart factory surgery. Sometimes the new buildings were put up over the old ones and slack periods were used to carry out the most critical operations. This was not easy for the production people but none of the exemplary teamwork skills have been lost over the years and together the problems were usually overcome.

Nonetheless the technology involved and the scale of the operation meant that there were delays and

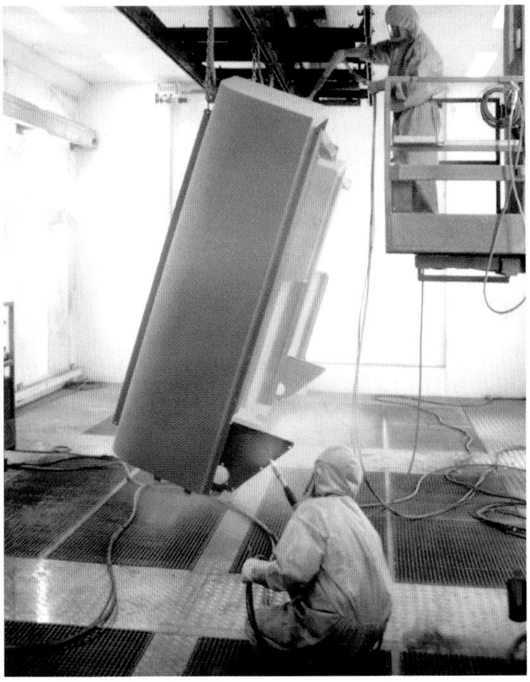

293 Large panel sections still have to be finished by hand

surprises. Without a doubt the switchover period from the old to the new painting facility was the biggest headache, even if the project team had made sure that the old painting system would stay in operation for as long as was needed to get the teething troubles out of the new facility. That was a wise decision and limited the factory downtime to a minimum.

Once the painting facility was up and running, the manufacturing throughput time could be reduced with the application of a high degree of automation. In addition the plant could run more flexibly and the paint finish, which was already at a very high standard, could be improved still further.

This future oriented centre for surface treatment is one of the largest in Europe outside of the

294 Automatic electrophoretic dipping

automotive industry. Since the environmental damage from second-rate painting facilities is well-known, the project team felt obliged to set new standards as regards pollution reduction and received support from an unusual quarter. In fact the company was able to obtain financial backing for this pioneering facility from the German Environment Ministry in recognition of its importance for other manufacturing centres around the world. It is in fact a model of quality and environmentally friendly technology.

Back to the other project details: the body shop was divided into two parts. The South body shop produces the large sections, whilst smaller parts are produced in the North shop. The first of these was restructured to take account of the need to run two lines. The dual component supply was designed to reduce rework costs and downtime whenever a model change takes place on the line and also to improve materials flow. The direction of the flow was mostly turned around by 180° and the individual workstations were brought up to the latest technical standards.

Once the cutter bar production had been moved out to the plant in Hungary, further changes could be made to the body shop without disturbing the flow of production parts. The North

295 A glimpse of the automatic powder coating

296 The 400,000th combine – a Lexion 480 – with a metallic silver livery on line 1

CLAAS

297 Robots can't do everything so skilled craftsmen are still in demand

shop was an easier task since the previous activities had been transferred out of there earlier. Particular attention was paid here to improving the working environment, increasing the process of efficiency and overall modernisation of the zone. Everyone was involved in this operation, including the workers, the production staff and the project planners. It is worth mentioning that maximum participation of all those involved was a major objective of the company management at every phase of this project.

The assembly area was also redesigned with a dedicated assembly-line for the different product families. Assembly line 1 is devoted entirely to the production of the *Lexion* range with the *Dominator* and *Mega* families coming off the number 2 line. The number 2 line was in turn completely redesigned and the area it occupies was increased, following the move of the small parts welding and painting facilities out of the area.

298 Assembly line 1 for the Lexion range as it looks today

The forage harvester line was moved to a new location and with its shorter, more concentrated assembly procedures, it now occupies less space than earlier. Last but not least, the quality control, inspection and final personalisation take place using the latest available technology.

The vast array of bits and pieces needed in the assembly process was reorganised with a new logistical concept and various basic assembly steps were redesigned. This has led to improved readiness along with lower inventory and faster handling times. "Just-in-time" is an integral feature of the process, as is the new generation *SAP R/3* management system introduced in 2003.

The remodelling project in Harsewinkel was concluded in 2003. Every visitor to the plant is impressed by the airy, light and pleasant surroundings in the factory area. With this ambitious project the *Claas* management has made a vital contribution to the company's future with a highly competitive and flexible production unit, one in which quality and motivation can both thrive together.

JOSEF LÖCHTE

Apprenticeships and Vocational Training

CLAAS can look back on a long tradition of training and education for youngsters. The initiation of an apprenticeship scheme goes back to the early days of the company and this commitment is reflected today in a large number of highly motivated apprentices and investments made into continued training in a wide range of fields.

It has always been the company's policy to recruit and develop technical and management skills from within. In addition the owners of the company have always been conscious of their social obligation to give young people a chance to develop their skills locally. From an economic point of view it obviously makes good sense to invest in the people who, with their technical skills developed in-house, will be best qualified to guide the development of many areas of the business in the future. The apprenticeship structure in Germany is the envy of the world and *Claas* takes advantage of it fully by investing much more in training young people than the industry average.

Let's look back at some of the milestones which the owners of the company have strongly influenced. The story can be traced back to 1950 when the first apprentice classrooms were developed and equipped with technical training aids. The chief trainer at that time was promoted to foreman in 1951. From then on the "Apprentice Department" was upgraded from a simple activity in the plant to a fully fledged department. This serves to underline the importance of the early development of personnel training in the minds of the company's owners.

More recently the company took another initiative by subscribing to what is known as the dual education system together with various vocational and technical academies. Helmut Claas became aware of the newly organised vocational academies (Berufsschulen) on one of his trips and decided that *Claas* would take part with a number of students.

299 A tool engineering apprentice undergoes practical training on a precision moulding

The first two students began their dual education in mechanical engineering together with the Stuttgart Vocational Academy. This system gives students an academic qualification which is tied closely to practical training in the company which sponsors them. The main qualifications are in engineering and management and have become a regular feature of the *Claas* training and management development schemes.

300 Learning how to programme a welding robot demnonstrated by Manfred Schön

The vocational training carried out by the company exceeds the basic requirements in terms of thoroughness and modernity. The minimum curriculum required by the authorities is just the start and those lucky enough to be selected receive the best possible start in their careers.

The facilities have moved with the times and have evolved into a Technical Training Centre which is capable of training mechanical and electrical skills in conjunction with teamwork elements as prescribed by the new industry curriculum which came into force in 1988. This led to the discontinuation of the classic workbench method, which was replaced by hexagonal shaped practical group work and training benches. What this means is that training in the basic skills required for carrying out the future tasks has been enhanced by much greater emphasis on teamwork and corporations skills, combined with a focus on individual responsi-

301 Instruction on how to use the electronic hand wheel of a CNC cutting centre by Alfons Gerdhennerichs

bility as well as independent training and work patterns. 16 years on and following a further update of the curriculum, these features are firmly embedded in the *Claas* training philosophy.

On the commercial side *Claas* has also set new standards with an approach developed within the company. It is a known as "dual qualification vocational training". This course is backed by the Chamber of Commerce and is offered alongside commercial or a foreign language studies offered by this organisation. When *Claas* instigated this in 1984, it was the only employer offering such a programme. The benefit was that the company gained commercially qualified youngsters with additional foreign language capabilities, which was just what the doctor ordered since the business was becoming more and more global. It has become even more vital in view of the fact that over 3,000 company employees now work outside Germany and German is not the most widely spoken language by any means.

This summary of the training organisation demonstrates how cooperation between schools and business can be structured in the interests of both parties. For over 50 years the company has made a concerted effort to reach out to teachers and pupils. Nowadays there is a wide range of activities going on with cooperation agreements with schools in Harsewinkel and surrounding areas. The parameters used in Harsewinkel have also been adopted in similar programmes at the company facilities in Metz and Bury St. Edmunds.

Alongside the efforts to provide young people with good qualifications, continuous development of skills has figured prominently in the company's training philosophy for older and more experienced employees. For a company like *Claas* with the clear objective of staying in the lead, there is choice but to work continuously at building up the skills and motivation of the whole workforce. This is an effort that can never be relaxed and has been recognised as a key success factor for many decades.

In 1982 a department was formed for personnel development and was able to strengthen the development of modern tools for human resource management. These include employee evaluation dialogue, trainee and skill development programmes, potential and performance assessment, objective fixing, career and succession planning. The overall company strategy is based on maintaining and expanding the knowledge potential within the group and involving each employee in the creation of added value. The company has achieved increased motivation and strong identification with the objectives, primarily by identifying those who are ready to improve their skills and by transferring responsibility to younger people with plenty of potential. This has helped the company to keep a high percentage of apprentices and trainees within the company after they have qualified.

302 Mechatronics – the fusion of electronic and mechanical technology is a key area of learning instructed by Klaus Ströer

Developing people's skills is not just a social responsibility. What *Claas* has clearly demonstrated is that intensive personnel training and development schemes are an integral part of a financially successful business. Not just in the short-term, though – for over 90 years.

GERHARD MEYER

The Distribution Network then and now

303 An early Claas self propelled combine being hoisted on board for export

The export business started to take off for Claas as a result of supplies demanded by First World War reparations. Most of these early sales were to European markets, but before long demand started picking up from overseas and Far East countries. Now as then the service provided by Claas has been a major feature in gaining a faithful customer base. Today's customers demand a full range of services including finance and leasing from competent local dealers, along with a dependable and fast supply of genuine spare parts to keep their investment in good shape. We look at the development of the sales organisation both within Germany and abroad, plus a profile of one of the early ambassadors of the company.

The History of the German Sales Company *(CVG)*.

The firm started early on its history with the steady build up of the distribution network both at home and abroad. The increased pace of mechanisation following the Second World War brought a growth in demand for combine harvesters in its wake. Then, as the market in Germany began to consolidate, a new direction was called for and in 1986 a new distribution company was founded for sales and service of *CLAAS* products in the domestic market.

The first *Claas* factory representative was Wilhelm Kock from Hamburg. He contacted the company in 1921 and took on the position as North German regional distributor with effect from January 1st 1922. This territory spread from Bremen in the west, the Danish border in the north and today's border with Poland. This cooperation lasted for over 50 years and Kock became part of a network of 15 distributors who were actively selling and servicing *Claas* products in Germany before the Second World War.

The 1948 currency reform and introduction of the D-Mark gave the necessary impetus to the new wave of mechanisation. By the end of the 1950s the combine harvester had finally taken its rightful place in German farming. *Claas* took a leading technological position from the very start. After a hesitant start a boom took place which led the company to expand its production facilities and all this ensured the leadership position for *Claas* in combine harvesters.

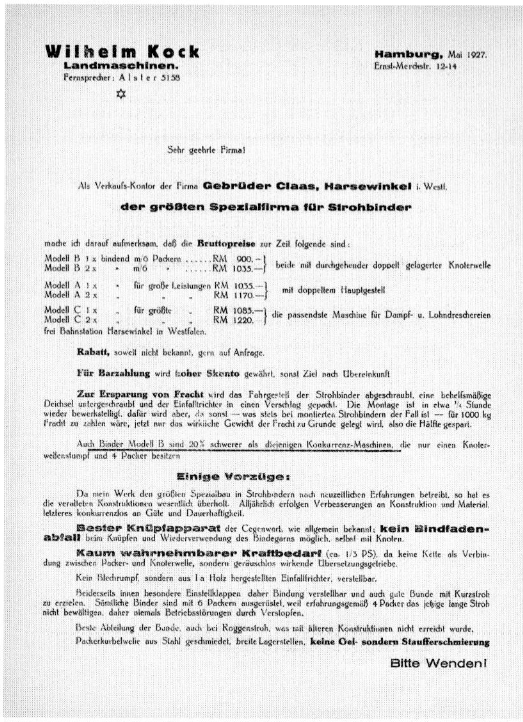

Wilhelm Kock
Landmaschinen.
Fernsprecher: Alster 5158

Hamburg, Mai 1927.
Ernst-Merckstr. 12-14

Sehr geehrte Firma!

Als Verkaufs-Kontor der Firma **Gebrüder Claas, Harsewinkel** i. Westf.

der größten Spezialfirma für Strohbinder

mache ich darauf aufmerksam, daß die **Bruttopreise** zur Zeit folgende sind:

Modell B 1 x bindend m/6 Packern ...... RM 900.—
Modell B 2 x " m/6 " ...... RM 1035.— } beide mit durchgehender doppelt gelagerter Knoterwelle

Modell A 1 x " für große Leistungen RM 1035.—
Modell A 2 x " " " RM 1170.— } mit doppeltem Hauptgestell

Modell C 1 x " für größte " RM 1085.—
Modell C 2 x " " " RM 1220.— } die passendste Maschine für Dampf- u. Lohndreschereien

frei Bahnstation Harsewinkel in Westfalen.

Rabatt, soweit nicht bekannt, gern auf Anfrage.

Für Barzahlung wird **hoher Skonto** gewährt, sonst Ziel nach Übereinkunft

Zur Ersparung von Fracht wird das Fahrgestell der Strohbinder abgeschraubt, eine behelfsmäßige Deichsel untergeschraubt und der Einfalltrichter in einen Verschlag gepackt. Die Montage ist in etwa ¼ Stunde wieder bewerkstelligt, dafür wird aber, da sonst — was stets bei montierten Strohbindern der Fall ist — für 1000 kg Fracht zu zahlen wäre, jetzt nur das wirkliche Gewicht der Fracht zu Grunde gelegt wird, also die Hälfte gespart.

Auch Binder Modell B sind 20% schwerer als diejenigen Konkurrenz-Maschinen, die nur einen Knoterwellenstumpf und 4 Packer besitzen

Einige Vorzüge:

Da mein Werk den größten Spezialbau in Strohbindern nach neuzeitlichen Erfahrungen betreibt, so hat es die veralteten Konstruktionen wesentlich überholt. Alljährlich erfolgen Verbesserungen an Konstruktion und Material, letzteres konkurrenzlos an Güte und Dauerhaftigkeit.

Bester Knüpfapparat der Gegenwart, wie allgemein bekannt; **kein Bindfadenabfall** beim Knüpfen und Wiederverwendung des Bindegarns möglich, selbst mit Knoten.

Kaum wahrnehmbarer Kraftbedarf (ca. 1/3 PS), da keine Kette als Verbindung zwischen Packer- und Knoterwelle, sondern geräuschlos wirkende Übersetzungsgetriebe.

Kein Blechrumpf, sondern aus I a Holz hergestellten Einfalltrichter, verstellbar.

Beiderseits innen besondere Einstellklappen daher Bindung verstellbar und auch gute Bunde mit Kurzstroh zu erzielen. Sämtliche Binder sind mit 6 Packern ausgerüstet, weil erfahrungsgemäß 4 Packer das jetzige lange Stroh nicht bewältigen, daher niemals Betriebsstörungen durch Verstopfen.

Beste Ableitung der Bunde, auch bei Roggenstroh, was mit älteren Konstruktionen nicht erreicht wurde.

Packerkurbelwelle aus Stahl geschmiedet, breite Lagerstellen, **keine Oel- sondern Staufferschmierung**

Bitte Wenden!

306 An early "mail shot" from Wilhelm Kock

By 1960 a domestic sales organisation had taken shape with a staff of seven clerks and five typists at head office plus six independent distributors and two *Claas* reps. In addition each distributor had an average of two people who worked exclusively for *Claas*.

305 Wilhelm Kock, the first company representative in Hamburg

The *Claas* distributors maintained the contact between the market and the plant. The country was still in an early stage of reconstruction with the East in communist hands. *Claas* had divided the territories between Kock in Hamburg for the North, Uhr in Soest for Westphalia, Dreier in Hersel along the Rhine valley, Bressel in Nurnberg for Franconia, Blecher in Munich covering Bavaria and Borgmann in Leonberg for Württemberg and Baden provinces. Finally Bracht in Bad Wildungen took on Hesse and Göricke in Steinhagen covered western Lower Saxony as *Claas* reps.

The most important farm equipment dealers in Germany also took on the *Claas* franchise as retailers, wholesalers and cooperatives. The firm received about 90 % of the orders each year with early sales conditions and usually these were paid for in advance. This trend reached its

307 Two CLAAS dealers from Bavaria in discussions with Walter Claas

peak from 1960 to 1963 during which period the annual production was accounted for totally by the spring order intake, and in 1961 and 1962 there was even a shortfall of supply. In retrospect this was the golden age for us all, especially for the domestic sales organisation.

During the mid 1960's the German combine market calmed down somewhat. Demand and the willingness of the dealers to commit themselves early both receded. As a result the sales organisation had to be reorganised into a division with six regional managers who replaced the distributors. Most of the sales reps were put on the *Claas* payroll at that time, reinforced by a new level of company representatives.

The team at head office began to develop new functions, in particular as regards improving their planning capabilities. Company planning worked closely with Marketing to produce short and long term plans and towards the end of the 1960s data processing made its debut in the order processing field.

In 1969 a difficult task arose with the takeover and integration of the *Bautz – Speiser* organisation. From this point *Claas* began to present itself as the harvesting specialist in the marketplace. The product range comprised combines, balers plus hay tools and forage harvesting. From now on it was a constant challenge to keep ahead of the market's changing needs.

Then the dealer in Mannheim was lost in 1983 as a result of succession problems and following a lengthy process the search for a new candidate failed. Since this dealer had been operating primarily on a wholesale basis, there was only one choice open and that led to the takeover of this function by the company and the creation of *Claas* Hockenheim branch facility.

A new site for this facility was found in 1984 near to one of Germany's main traffic highway and all the typical wholesaling functions were incorporated under one roof – sales, service, parts and repairs with a local retail sales partner involved in every transaction.

In 1986 the next step was taken for the domestic organisation. Traditionally this function had been mixed up with other corporate and staff functions, so it was dependent on many outside

308 Claas factory representatives presented the brand at shows and exhibitions

309 Photo session for the sales team during a technical course in Harsewinkel, mid 1960s

sources which didn't always associate themselves closely with the market. With the launching of the new legal entity *Claas Vertriebsgesellschaft Deutschland* (*CVG*), the sales and service company for the German market was inaugurated with all the activities grouped under a dedicated management team.

Two regional parts depots were merged to form a new *Claas* harvest centre for Bavaria, which was modelled on the Hockenheim operation.

The reunification of Germany began with the fall of the Berlin wall in 1989, followed by a transition period which ended in October 1990 with the ratification of the reunification treaty. During this period it was once again possible for westerners to cross over and take a first look at what the years of neglect had done.

Mechanisation was obviously going to be a major issue, but there were several major producers of harvesting equipment in the country, which

310 The CLAAS Hockenheim team less a few sales reps who were in the field

311 Season start with the CVG team in the new Landsberg centre, 1995

produced simple and robust machinery for the communist states and it seemed at the time that they would either become serious rivals or could be potential partners. In the end, though, the companies drifted into oblivion, with only a few areas of activity surviving.

The conclusion of the transition period was a historic occasion which had an enormous impact on the company's development, both inside Germany and across the countries of Central Europe. In its wake there was a need for quick and decisive action to make sure that Claas could build on its old image and become the dominant player. Whilst the company had contributed to the pioneering stage of farm mechanisation in pre-war years in the former East German regions, there was hardly anyone around who would remember it.

This situation brought about a major change to the *CVG*. The urgent priority was identified which was to set up a strong distribution network in the new region to provide the farming community with the same high level of technology as in the west. After all the opening up of the east added 6 million hectares to the sales area. To put this into relation, West Germany had 12 million hectares, so 50 % more area was added overnight.

However the farms were seriously run down, management was based on an authoritarian plan economy, the ownership structures had been wiped out by confiscation and regrouping of smallholdings and the currency was worthless. Despite these hurdles *Claas* had set up a three pronged structure by the end of 1990 consisting of new dealers with local management, existing dealers from West Germany who set up new branches and four main cooperatives.

The top priority for this new set up was to ensure a competent after sales back up to *Claas* standards. Two *Claas* branches were created near to major traffic arteries on sites which had previously belonged to the communist run farming cooperatives, one north of Berlin and the other near Leipzig.

In 1995 these two branches became fully fledged *Claas* harvest centres and are now known as *Claas* Landsberg and *Claas* Wittstock. The harvest centre concept became part of the core distribution strategy in several other countries, including France, Great Britain and the USA.

Recruitment of new and qualified personnel to cover the new market region was an important parallel activity. The majority was recruited locally and then thoroughly trained to tackle the new and unfamiliar tasks which are part of our lives in the West. All of the recruits had grown up within the confines of a communist system which didn't encourage initiative and creative thinking. A major rethink was necessary for most of them. A number of experienced members of staff were also sent from the western regions to help create a good mix of old and new and speed up the integration pro-

312 The new centre in Wittstock was inaugurated in 1999, and features its own test area

cess. Today we can say that there is a very good balance between the staff originating from the East and those from the West, an achievement of which we are proud.

The ambitious target of achieving the same high market share in these new regions and keeping the undisputed market leadership was reached fully in the first year of operations – this was without question a great success which has paved the way for continued expansion ever since.

The increased pace of combine and forage harvester development coupled with a steady growth in size of the equipment meant that many dealers were reticent to make trade-ins because the risk of tying up so much capital was a serious threat. However these second hand machines were sought after in many countries in Eastern Europe and the former Soviet Union. As a result of this trend, the decision was made to create used equipment centres and now there are three such centres – in Hockenheim, Landsberg and Grasdorf.

This decision became a main success factor in the development of the *CVG*. These centres help the sales partners with trade-ins and can also provide the dealers with a broad range of used equipment if that's what the customer needs. The sales activities are increasingly international. Ease of purchase plus the availability of experienced, well qualified experts makes these centres a good choice for customers around the world.

The latest trend which is still taking shape results from the continued growth in size and sophistication of the products. As volumes fall and unit value climbs, *Claas* sales partners need to become exclusive dealers. The availability of exclusive partners is a prerequisite for increased expertise and quality of service. This trend is one that is appreciated by the majority of our customers.

As a result, *Claas* has had to bite the bullet and terminate some large dealers. However, there are not always viable alternatives on hand, with many dealers having given up over the last few years. The new solution which seems to be very promising is the establishment of joint ownership companies which manage a sales territory on an exclusive basis.

In summary *Claas* has managed the ups and downs well and with fine products and service kept its leading position in Germany in combines, forages and large square balers for as long as most of us can remember.

Johannes Jansen, Wilhelm Isenberg

Export markets and Globalisation

CLAAS laid the foundations for its strong position around the world today by developing the export business from a very early stage. The very first export contacts were forged with France and England, and these two major markets account for a large part of the business nowadays. The first combine harvester to be tested in France was in the field as early as 1936, at the same time as it made its breakthrough in Germany. There were close links to the UK prior to the Second World War, and the Royal Show was a popular showcase for CLAAS even then.

The earliest record of export business goes back to 1922 when the *Claas* general agent *Trier and Küas* in Wiesbaden supplied *Claas* straw trussers to French farmers as part of the reparation programme invoked by the treaty of Versailles.

Apart from the business in Wiesbaden, Mr. Trier Senior had set up a company in Paris called *Gillon, Carpentier & Cie.* with a French colleague. Despite being married to a French citizen, his German nationality meant that he had to stay well in the background. Later on the company was turned into *S. Trier & Cie. Succ.* and it first displayed *Claas* machines at an exhibition in Lille in 1924.

313 The founder of the Trier & Küas Company

314 An early Trier & Küas brochure

The well established relationships to neighbouring countries were of course disrupted by the events in 1939, but immediately the war ended, the owners set about starting again as quickly as possible. The old links were reforged and new contacts were built up.

315 The farm equipment show in Lille, 1924

United Kingdom:

The *Claas Super* combine attracted a lot of interest, particularly in England where 100 units were sold in 1948. The volume could have been much larger if the Agriculture Ministry in England hadn't imposed strict quotas. *Claas* was facing stiff competition from combine harvesters made in America since these were running in quite large numbers. During the war the British government had provided the machines to farmers for next to nothing. As a result mechanisation had taken hold much earlier here than elsewhere in Europe.

Word soon got around in England when the *Claas Super* combine arrived. From the word go it was obvious that it was much more suitable for local conditions than the American products. As a result it emerged triumphant and by 1951 the magic figure of 1,000 units was reached. From then on *Claas* has maintained a leading position across most product lines in the United Kingdom.

August Claas had been a regular visitor to the *Royal Show* from as early as 1923. He used the occasion to exchange views with customers and opinion formers. Foremost in this list is the family of Lord Walston, who have always been first in line when it comes to trying out new *Claas* products.

France:

Meanwhile some 6,000 combines were in service in France by 1949. As a result of government restrictions *Claas* was virtually excluded from the market. From then on the business took off and followed the same positive development as elsewhere. Sales increased from one year to the next. The service teams were permanently in action, instructing customers, monitoring the machines' performance in the various regions and operating conditions as well as providing feedback to the engineers at the plant. It took awhile until farmers got used to using the machine properly and harvesting at the right time. Individual instruction was needed and the *Claas* teams quickly gained a reputation as the helpful ones.

316 Royal Show 1934, Ipswich

317 August Claas chatting to England's first Claas customer, Mr. Young (left) and Bill Mann (centre), the importer

Close to the customer

The company was always proud to demonstrate the quality of its products and the early marketing activities focused on carrying out demonstrations and presenting the products at exhibitions. These were occasions where both sales and service teams could work closely together and convince the customer to trust *Claas*. A simple approach and one which has helped to develop the *Claas* reputation as being close to the customer over many years.

Initially factory sales representatives scoured the market looking for suitable dealers or agents. As time went by *Claas* appointed importers in each country with responsibility for import and distribution. The relationship with these companies was always amicable with an open exchange encouraged in both directions. The emphasis on long-term relationships with the importers has led to strong links and an unusually close personal bonding. Rapid market expansion sometimes meant that future growth could only be assured by direct *Claas* participation. As a result of this, the company set up wholly-owned subsidiaries in France, Italy, Spain and the UK many years ago.

To give you a flavour of the interest in *Claas* products at the end of the 1940s / early 1950s, here are some assorted enquiries received by the company:

318 Marie Mattheis, Export Manager in a discussion with Paula Claas

Sweden:

We wished to know if you can already start new supplies and connections. We are interested in combines and balers.

Italy:

We are very interested in machines of your brand and hope that we can make a deal in the near future, despite the difficulties regarding import of agricultural machinery in any significant quantities.

Similar requests came from all over Europe and many overseas markets, North and South America, South Africa, India and New Zealand. Here are some more examples from further afield:

Iran:

Demand for farm equipment is very high here. We would be prepared to work together with you. We are interested in combines and seed drills.

Brazil:

We are very interested in combines suitable for harvesting wheat and maize. Please let us know forthwith how many machines you can supply us this year - 1949.

August Claas: "the whole world is chasing after *Claas* machines. It is regrettable that we cannot export freely, neither can we get enough raw materials. However these inquiries which emanate from all the continents prove that there is a high demand for *Claas* machinery and quality made in Germany is appreciated around the world again".

Paula Claas and the export business

The development of the company's export business was influenced greatly by the efforts of August Claas' wife, Paula. She maintained close personal links to the importers and the success of the company in the export field can be attributed to her skills together with her husband.

Claas presented the product range at all the major international farm equipment exhibitions, for instance in Paris and Brussels. They became a major magnet for the farming community looking for the latest in developments. Customers would come to relate proudly how they had years of trouble-free and satisfactory use from the company's products. One very telling comment on the *Claas* image: "I bought your machine because the *Claas* name is on it".

However it goes without saying that competition, particularly from America, was always very intense. That meant that *Claas* could only prosper by consistently offering its customers high quality and better performance.

By 1952 *Claas* products were running in about 30 different countries in Europe, South America, Africa and the Middle East. The broad range of harvesting conditions encountered lead to new challenges in the field. The diversity of grain types on this planet is enormous and the *Claas* engineers were always looking for new fields to conquer from an early point in time with, for example machinery for efficient harvesting of rice, maize and sunflowers. All of the customers, including those in less demanding markets, benefited from the heavy duty features which these crops necessitated.

Let's look at some of the farming regions of the world and how *Claas* has faired in them.

South America:

The owners of the company got involved personally in developing products for export markets. For instance in 1950 August and Helmut Claas spent two months in South America (Argentina,

319 The visit of the company owner to South America was well documented in the press

320 A farming family in Uruguay poses proudly with their Claas Super ...

Brazil and Uruguay) researching potential markets for the products and building up contacts there. *Claas* combines had already been successfully tested in Brazil and new sales opportunities developed in the main South American markets in the following years.

Africa:

In 1954 the *Super* combine was first used in South Africa to harvest maize, sorghum and sunflowers. The importer, a cooperative called *Boeresake* tested the *Claas* machines and confirmed: "this combine is exactly what our country is looking for". Then of course all eyes were on the Super when it turned up on the local exhibition stand and this exposure was followed by a very successful run of sales. The positive development of farming in African states such as Kenya, Zimbabwe and Sudan in those years led to a long period of investment and success for *Claas*, which unfortunately petered out for different reasons.

In North Africa *Claas* was able to build up close links to the authoritarian regimes in Algeria and Libya, plus the more liberally minded neighbours in Morocco and Tunisia. In the mid-1970s a licensee agreement was signed with the Algerian government to produce Mercator combines and Markant balers locally.

Australia:

The Australian market offered plenty of potential for *Claas*, in view of the size of the arable farming areas. Despite the distances involved, preparations were made for a successful launch. In 1952 *Claas* showed the *Super* to a somewhat bemused group of farmers during the farm equipment show in Perth. This was followed by a series of 14 field demonstrations under the aegis of Bernhard Specht (see next chapter) and the service team, which impressed the farmers considerably. The aim was to show the product superiority in comparison with locally available combines. The company had dispatched three combines for the field trials, one in the west, one in the east and one in the south. But without proper local representation, customers were sceptical.

The missing link to long-term success was the local distribution partner. In those days communications were difficult and correspondence took ages. The trip to Australia was also a lengthy affair and the telephone lines were unreliable. As a result it took a long time before *Claas* could find a suitably competent sales and service partner to cover the whole country. However the

321 ... and here it is in the 1951 harvest, complete with auxiliary engine

322 Tunisian President Habib Bouruiba opened the harvest season personally with a Claas combine in 1959

right importer was found and the first machines sold just one year after the demo programme.

Australia suffers from an unreliable climate which causes major yield variations and fluctuating farm incomes. As a result investment patterns are very volatile. Conditions are less severe in neighbouring New Zealand where *Claas* has established a leading position across the whole range thanks to a long relationship to the local, highly competent distribution team.

North America:

Canada has always been open to *Claas* technology, whilst the USA has historically been a tough challenge for all European competitors.

The first combine order placed in Canada dates back to 1952. There were already 100,000 combines running in the country, and they virtually all came from across the border. *Claas* organised demonstrations around the country to coincide with the introduction. These were often made public on the radio and in the newspapers and attracted a lot of attention. Farmers were impressed by the combine's ability to both reap and bale the straw in one go, which the American products couldn't do.

323 Typical shot of a late 1950s shipment

Apart from the recuperation of the straw, the machines stood out due to their high work rates, excellent cleaning and low losses, features which were confirmed by a letter of recognition from the Farm Ministries in both Ottawa and Alberta. This was just what was needed to get sales going and before long representatives had been appointed in all the main provinces. The company quickly established a solid reputation and a large volume of combines were sold.

Even during the boom years of the 1960s, when the Harsewinkel factory was running at full capacity, the company kept looking for new markets. The management realised that saturation would occur sooner or later in the established markets, so it made good sense to keep developing the export business in new regions.

324 Claas on show in Ottawa, 1953

This explains why *Claas* entered into an agreement with the Tractor Division of the *Ford Motor Company* in the mid-1960s with the aim of gaining a strong foothold in the United States, the largest single world market for harvesting equipment. *Ford* was granted distribution rights for the whole of North America, the combines were sold under the *Ford* label in blue *Ford* livery. It was however necessary to make the combines suitable for maize and soy bean harvesting and this meant tying up substantial development resources.

Initially sales did not come up to expectations as it became apparent that *Ford* didn't really have a strong enough distribution organisation to make a breakthrough against the well-established competition. To make matters worse the exchange rate turned against Germany. When *Claas* started, the dollar was worth about 4 DM. Ten years later, it was worth only 2.40 DM and by 1970 had dropped to 1.70 DM. In the end the *Ford* project was discontinued and a new strategy developed.

The way forward in such an important market could only be with a wholly-owned import and distribution company. As a result *Claas of America* was set up Columbus, Indiana in 1979 with the responsibility of marketing the whole *Claas* product range in North America and to fill the gap left by the termination of the previous arrangements. Once again the lack of top rate dealers capable of challenging the established competitive long liners meant that this organisation didn't thrive either.

A further project materialised at the end of the 1980s with the signing of a supply deal with *Massey Ferguson*. *Claas* offered *MF* to supply the *Dominator* combine for the North American market with *MF* branding and red livery. Once again the dealer organisation failed to meet expectations, except in some regions of the USA and more particularly in Canada. However this arrangement came to grief when *Agco* took over *MF* a few years later and decided to concentrate on selling their own brands (*Gleaner, White*) and discontinue links with *Claas*.

325 Overseas order on its way in the mid 1960s

326 Erika Claas joined the company delegation for a symposium in Uzbekistan in September 2000

You will have realised that *Claas* doesn't give up easily and negotiations continued with potential new partners in North America. These efforts came to fruition with the conclusion of a joint venture with *Caterpillar* in 1997 and this looked like a perfect solution. *Caterpillar* dealers needed a combine to add to the *Challenger* belt drive tractor in North America. The deal with *Claas* would build up the combine business for *Caterpillar* dealers in North America with the top-of-the-line *Lexion* range, and *Claas* would market the Challenger belt drive tractor range under the *Claas* brand in Europe. Even if things didn't work out quite as expected, *Claas* has managed to build up a reasonable position in the combine business with the *Lexion* range, manufactured in Nebraska.

Claas has been extremely successful with other product lines in North America, especially with the *Jaguar* forage harvester range which came from nowhere to reach a leading position across the nation in a matter of a few years. The green harvest and baler ranges have also achieved satisfactory results thanks to a highly committed network of dealers who have become loyal partners of the company.

Eastern Europe and the Soviet Union:

Far away from the free markets of Western Europe and North America, *Claas* tried to open up relations with the Eastern bloc states. The USSR was a particularly difficult candidate. Whilst the company took part in agricultural equipment shows in Moscow and Kiev in 1983 and 1984, the State was only really interested in purchasing machines like the *Commandor 228* for test purposes. The assumption is that the prime interest was to "borrow" a few ideas for their own national manufacturing rather than serious interest in larger volumes.

On the other hand Hungary became a very important part of the business, with a close business partnership which flourished from 1969. Volume purchases were managed by the State trading company *Agrotek* in Budapest who also distributed the machines to the large farms which were structured along American lines. The first large customer was *IKR* Babolna, a model State Farm which later became the *Claas* importer after the fall of communism. Before this happened in 1989 *Claas* had sold a total of 5,000 combines in Hungary. This was primarily on a barter basis so *Claas* had signed up a variety of licence agreements with Hungarian manufacturers who supplied the company with items such as cabs and maize headers.

When the Iron Curtain collapsed *Claas* wasted no time in setting up shop in these markets. In Hungary, Poland, Bulgaria and Romania, for instance, new distribution arrangements were set up within a year or two with a strong emphasis on service and competent support. This experience was transferred to the other central European markets step-by-step. Apart from setting up an independent importer, *Claas* also established local offices to provide on the spot support and expertise to the fledgling companies.

The former Soviet Union dissolved into a number of sovereign states, each of which had a major stake in agriculture. They had in common outdated and troublesome equipment, low yields and large labour forces. They also all had in common a strong interest in up-to-date technology and improved working methods for better yields. The political structures vary from one republic to the other. As a result many key regions can now be covered by independent dealers. In other republics, business decisions are centralised and here the task is to maintain close links to government departments. A central parts depot was established in Moscow some years ago to ensure rapid parts supply in the harvest and to eliminate transport and customs delays. Before long the first *Claas* manufacturing facility will be up and running in Russia.

India:

The first *Claas* combine, a *Super Automatic* was shipped to India in 1972. One year later a further 21 units were sent there, after having been adapted to local conditions. The huge population and resources of this country make it an essential part of the company's global strategy and a local manufacturing presence is a prerequisite for taking part in the mechanisation of Indian agriculture. With the production of the *Crop Tiger in* India, the company is well positioned for success in Southeast Asia with the ideal product for the prevailing farming structures and crops in this vast region.

China:

The initial contacts with China go back to 1978 with the display of *Claas* machines at an exhibition in Beijing. The government ordered a large number of different harvesting machines a year later and this was followed by lengthy negotiations with representatives of the Chinese government on a combine manufacturing licence in 1981. These negotiations came to nothing and after a break, *Claas* has resumed talks aimed at building up new arrangements in this market which will gain steadily in importance as the labour supply dries up and mechanisation takes over.

The early emphasis on developing the export business has paid off since 70 % of the total turnover takes place outside the home market. Being active in so many different markets also has the advantage of balancing out changes in demand and helping to provide a more stable business environment.

Günter Ellermann

327 Combine demonstration and celebration with the President of Turkmenistan in Askabat, 2001

Bernhard Specht – the first Global Ambassador

Every company has its legendary names, people with extraordinary skills who have a major influence on developments in their lifetimes. Bernhard Specht is one such person without whom this chronicle would not be complete. He started work for the company in 1927, was involved in the early years of combine development and then became responsible for service worldwide. During his 50 years of service there is hardly a country that he didn't visit either to present new machines, to train salesman and mechanics or to help personally with difficult repair jobs. Thanks to his efforts and those of his colleagues, the reputation of *CLAAS* was reinforced globally and his travel reports are rated as valuable company documents.

329 Bernhard Specht took part in the first combine trials in 1931

The best way to get the feeling of what it meant to be in the field in those days is the following report from Bernhard Specht after a visit to South America in February 1954, including a stop in Chile where *Claas* combines were to be demonstrated live. He was a frequent transatlantic traveller at that time and sent a terse telegram to Harsewinkel: "it all worked perfectly." When he returned everyone was so interested in what had happened that the following report was filed with the editors of the in-house journal.

"As you know we introduced our Super to South America a few years back. The farmers in Brazil, Uruguay and Argentina were highly impressed by the quality of combining and cleanliness of the crop. The built in Claas straw baler is very much appreciated in the Latin American countries, because it simplifies the harvesting task significantly and that's very important, for instance in southern Chile. In this part of the world straw gathering is just as important as it is in Western Europe. The straw is required for use in the stables and then spread on the fields as humus. The other combine makes don't collect the straw but just spread the stalks on the field after threshing.

Southern Chile is hilly and the farmers require harvesting equipment that can run on this terrain. Without a doubt the Claas machines are at the top of the list in this regard and offer superior threshing and cleaning. When I look back at this year's cereals harvest in Chile I can say that our combines – including our self-propelled model – were subjected to extremely rough conditions. Despite everything being thrown at them, the Super and self-propelled combine produced excellent results. You don't have to take my word for it, because this is the view of the farmers who came in large numbers to see our combines in operation.

328 Paula and Bernhard Specht with their children Bernhard Junior and Christa

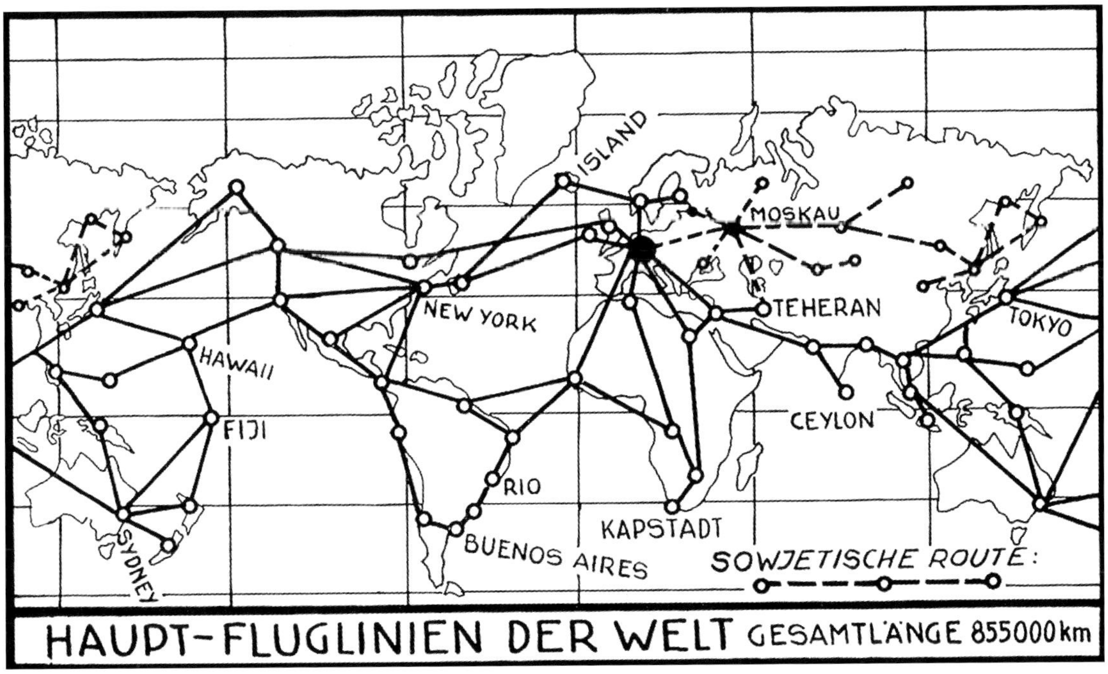

330 The global aviation routes in 1953 were still very sparse

331 From the farm tracks in Chile this journey went on ...

333 ... via the Panama Canal to the next job

We've definitely made our mark now in South America. The Super has built up our image thanks to its exceptional reliability. That paved the way for a very attentive reception for our self-propelled combine and I got the feeling that the Chilean farming community really trusts us. I reckon that the name of Claas is now as well-known in the arable farming centres of South

332 Juan Greising (right) gave this signed picture of Bernhard Specht's arrival at Montevideo in 1954

334 Stopover in Nairobi ...

America as it is in Germany. As regards the self-propelled combine, this is considered a further significant step forward for harvesting there.

It was a pleasure for me to meet so many farmers who had their origins in Germany. Many of them have been there for generations, despite which they were very happy to be able to speak to me in German. I observed that they've not changed their working attitudes one bit and just like their contemporaries back home they all work very hard and with a high tempo. They are decisive and energetic and are looking for equipment which works well, works fast and is totally reliable.

After I had finished my task in Chile I embarked on a lengthy tour across the large expanse of Uruguay. I covered thousands of miles and car-

335 ... en route to Cape Town

336 ... where a warm welcome was always on hand

337
Contemporary ad for South Africa tourism

ried out combine demonstrations again and again. I was able to show our combines at work in a vast range of crops and witnessed how our self-propelled combine distinguished itself in the toughest conditions, exactly as expected from our proud reputation as a German engineering company. If I listed all of the positive statements, you would probably think that I was exaggerating, so I'll leave it at that. The best proof is the number of export orders for South America which we are currently processing.

On this occasion we were harvesting primarily maize and sunflowers. I would like to mention that our South American General Representative – Greising in Montevideo – had prepared the demonstrations very conscientiously so that the farmers were left with no questions unanswered. Greising believes that honesty is the best policy and the local farmers appreciate this. It also explains how the required atmosphere of confidence has evolved. I came across more than one farmer who said to me after the demonstration: "the Claas combines actually do more than Mr. Greising said they would". In particular the demonstrations in maize showed that the SP combine is a fast worker. Our straw baler processed the maize straw very well, which is important since it is considered to be good winter forage. The farmers praised the ability to bale

338 … and Africa's wild animals

the straw and then stack it. They also explained to me that they have not seen such good cleaning in maize and sunflowers with any other combine they've come across.

On March 26 I flew to the capital Montevideo from Santiago de Chile, where I was met by Juan Greising, President of the company. He accompanied me to Nueva Helvetia (New Switzerland) for a special combine presentation. It went perfectly and Mr Greising was so kind as to invite me to the traditional South American meal called Assado (meat on a skewer). Following this we had a very intensive discussion on the subject of combine harvesters.

Unfortunately I had to finish my stay in Montevideo and in Argentina because the Harsewinkel

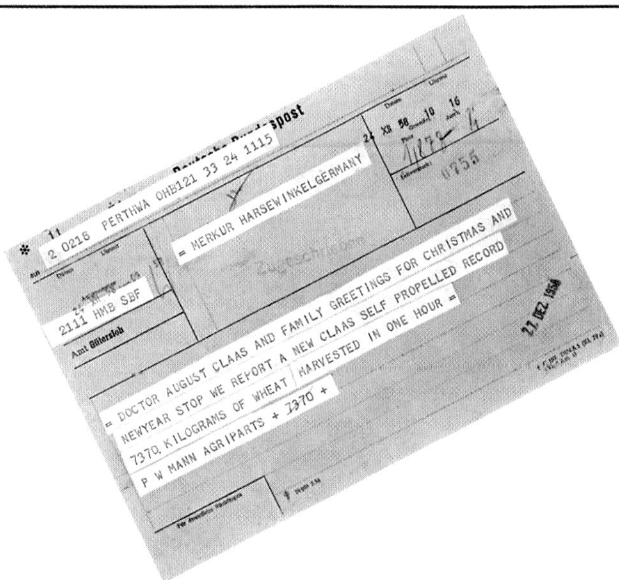

2 0218 PERTHWA OHB121 33 24 1115

= MERKUR HARSEWINKELGERMANY

2111 HMB SBF

= DOCTOR AUGUST CLAAS AND FAMILY GREETINGS FOR CHRISTMAS AND NEWYEAR STOP WE REPORT A NEW CLAAS SELF PROPELLED RECORD 7370 KILOGRAMS OF WHEAT HARVESTED IN ONE HOUR =
P W MANN AGRIPARTS + 7370 +

Neujahrsgruß mit Rekordmeldung!

Aus Perth im fernen Australien traf am Heiligen Abend dieses Telegramm ein. Es lautet in der Übersetzung:

Dr. August Claas und Familie Grüße zum Weihnachtsfest und zum neuen Jahre. Wir berichten einen neuen Rekord des CLAAS-Selbstfahrers: 7370 Kilogramm Weizen in einer Stunde geerntet! - P. W. Mann

339 A telegram from Australia at Christmas 1958 underlines the company's service efficiency

340 Combine being offloaded in Africa

colleagues wanted me to come back. So I made my way to the airport. By the way this is a new and modern building which documents the energetic development of this country. From there I made my way home". We hope you enjoyed this lively contemporary report from South America and a proud Bernhard Specht.

341 Bernhard Specht on assignment in North America in 1970

During the 50 years he spent with the company Bernhard Specht went round the world several times a year. He always went on his own and in his travels he probably did not leave a single country out of his schedule in which *Claas* combines were running. A legend in his own time!

Horst-Dieter Görg, Willi Kemper

Service, Parts and Training

The founding fathers and the generations which have followed have made customer service an enduring part of the company philosophy. The local service function was built up with the network of dealers and importers. Quality parts supply is characterised by high availability and rapid dispatch to the customer. Well motivated staff, continuous training, availability of technical documentation and special tools have always had a very high priority in order to ensure that service standards around the world are second to none. We asked several members of staff to record their experience for the Chronicle.

C*laas* has built up a long reputation of being close to the customer and particularly service oriented. This is an integral part of the philosophy and has been practised by the owners from the earliest days. Without a doubt it's one of the factors that has helped build up the success the company enjoys today, wherever it does business. Despite the many obstacles, the owners of the company can say with some pride that they have never left a customer in the lurch.

A history of service

Little did I imagine when I joined the company in January 1959 that this was going to be the start of 40 years of exciting and interesting work in the service area. Following two years on the assembly line the service adventure began with my first assignment in southern Germany.

Traditionally the service engineers were employed most of the year on the factory testing line or in the engineering shop. They were lent out to the service department for the harvesting periods or to back up special operations such as new product introductions. This meant that field expertise could be relayed directly to the engineering and production teams. The name of the dispatcher was Karl Gerwin. He was also the parts manager, just to show you how closely parts and service have always worked closely together within the company.

342 The "requisitioned" Beetle belonging to August Claas on its way to England

343 The first 16 Hercules salesmen pose during a 1953 factory training session

Gernot Werner joined the company at the end of 1954 with the task of building up training and technical documentation. New markets, languages, bigger product line and increased sales volumes meant that new structures were needed and the service function had to be expanded with both desk and field jobs, not to forget the processing of warranty claims.

Working conditions meant we had to improvise a lot, the hours were long and a service vehicle wasn't always on hand. Even the private vehicles belonging to the owners had to be requisitioned from time to time, as happened to me in 1963. The *VW Beetle*, personal property of August Claas, had to be put into urgent service for customer visits in England. However I had to be very careful with it because the garage would always check carefully whether everything was undamaged.

Then in 1965 Erwin Leiter took over the management of service and parts. The service department was then divided into field service, warranty processing, technical documentation and service training with the addition of product monitoring from 1966. In addition service inside Germany was managed centrally by the team.

Service inspectors were nominated for the field jobs which involved supporting the German dealers, the import companies and subsidiaries across the full service and training spectrum. Service engineers could be loaned out to them for special projects, reflecting the importance placed on a strong presence of the company field staff close to the action. A similar field organisation was introduced to the subsidiary markets and some of the importers adopted it.

Towards the end of 1966 service and parts were regrouped in the central parts depot. The newly instigated product monitoring function with quality statistics had the task of analysing market information and pass it on to the relevant departments in concentrated form. These departments were required to work out solutions and come up with quick decisions to overcome problems. The quality control meeting which involved all the department managers was extended to all the production companies over the following period. The product monitoring function encompassed checking production machines with "critical customer eyes" and pre-delivery inspection of machines picked up directly by customers.

After I had completed a two-year mechanical training I was given the responsibility for service product monitoring in 1970. At this time the *Claas* service organisation comprised over 60 field staff following the takeover of *Bautz and Speiser.*

The service management function passed to Hans Fischer in 1974 following the setting up of a separate parts function. One of the main chal-

344 Joint Claas, Bautz and Speiser field service training in 1970

345 Demonstration of the Matador in the Rhine Valley

lenges of that period was the creation of service structures in Eastern Europe and overseas markets. The staff was for instance confronted with assignments in deepest Africa or accompanying the first sugar cane harvesters which entailed month-long stays in tropical regions in less than comfortable conditions.

From 1978 all technical literature such as operators manuals and parts lists was digitalised and networked. New languages had to be introduced as well. Microfiche systems were introduced as a new information medium in 1984, so the cupboards full of parts lists could be consigned to the scrap heap. I took over responsibility for central service mid-1986.

That same year the German sales company was spun off (see page 157) and the responsibility for service in the home market was transferred to the new entity. Pretty much the same time the manual warranty processing was switched over to a new electronic system and product monitoring could be improved considerably following this step.

The introduction of the *Lexion* combine range in 1995 was the occasion for the company to break new ground again in the industry with the first diagnostic system for our dealers called *CDS 3000*. The breakthrough was that malfunctions could be analysed in the field, even during the harvest, using electronics. The system development was taken on by the service training team.

The end of 1996 saw the creation of the *Claas Academy* and the integration of the training function under a single roof with sales training. At the same time the first CD-ROM was produced and formed the basis of the new electronic parts catalogue. The *Claas* service managers have for many years worked closely with the

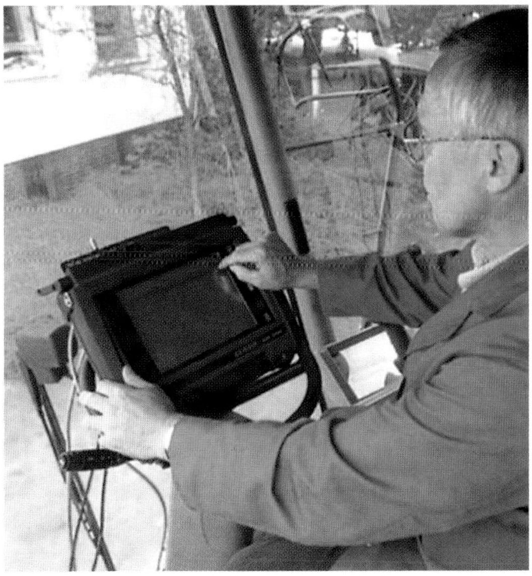

346 CDS 3000 diagnostic unit being demonstrated during a training session

industry within the German Agricultural Equipment Association (*LAV*) to define industry standards.

Konrad Siegers took over the responsibility for central service when I retired in January 2001. He is faced by a number of new and fascinating challenges, principal amongst these being the continued rapid growth in product diversity and complexity as well as the application of electronic components and systems.

The result is continued restructuring and expansion of the service organisation with the leitmotif "Service on the move". Here are some of the most important projects which are currently being managed:

- Global introduction of *Service Online* (paperless warranty processing)
- Integration and development of tractor service
- Reinforcement and improve qualification at dealer level with *CDC* (*Claas Dealer Consult*)
- Introduction of new customer service products (such as *Maxi Care* including warranty extension, component protection, service contracts etc) for improved product support and added customer value
- Remote product diagnosis with teleservice

These future oriented projects are assigned to maintain the leading position of *Claas* service in the global agricultural equipment business for years to come.

Bernhard Blömer

Right parts, right place, right time.

This has been the prime objective since I joined the company as Parts Manager in 1971. Fortunately the company had always invested wisely in exemplary service standards and the Central Parts Depot based at the factory site in Harsewinkel was extremely modern and efficient even then. For instance, when I joined a driverless transport system had just been introduced to control the whole materials flow.

Initially there was a need to develop the various regional depots in Germany. The company had already started to sell service and wear parts to contractor customers during the quiet winter period. In the early 1970s a key system was developed to control the parts business, which enabled parts families to be constructed and managed.

When the company started selling *Dominator* combines to Hungary in 1971, the parts function was required to show what it was capable of. The large farm structures in Hungary demanded quick responses and would accept no parts supply failures. Needless to say everyone swung into action to make sure that the *Claas* reputation for service could be defended and thanks to the exemplary support which the customers received in Hungary, further service centres were added in Czechoslovakia and Bulgaria. This early success has laid the foundations for continued success of the *Claas* brand right across this region following the collapse of the Iron Curtain.

347 Dispatch area – former parts depot in Harsewinkel

348 View of a gangway – Harsewinkel parts depot

In the home market the regional parts organisation had contributed greatly to the company's superb service image. *Claas* was the only manufacturer who maintained parts so close to the customer. With the development of the *CVG* subsidiary, these depots were transformed into *Claas* centres. Following reunification two new regional depots were established in eastern Germany, to ensure that customers could be sure of highest standards of service in this new market.

The direct responsibility for the North American parts business was taken over early in the 1980s. Without a doubt it was a tough challenge to compete directly with American manufacturers on their home ground. However with a well-established dealer organisation and significant machine population, the company is now a serious contender in the marketplace with innovative service approaches.

In the mid-1990s first deliberations were made about extending the main depot in Harsewinkel or even leaving our historic base in the interests of efficiency. We discussed a lot about how to centralise efficiently with a new and highly efficient Central Parts Depot. We began asking suppliers for bids on the project in the spring of 1997. After analysing the various offers we decided in September of that year to spin off the storage function, split it completely out of the factory and give it to a service provider. The winning bidder was *Stute Verkehrs GmbH* based in Bremen who was selected to erect a new centre in the town of Hamm, some 50 km from Harsewinkel. Following the comprehensive project planning phase the groundbreaking ceremony took place in September 1998. A joint company was formed between *Claas* and *Stute* (*CS Parts Logistics*), each holding 50 %. This structure should provide a stable long-term basis

350 High level stacking of parts in the new facility

349 Parts ready for shipment – new depot in Hamm

with an ideal combination between the expertise of a logistics specialist with the unrivalled equipment and market knowledge of *Claas*.

How do you transfer all the stock without disrupting the supply to dealers and customers? The quietest time of the year is the autumn and winter, so in late 1999 the parts began to be moved out of the old depot and were all in place by April 2000, in time for the new season. The move involved 1,000 truckloads and 9,000 tonnes of goods. The 2000 harvest season was the bedding down period for the new centre which was renamed *Claas Parts Distribution* or *CPD*. This centre now sets the standard for

351 / 352 *Bird's eye view of CPD in Hamm and (inset) dispatch area*

reliable parts supply to our worldwide distributor network and is recognised as a vital component in the development of the business in years to come.

In addition decentralised parts depots have been set up to cover the expanding markets in Russia and the Ukraine. The rationale behind this is to supply customers quickly without customs and other delays, and the expectation that these will become very major markets one day in the future. In addition *Claas* has used the opportunity to build up a qualified local parts team.

The times have long passed when the manufacturer could sit back and wait for customers to buy parts, so *Claas* has gone to great lengths to reinforce sales of *Original Claas parts*, accessories and ancillary items. As a result customers can benefit from regular promotional programmes, kits and packages to keep their equipment running correctly without the risks inherent in using pirate parts.

With the instigation of tractor sales within the *Claas* Group, the parts function has taken on new challenges which include the Central Tractor Parts Depot in Le Mans. *CPD* has already taken on the task of distributing tractor parts in most markets outside France and the management responsibility for the Le Mans facility is now integrated within *CPD*.

The company has all the resources it needs to ensure the finest in parts supply well into the 21st century in all the markets where *Claas* products are in operation.

BERND ALBRECHT

An Academy for a qualified community

In 1996 the responsibility for product training activities was regrouped in the newly created institution entitled *Claas Academy*. Prior to this the product related training activities were split between the marketing team who trained the sales people and the service training department for technical issues.

353 *New Claas Academy headquarters in Harsewinkel*

354 Classroom training in modern surroundings

Whilst the majority of courses take place in German, there are plenty of other language skills available with programmes in English, French and Spanish. Most mature markets offer local training as well, based on tools and material created centrally. Russian is a more recent addition which has been growing steadily in importance in line with market developments.

The tractor training facility based in Evreux, France has been incorporated into the *Academy* function and integrated into the worldwide training activity schedule. Here too there are similar language skills to the team working in Harsewinkel.

For quite a few years after its inception the *Academy* had to work with the existing facilities. The erection of a new purpose-built centre in Harsewinkel was a major milestone since it meant that both sales and service training could be carried out in the same facility with the latest in training aids. The training rooms are comfortable, spacious and airy, equipped with the latest in audiovisual and other equipment. As a result the *Academy* features an ideal environment in which to gain in-depth knowledge into today's high technology machinery. Some 3,200 participants visit the centre each year and come from more than 30 countries.

355 Modern training aids facilitate learning

Another regular feature of the sales training calendar since 1993 is the *Claas Expert Camp* which takes place during the actual cereals, maize or grass harvest and gives about 130 sales people the opportunity to evaluate directly the features of *Claas* in comparison with selected competitors in the field. All of the participants benefit from the hands on approach and direct customer benefit analysis to help them justify the operating benefits of the brand. These camps have taken place in Germany, France, Hungary and even the Ukraine where political decision-makers were also included.

Looking back over the last ten years the technical complexity of the product range has increased rapidly. In response a specialist team within the *Academy* has developed specific computer animation packages which enable complicated componentry to be explained clearly to the students. The standard of these training supports is "*world class*" and can be accessed by schools and colleges plus other interested parties via the Internet.

356 Induction training on the Lexion

In a similar project the company has developed together with the French *Thales* Corporation a computer based training programme (*CBT*). This is an autodidactic program which explains the *CEBIS* operating and control functions of the *Lexion* combine family. It has been designed so that technical changes in the operation and functions of the machine can be modified in the software rapidly and without much effort. What used to take rather a long time can now be learnt in one to two hours, which is a good example of how training can add to operational efficiency and cost reduction.

Ludwig Caspers, Wilhelm Kemper

CLAAS Advertising and Public Relations

357 Claas "Technoparc" in Harsewinkel

Claas has always been a leader in marketing its products and services. It began with advertising, primarily in Germany, followed by promotional films. As the farming business changed, the approach became more international whilst strengthening the brand became a central strategic issue. Emotional factors began to assume more importance alongside the technology platform. The Technoparc was opened in 1992 to give customers a closer contact to the company's products and philosophy. A new event culture with live presentations evolved along with a dedicated demonstration team. The company's heritage is now given more attention with a classic machine activity. Today's customers identify themselves with the brand via Claas brand clothing and models. Design has become an integral part of every machine and closes this section on how Claas is perceived in the world.

The Awakening of the Corporate Image

Not many companies bothered much about their public image until after the Second World War. *CLAAS* was no exception but advertising was gradually organised, press photos were released and the medium of film was used to position the company in the market place. In the mid-1950s, the Press and Advertising department was formed and was the forerunner of today's sophisticated Marketing function which has contributed a lot to the success factor of the company over the last two decades. One of the contributors to the early days of Marketing recalls some of the highlights.

How I "invented" advertising at Claas ...

On April 1, 1952, when I returned to *Claas* directly after having completed a six-month full-time course at the Hamburg Advertising College and graduated as 'Betriebswerbeassistent' (PR assistant), I was entrusted with doing the advertising for *Claas*. Before that, I had already worked as a draftsman and 'handyman' for Dr. Brenner, the chief designer of combine harvesters.

I had worked out how advertising at *Claas* was carried out earlier on. There were no marketing plans in those days. Theo Claas, the commercial manager, would walk into Dr. Brenner's office and say: "It's about time we ran an advertisement in the trade press again". Brenner, who was not only a technician but also quite sales oriented, would draw a sketch on a sheet of paper and explain his idea in a few words. A freelance graphic artist in Bielefeld would rework the sketch into a template, and an advertising agency would place an order for the ad with the magazines it had recommended to *Claas*.

Apart from advertising we promoted our products with sales brochures – albeit of quite simple design – illustrating each of the machine types that *Claas* produced at the time (straw balers, seed drills, pick-up balers and combine-harvesters). We also went out and displayed machines at the major agricultural exhibitions in Germany – the DLG exhibition, the Green Week in Berlin and so on. That was about it.

This situation was bound to change since the com-

358 The first ads from the 1950s

bine harvester was gaining steadily in importance and needed to be promoted in the rapidly growing market. Our aim was to move from a rather sporadic media schedule to a more systematic approach with more continuity and a clear style. We began to run regular advertisements in the agricultural trade press, which at the time consisted mostly of regional weekly papers and some monthly journals.

Next to that, we set up a card index of prospective customers by obtaining farmers' addresses (medium and large farms, followed by contractors) using address agencies. Soon enough, we had a database of around 45,000 addresses and we could send mailings from time to time about new products or special developments from *Claas*. At the time, the main focus was not on marketing *Claas* itself but first and foremost our new combine harvester. Combine harvesting was a new process in Europe and there were plenty of detractors. Well known academic agricultural experts published reports in the trade journals in which they put forward a critical view of the combine harvester and went on to say that this 'American harvesting method' had no future in this part of the world. This prompted a response from Dr. Brenner who, in turn, championed the cause with elaborate articles based on the increasing bank of experience and the promising results obtained with our tech-

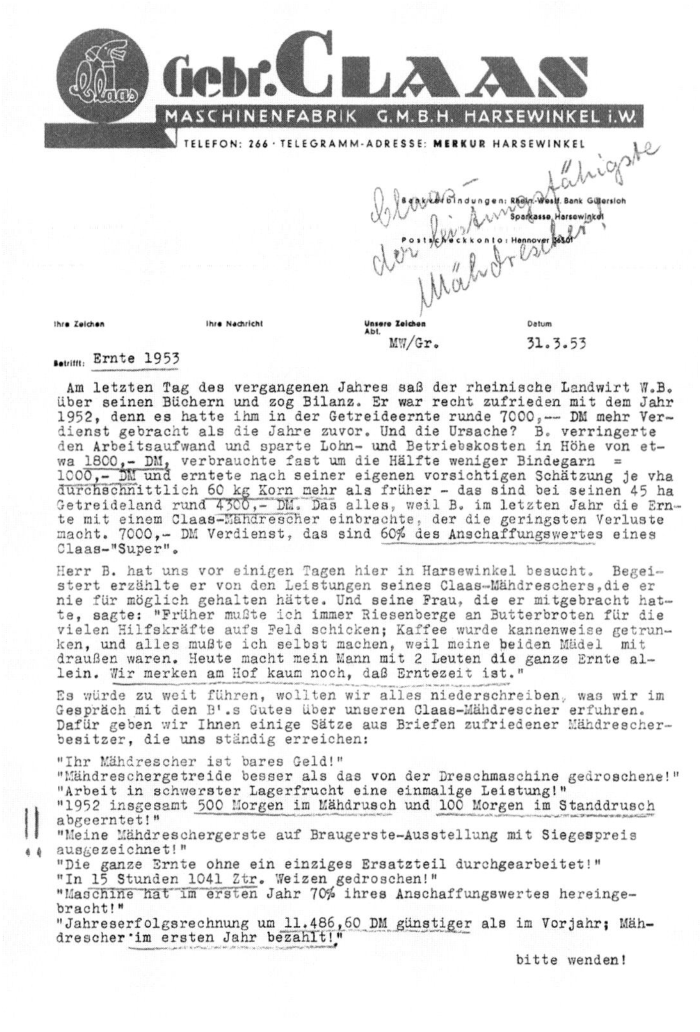

Gebr. CLAAS
MASCHINENFABRIK G.M.B.H. HARSEWINKEL i.W.
TELEFON: 266 · TELEGRAMM-ADRESSE: MERKUR HARSEWINKEL

Claas – der leistungsfähigste Mähdrescher!

Bankverbindungen: Rhein.-Westf. Bank Gütersloh
Sparkasse Harsewinkel
Postscheckkonto: Hannover 36501

Ihre Zeichen | Ihre Nachricht | Unsere Zeichen Abt. MW/Gr. | Datum 31.3.53

Betrifft: Ernte 1953

Am letzten Tag des vergangenen Jahres saß der rheinische Landwirt W.B. über seinen Büchern und zog Bilanz. Er war recht zufrieden mit dem Jahr 1952, denn es hatte ihm in der Getreideernte runde 7000,-- DM mehr Verdienst gebracht als die Jahre zuvor. Und die Ursache? B. verringerte den Arbeitsaufwand und sparte Lohn- und Betriebskosten in Höhe von etwa 1800,- DM, verbrauchte fast um die Hälfte weniger Bindegarn = 1000,- DM und erntete nach seiner eigenen vorsichtigen Schätzung je vha durchschnittlich 60 kg Korn mehr als früher - das sind bei seinen 45 ha Getreideland rund 4300,- DM. Das alles, weil B. im letzten Jahr die Ernte mit einem Claas-Mähdrescher einbrachte, der die geringsten Verluste macht. 7000,- DM Verdienst, das sind 60% des Anschaffungswertes eines Claas-"Super".

Herr B. hat uns vor einigen Tagen hier in Harsewinkel besucht. Begeistert erzählte er von den Leistungen seines Claas-Mähdreschers, die er nie für möglich gehalten hätte. Und seine Frau, die er mitgebracht hatte, sagte: "Früher mußte ich immer Riesenberge an Butterbroten für die vielen Hilfskräfte aufs Feld schicken; Kaffee wurde kannenweise getrunken, und alles mußte ich selbst machen, weil meine beiden Mädel mit draußen waren. Heute macht mein Mann mit 2 Leuten die ganze Ernte allein. Wir merken am Hof kaum noch, daß Erntezeit ist."

Es würde zu weit führen, wollten wir alles niederschreiben, was wir im Gespräch mit den B'.s Gutes über unseren Claas-Mähdrescher erfuhren. Dafür geben wir Ihnen einige Sätze aus Briefen zufriedener Mähdrescherbesitzer, die uns ständig erreichen:

"Ihr Mähdrescher ist bares Geld!"
"Mähdreschergetreide besser als das von der Dreschmaschine gedroschene!"
"Arbeit in schwerster Lagerfrucht eine einmalige Leistung!"
"1952 insgesamt 500 Morgen im Mähdrusch und 100 Morgen im Standdrusch abgeerntet!"
"Meine Mähdreschergerste auf Braugerste-Ausstellung mit Siegespreis ausgezeichnet!"
"Die ganze Ernte ohne ein einziges Ersatzteil durchgearbeitet!"
"In 15 Stunden 1041 Ztr. Weizen gedroschen!"
"Maschine hat im ersten Jahr 70% ihres Anschaffungswertes hereingebracht!"
"Jahreserfolgsrechnung um 11.486,60 DM günstiger als im Vorjahr; Mähdrescher im ersten Jahr bezahlt!"

bitte wenden!

360 Info mail for interested farmers on the harvest of 1953

359 This picture of 52 Super combine-harvesters made Manfred Wagner the corporate photographer

361 The Claas exhibition stand and the Westphalian House

nology. Gradually we managed to silence the critics.

As already mentioned, our main platform was advertising in the trade press to present *Claas*, its products and product benefits to the agricultural community. The size of our advertisements increased quickly. First, we ran half pages, but soon afterwards we changed to full pages, breaking new ground in the ag equipment sector. During the selling season we ran ads in the weekly papers every two weeks.

The card index of prospective customers was kept updated for mailings and we also began to make our machine brochures more colourful and informative. The product brochure turned out to become the most important source of information for prospective customers. In this context, our cinema ads also deserve a mention, being a long lost way of reaching the market. In those days the adverts were placed by the dealers either in the local cinema or in the mobile cinemas moving from village to village at the time. They were provided with finished slides which were flashed up before the films. Exhibitions have also always been a main source of information and exchange and they have continued to be one of our most important areas of Marketing investments to this day.

362 The first Claas press conference in August 1955, including a machine presentation ...

I was on my own when I began to 'invent' publicity for *Claas* in 1952. I did everything by myself, drafting sketches for the ads and brochures, copywriting, photographing, proof reading layouts from freelance graphic artists, handling orders for typesetting and much more. Today, this would be called 'learning by doing'. Eventually, I was granted my first secretarial help, and in 1955 the first graphic designer came on board. More employees followed: a secretary, a copywriter, a retouching expert and a production layout assistant. Finally, *Claas* had an advertising department to match the size and importance of our brand.

How I became Corporate Photographer

There was no great need for pictures after the war, but now and then we had to take photos of

363 ... with Dr. Brenner, Franz and August Claas (from left to right) following the action

one of the machines at the factory for advertisements, brochures or operating manuals. Then we needed pictures of the machines working out in the field, particularly the combine harvesters and balers. Only Theo Claas and Dr. Brenner had their own camera – a Leica – for private use, so one of them always had to be called when a photo was required. When I had been working for Dr. Brenner, we had agreed that I would be responsible for the photos. I would get the machine to be photographed out of the factory, put it in front of a black wall that we had specially prepared for that reason, and then call one of the two 'photographers'.

One day, Theo Claas had taken photos of several straw balers for a brochure when I asked him to take another photo of the 52 *Super* combine harvesters which were neatly lined up behind the shop floor. I suggested he would get the best shot if he climbed on the roof of the shop floor. "Well, you'd better climb up there, then", he replied, handed me the camera, and showed me which button to press. I had just got myself a new job because when I returned the camera, the boss said that I could take the photos myself in the future. Consequently, I bought a book on photography, taught myself the necessary basic know-how and thus became the "Corporate Photographer".

From still photography to moving images

At this point, let me tell you about another promotion medium from our early advertising years: the movie. Moving images are still a better way than printed paper to demonstrate and explain how a combine harvester works. Very soon, I was told: "if you can take photos, you should also be able to film", and so I quickly learnt how to use an amateur film camera. As early as at the start of the 1950s, we began to make short information films in colour, which mainly dealt with the use of our machines. Since these were silent films, of course, the presenter had to provide a running commentary live. At first, I only possessed a simple Siemens cassette camera, and I had to load the cassettes in the dark room myself with 16mm reversal film. To comply with the growing demands, I was issued

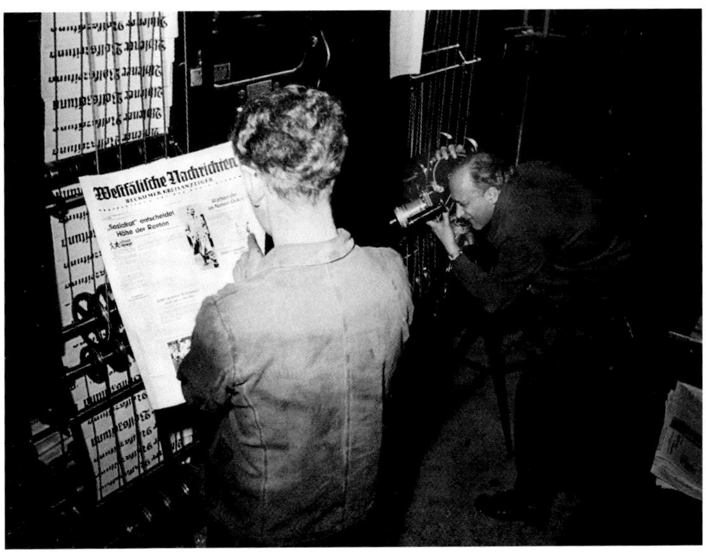

364 The newspaper Westfälische Nachrichten of April 21, 1956 reports on a visit to the Claas combine harvester factory

365 "The Verdict". The title of a special testimonial on Claas products, highlighting the benefits of using combines

a *Bolex H 16* with three lenses and all the trimmings which at the time was semi-professional.

Inevitably we were soon asked to add sound to our films. Our first approach to live recording was to use the new tape recorder technology which had just come onto the market and run it parallel to the cine projector. Then we discovered a wire recorder which was even more suited for our purposes because it came combined with a record player. This made it possible to play music before and after the commentary and fade in and out. We did all that ourselves! I would select suitable music from the *Claas* family's record collection, record the commentary we had prepared, and fade in the music – and all this while the film was running. This is how we produced our first sound films. We used to do it in the evenings or at the weekends when it was quiet in the factory.

In 1954, we moved into the new office building of the company which had a huge state-of-the-art projection room in the basement with a projector set up in a separate operating room. When we were filming outside the factory though, at important sales conferences or local farmers' meetings for instance, we had to take our film equipment with us.

Eventually, we reached a point where we weren't satisfied with our home made films any more and in 1956 the management agreed with us and we got permission and funds for a professional film with sound and colour. At the time, we had an importer from the Netherlands who recommended the *Parsival Filmbedrijf* of Tilburg who would do it at a reasonable price. With a team of only two people, which was therefore extremely mobile and efficient, we made the first industrial film about *Claas*. It was "*a visit to the Claas combine harvester factory*" and was around 40 minutes long. The film documented a cross-section of our entire production, showed the machines in the harvest and also covered the shipping, export, and the service departments. Some of these scenes are still used today in historical productions.

To liven up the film, we created a storyboard with three journalists visiting *Claas* – hence the title – who were on a guided tour through the factory. As a result of this visit, a regional newspaper, *Westfälische Nachrichten* of Münster published a long report about *Claas* written by Walter Werland who was both editor of the paper and our house journal, the Knoter. The last scenes were filmed late at night at the printing press in Münster at the same time as they printed the edition containing the article on *Claas*.

Using films as promotional tools has always been appreciated by our clientele. It is the best way to show the company, its international position and its products to visitors to the factory, dealers at home and abroad and at exhibitions. Of course, this is especially important due to the seasonal nature of the business. As time went by we worked with a number of well known film producers. At first, we made several films with Munck's *Industrial and Agricultural Film Institute* of Stuttgart. These included a few short films of three to four minutes in what was known as the "agricultural film show" which they distributed on their own. We also carried out a number of larger product projects such as films about the new *Super Automatic*, the *Hukkepack*, or the *Super* series (the combined longitudinal / transversal flow system of the pull type *Claas* combine and its advantages). Other interesting stories included the grain harvest on the seabed, which dealt with reclaiming land on the Dutch polders and harvesting it with a huge fleet of *Claas Matador* combines. The big *Matador* and the smaller *Columbus* featured in another film which is still of historic interest today.

We also benefited a lot from our links with the Berlin *Institute of Film and Photography in Science and Education* who distributed the films to the target users. We produced films showing pull type and self-propelled combines as well as balers in the field with *RCF Film* of Berlin. In the years that followed, we produced an entire series of PR and product films in cooperation with other renowned film companies, such as *Ufa-Film*, Düsseldorf; *Inselfilm*, Munich; *Allcom*, Hamburg to name just a few.

As the company grew in size and importance, the tasks for the publicity department grew in line. At a certain point in time the question arose whether we should keep on adding our own staff or hire an advertising agency. We went for the second option. In 1961, we worked with an agency from Duisburg for a short time but they were only assigned limited tasks. In 1968, we decided to work with a local agency in Bielefeld – young, dynamic and quite creative – but we were not very happy with this cooperation. In 1970 we contacted the *Dr. Seibold Marketing Agency* from Bad Dürkheim because they had plenty of experience in the agricultural sector and thus spoke our language. Our successful cooperation with the Seibold team lasted more than 13 years until the management recommended a change in 1984 in order to get some new ideas.

The Advertising Department becomes the Department for PR and Advertising

We had been a major advertiser in the agricultural trade press from the early 1950s and the company had become a major factor for them. The editors realised that it would be advisable to publish information on interesting events such as new product releases, for instance. This task could only be performed by the advertising department. So we gradually started our PR work. We began sending out press releases together with photos to the journals and as early as in 1955 we invited the trade press to the first press conference in Harsewinkel. The occasion was the *25th anniversary of combine harvester* development at *Claas*. Around 30 representatives of the press turned up and were given comprehensive information on the combines, both in the meeting room and in the field. In fact, field and hands-on experience have always figured high in our marketing efforts to this day. Even though the agricultural press has changed out of

366 These flyers announce the latest Claas film productions ...

all recognition, it has kept its place in all our main markets as the most influential advertising medium in the market with a major influence on attitudes and opinions.

It made sense for us to build up good personal relations with the editors and the agriculture desks of all the major journals as well as influential freelance journalists. Our press conferences proved particularly helpful in this respect because unlike other press conferences, they offered a lot more. We didn't simply release product information on *Claas* – our programme included guests speaking about topical subjects, visits to seed-growing establishments, wineries, stud farms, agricultural schools and other highlights.

Approximately every two years, we invited around 35 journalists to attend these events. Initially we were limited to domestic journalists and later these meetings became increasingly inter-

367 ... and here is a professional film team in the Dutch polders

national. We didn't just stick to Harsewinkel either, we once chartered a plane to Italy and visited the rice harvest, then we took a trip to the Netherlands by bus for a demonstration of polder agriculture, we toured the baler factory in Metz stopping off at Verdun and once flew to Hungary to watch combines and self-propelled foragers in the maize harvest. These events became real highlights for the journalists and *Claas* set the standards for the industry over many years. As early as in 1975, Dr. von Bokkelmann, the chairman of the *German Association of Agricultural Journalists*, wrote to us: "... the only other ag equipment company in Germany with which we have similarly good relations as with your house is Fendt". The advertising department had truly become the PR and Advertising Department.

We also employed a freelance PR adviser in 1963 to help us to improve our public relations and raise them to a more professional level in the first few years. With his support, our first business press meeting took place. Representatives of the regional and national daily papers were invited as well as the news services and the first meeting took place in the autumn of 1966. We presented the main highlights of the season and the current market situation. This information event was held annually ever since then and paved the way for today's annual financial press conference.

The actual financial press conference began with the presentation of our first printed annual report in 1978. The report was very simple and contained only facts and figures. Today, we present our annual report to the international media at such a conference after the end of each business year, the report is very comprehensive, appears in several languages and is an important investor relationship tool.

The company magazine "*Knoter*" or Knotter would be described now as an internal Marketing tool. It was published by *Claas* originally to spread in-house information. The Knoter was founded during the Second World War and was first sent to those *Claas* employees who were called up for military service. After the war – to be more exact, Christmas 1948 – *Claas* revived the Knoter in order to improve information flow internally. Walter Werland, the editor of a daily paper, was the editor in chief at the time. The first post-war edition had a size of 24 DIN A 5 pages (5.7 x 8.2") and contained a word of greeting by August Claas "to his loyal industrial family". At first, it was published quarterly, but over the years, the frequency increased. The Christmas Edition of 1952 had 100 pages and contained, among other things, a detailed appraisal of August Claas written by Professor Dr. Brenner to mark his 65th birthday. In 1953, the size of the paper was increased to DIN A 4, which gave us more design flexibility and room for larger illustrations.

The *Knoter* ceased publication in 1972, as part of the drastic cost cutting measures which were needed to overcome the difficult business situation. In April 1973, though, the '*Claas Intern*' was founded. The initiative came from the personnel management and the Works Council since there was now a legal requirement for companies the size of *Claas* to inform their employees in writing about the business situation at least four times a year. The first edition comprised seven pages of typed text and some photos and was printed in the simplest possible manner. Over the years, *Claas Intern* also increased in size and appearance. Today, its full colour layout, paper and print quality meet magazine standards.

Manfred F. Wagner

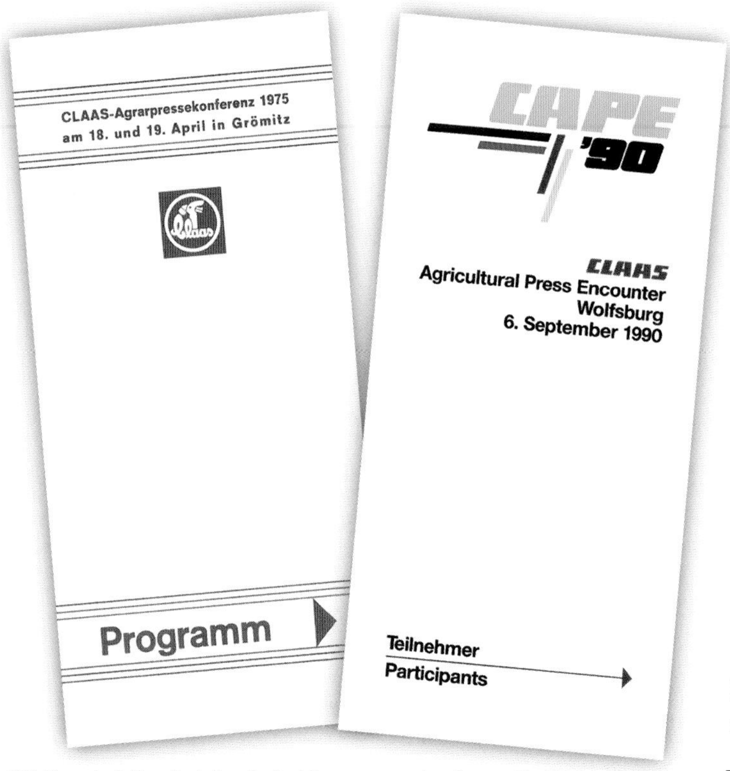

368 Press invitations including the first German cross border event in 1990

CLAAS on Show

Fairs and exhibitions, both at home and abroad, have featured in the events calendar at *CLAAS* right back to the 1920s. When the drive for mechanisation took off in the period after 1945, exhibitions became an essential source of information for the farmers. In this period where the technology was still in its infancy, it was vital for the public to compare what the different manufacturers had on offer and evaluate rival systems. In the 1950s the *CLAAS* exhibit on the open air show grounds distinguished itself from others thanks to the *Westphalian House* positioned at the centre of the stand. Nowadays the products are mostly indoors and events like the *AGRITECHNICA* take a vast amount of planning and organisation.

When talking to the old hands at *Claas* it is apparent how important fairs and exhibitions have always been as a promotional tool and for what we now call "image transfer". Machinery was on display of course, but the company simultaneously demonstrated its unique status as the harvesting specialist at these shows. One recurring theme is the effort made to make visitors feel at ease. The guests need to feel at home with us. As far back as 1924 *Claas* erected a tent to keep visitors protected from the elements at the open air DLG show of that period.

In the 1950s the legendary "*Westphalian House*" was constructed. This was designed to be put up quickly and was used both at big national exhibitions and the multitude of smaller shows round the country. It was a unique symbol and symbolised the roots of the company. Finally it fell out of use though and was sold to a *Claas* dealer in 1983.

370 The Claas stand at the 1924 DLG show in Hamburg

The DLG exhibition was initiated in 1886 and moved from place to place until it finally went indoors like the French *SIMA*. This in turn changed how the company went about exhibiting. Proper stands were constructed by carpenters using plywood dividing panels which were

369 Demonstrations of the first combine were always a crowd puller in the 1930s

then wallpapered and painted. The effort involved was high and as a rule ten or more assistants had to be seconded from the factory two months ahead of time to do the joinery, electricals and exhibits. This function was later outsourced as the need for specialisation became apparent.

Nowadays car makers show off their concept vehicles at shows. *Claas* did this too, for instance as long ago as 1970 when the combine that became known as the "Dustbin" was presented at the 1970 German DLG show. The machine was guarded day and night and fenced off to avoid the visitors from getting too close. However, the Dustbin never saw the light of day.

Anyone who has taken an interest in exhibitions will remember that *Claas* has always done an excellent job of matching the company's tradition as the inventor of the European combine harvester with its high technology and innovative power. Back in 1980 the theme of the DLG exhibition was fifty years of *Claas* combines and the presentation of the 300,000th combine will stay imprinted on many minds – it was a *Dominator 76 H* Hillside combine.

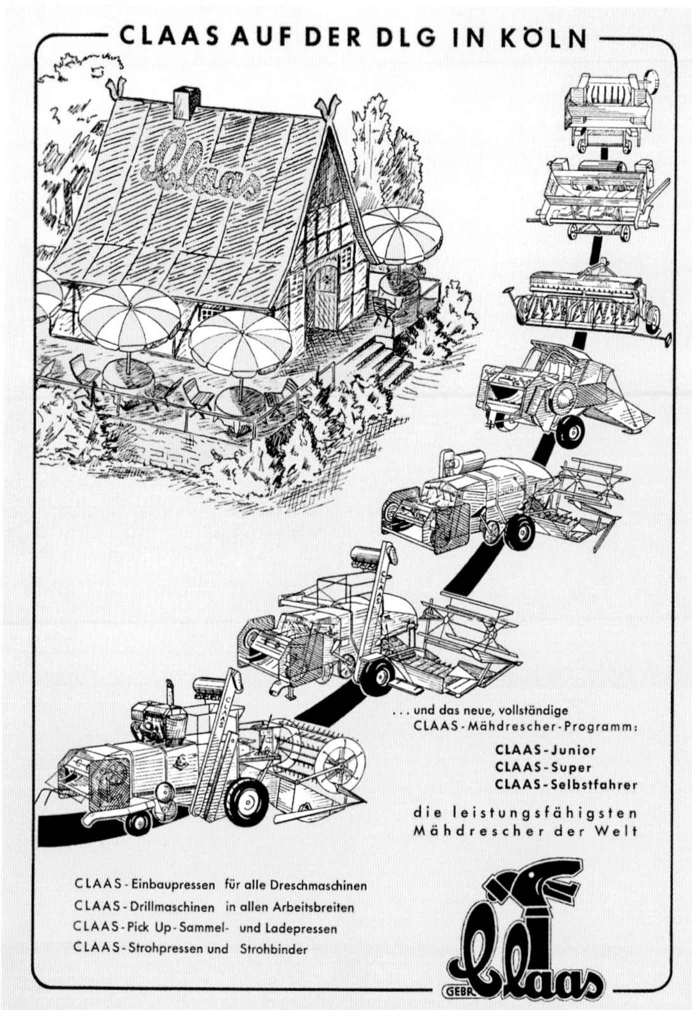

371 Claas ad for the 1953 DLG show with the Westphalian house

372 Claas at the fair in Verona in 1963

In the subsequent years, the face of farming began to change in Western Europe as producer prices began to fall and subsidies were squeezed. Small farms began to gradually drop off the map as farm sizes grew and at the same time the role of contractors gained in importance. This had a major impact on the way the company presented its wares, especially for the self propelled equipment which became progressively bigger and more expensive. The customers needed to be sure they were making the right investment choice.

The traditional types of exhibitions were not suited to this new trend and *Claas* was among the driving forces in the creation of the specialised equipment show in Germany, christened the *AGRITECHNICA*. It took off in 1987 and has been organised on a bi-annual basis ever since and whilst originally staged in Frankfurt it has now taken root in Hanover. To avoid overlap it takes place in November in odd years whilst the *SIMA* has been scheduled in the late winter of the same year, so the two biggest markets are catered for and are easily accessible to international guests.

This restructuring of the exhibitions occurred at a time when the importance of innovative Marketing approaches had been reinforced by the arrival of a new department head who was intent on building closer relationships with *Claas* customers and focussing on the farmers of the future in this period of rapid change.

The most well known innovation was the creation of an exclusive *Claas* customer event in the field which took the machine presentation to new levels and added the enjoyment of a field demonstration. Unconventional methods were encouraged by the management at that time so the Marketing team just got on with the preparation of the first field day without anyone really taking much notice. The show took place

373 The so called Dustbin was the centre of attraction in Cologne in 1970

in a circus tent near Harsewinkel with the premiere of the *Claas Field Days* taking place in 1987. It was an immediate success and became a regular event for many years and customers looked forward to the latest ideas with plenty of anticipation.

From then on many *Claas* events took place in circus tents which grew in size and the demand for places expanded. In 1989 the management asked the Marketing Manager to organise a world wide dealer meeting, of course in a tent. Scheduled to take place in September 1989 there was a need for something spectacular since there would not be anything to harvest at that time. During a creative evening session during the *SIMA* the team came up with the idea of flying in the newest product – the *Dominator 98 SL Maxi* – suspended from a *Chinook* helicopter.

The chaps at the local *Royal Air Force* base were keen to help and provided all the technical requirements. A prototype was reinforced for attachment to the helicopter and the first test flight showed that the machine was too heavy. As a result a fair amount of weight was stripped out for the second test. The threshing system, the straw walkers, chains and drives were all removed but the combine had to move so the engine and transmission were still fitted. On the great day the helicopter broke down shortly before the flight, and arrived much later than planned. However, nobody who was there will ever forget the sight and sound as the *Chinook* circled with the combine underneath and landed gently on the field as the sun set.

The event culture at *Claas* became one of the most potent communication tools as the farming environment changed yet again with the ope-

374 The flight of the Dominator 108 was the most sensational stunt in 1989

375 Claas at the premier French show, the SIMA, in 1997

ning of the Eastern European countries from 1990 onwards. The *Field Days* were renamed the International *Claas Forum* and became a vital meeting point for farmers and contractors from east and west. They also helped the company establish its presence in North America and take a leading position in the forage harvester market. The introduction of the new *Jaguar 800* range in 1984 and the *Lexion* combines in 1987 were unforgettable highlights, and customers were able to comprehend the technological leaps forward made by *Claas* and see for themselves in the field what it would mean for them.

In addition to shows in Europe, the idea spread to the USA, where the whole forage harvest chain was presented to the dealers in Florida in 1998 and the presentation / demonstration idea even took hold in Uzbekistan with a special high level symposium in 2000. Finally the last two shows took place in Hungary in 1999 and then in Chantilly, north of Paris in 2002.

Another essential part of the "*Claas* on show" package is the demonstration team. This activity goes back to the pioneering tradition instigated by Bernhard Specht and others, as described earlier in this book. The demonstration team organises individual demos on specific farms which have been identified as potential new *Claas* users right up to the event style demos with thousands of viewers.

The objective – then as now – is to prove the superiority of our products to farmers and contractors who use other brands. This entails thorough preparation and in view of the size of

376 The products are the stars at Claas events, the guests fascinated by the ideas of the Marketing team

377 Muddy demo with a full rubber belt drive combine in the 1990s

the machines, individual demos can only work if the logistics are perfectly organised. The company owns its own tailor made fleet of flatbeds for moving the big machines from place to place, offload and reload in a short space of time.

The days when a complete combine or forager could be moved form site to site in one piece are long gone. Nowadays, wheels have to be removed for transport, so an on board crane is fitted and compressed air tools carried. With the specially designed trailers, the *Claas* demo team can offload a *Lexion* combine or *Jaguar* forager and have it running in less than 20 minutes. The sight of the *Claas* demo team convoy on the road with a cutter bar of up to 9 metres in tow is always exciting for us and for our customers.

The company is permanently on show at the headquarters site, thanks to the *Technoparc* which is described in more detail in the following chapter. The unusual aspect of this facility is that is linked with an adjacent test farm where the customers can drive our machines throughout the year. Since most of our professional visitors come and see us in the winter, a combine test track was set up to demonstrate some key

378 The demo team on the road, lost in France 1989

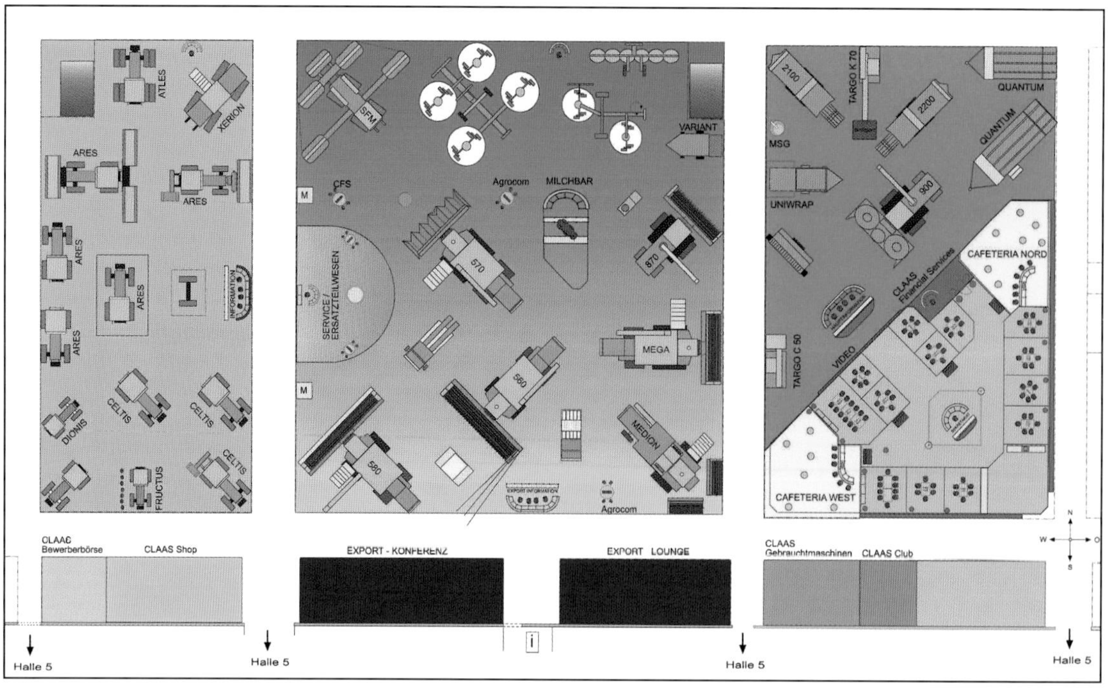

379 It's a long way from the layout of the exhibition stand ....

features regardless of the time of year. A separate hall houses machines and demonstration gear, and the demo team spends many days in winter sharing their knowledge with customers.

Planning of events in the early days meant we started with cardboard models lined up on the kitchen table. Later a drawing board was used and nowadays engineering tools such CAD are used and computer simulations made. New products, more intensive customer care and in particular the arrival of the *Claas* tractor range have led to a rapid growth in space requirements. Whilst 1,000 m² was enough for the *AGRITECHNICA* in 1995, this had quadrupled to 4,200 m² in 2003, the first year with the tractor range. In addition international guests are looked after in their own specific reception area, where they can be attended to properly.

Customers have come to expect a powerful presence from *Claas* on shows and at events. The company has stood out for twenty years with innovative, internationally oriented marketing approaches which have added an emotional dimension to the pure product features. As a result the *Claas* brand has developed to become the favourite and often best known brand for harvesting equipment in many countries. Now the challenge will be to create the same image with all the products that carry the *Claas* name. The challenge is safe in our hands.

CHRISTIAN VON DAVIER

380 ... to the final presentation at the AGRITECHNICA in Hanover 2003

The *Technoparc* – the Company's Visiting Card

At *CLAAS* the doors are always open for anyone interested in our business. In an average year some 20,000 farmers, contractors, distributors, students, journalists and other guests from over 140 countries make their way to the *Technoparc*, the corporate exhibition and presentation centre inaugurated in 1992. The museum shows a cross-section from the history of the company and its landmark products. We like to spoil our visitors and they are taken though the company philosophy with state-of-the-art presentation technology, they are fed and watered and can also drive the machines on our nearby test farm all year round.

The idea of creating a new exhibition centre with customer information facilities started circulating in 1990. As part of the build up of marketing power and the success of the customer events, it was a logical next step to look at ways to take care of our business partners in a modern, comfortable environment which matched the premium positioning of the brand. The building needed to be as close as possible to the factory and management offices, because contact between the *Claas* managers and end users was at that time considered to be a vital factor. At a later stage the main factory gate and perimeter were moved forward so that the Technoparc became an integral part of the factory complex.

381 This is an early model of the Technoparc

The choice of location focussed on the parking area and petrol station in front of the main factory entrance. This position also had the advantage that an existing building could be attached, and this could house the museum which was part of the project. The marketing team looked at similar facilities at other local companies and this helped form what became the multivision centre.

The decision was made to go with a triangular shaped building which filled the available space completely. The whole structure was to be supported on concrete pillars buried 10 metres in the ground, large areas of glass and a spectacular roof structure held together by steel rods with convector heating built in below the roof.

382 First construction phase, early 1992

Whilst many companies boast about the enormous budgets put into such prestige projects, the Marketing team was given the challenge to build the whole centre for approximately 2 million Euros! That's not very much for a 1,500 m² building which was supposed to house the largest machines the company made, the 650 m² conversion of the museum hall, meeting and presentation rooms plus a cafeteria and customer shop.

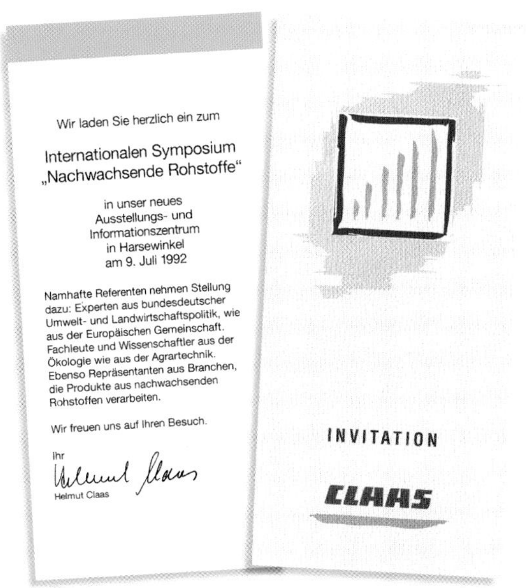

Wir laden Sie herzlich ein zum

Internationalen Symposium „Nachwachsende Rohstoffe"

in unser neues Ausstellungs- und Informationszentrum in Harsewinkel am 9. Juli 1992

Namhafte Referenten nehmen Stellung dazu: Experten aus bundesdeutscher Umwelt- und Landwirtschaftspolitik, wie aus der Europäischen Gemeinschaft. Fachleute und Wissenschaftler aus der Ökologie wie aus der Agrartechnik. Ebenso Repräsentanten aus Branchen, die Produkte aus nachwachsenden Rohstoffen verarbeiten.

Wir freuen uns auf Ihren Besuch.

Ihr

Helmut Claas

INVITATION

CLAAS

383 Invitation to the inaugural symposium on renewable resources, July 1992

384 A view along the "village street", on the right the two floor section, museum in the background

This was a tall order but there was no alternative if we were to be given the money for this investment. The chosen design was the most cost effective although the Marketing project team had an uphill task to keep the costs under control. In early 1991 this meant that the glass pyramid in the roof had to be scrapped along with a basement floor and air-conditioning.

Step by step the project advanced and practical solutions were found to all the problems which arose. The idea of having a "village street" with street lighting down the centre aisle were abandoned when we realised that this would interfere with the movement of the exhibition machines. The paving used in the main exhibition and museum areas had to meet a variety of conflicting requirements. On the one hand we expected ladies with high heel shoes and they would need to walk comfortably on the paving, whilst on the other hand the big machines had to have a sturdy base and inevitably there would be drops of oil, especially with the ancient machines in the museum area. A lot of effort went into designing an interesting museum presentation taking our visitors from the origins of farming through the middle ages, mechanisation and industrialisation to the modern day.

The flow of customers needed to be as smooth as possible. Different groups would either stick together or explore the exhibition centre individually. The *Claas* shop was designed on the ground floor along with four meeting rooms,

385 The author produces and updates the company presentation and is proud to present it personally to groups from around the world

386 Satisfied customers in the Claas shop

a control centre, storage room, toilets and a lift. Whilst the exhibition area used the full roof height the rear part was divided on two floors. The upstairs floor was dedicated to catering and presentation in the multivision centre. With some 180 customers a day the catering was quickly handed over to the same external catering company which is responsible for the factory canteen.

Behind the cafeteria was the ideal location for the multivision centre where customers could be welcomed and given a professional presentation on the company, its products and its values before going round the plant.

The construction phase

The final go-ahead was given in March 1991 following a presentation to the Board of Directors and a lot of work to get the budget back in line by the Marketing and factory construction project teams. Construction began in June 1991, starting with levelling of the site and the foundations. The pillars were the first visible sign of progress followed by the 2,800 m^2 roof construction. The roof reaches a maximum width of 43 m and a height of 15 m, whilst the volume of the building amounted to 18,000 m^3. The topping out ceremony (which is always a big event in Germany) took place on January 27, 1992 and preparations could be started for the inauguration in the summer of the same year.

The first decade

Without a doubt the *Technoparc* as proved itself to be one of the most worthwhile marketing

TECHNOPARC

388 The original Technoparc logo

investments of all time. In particular it came at a time of major change within the industry, the opening of new markets and introduction of many new products. Unlike other exhibitions, this one is available all year round and thanks to the test driving facilities on the adjacent farm, customers can really get close to the company and the company maintains its close links to the

387 The Technoparc team posing with the 20,000th Jaguar forage harvester

customers. Every effort is made to ensure that each visitor is looked after individually and the management frequently visits the Technoparc to enjoy informal contacts with customers, dealers and opinion formers from around the world.

The centrepiece of every visit is of course the factory tour. Following the major investments in the Harsewinkel plant which were described in detail from page 145, this has become a major attraction for visitors who are in the process of making up their minds about future investments. We encourage the exchange of information with our visitors and offer discussion groups with the company's product management, service, sales and engineering experts.

We know that our customers are keen to take back souvenirs and articles which show the brand to friends and neighbours. As a result the *Claas* shop offers a full range of models, books on the company and articles from the company's range of clothing and merchandising objects.

Multipurpose use of the *Technoparc*

The *Technoparc* was designed with maximum flexibility in mind and can also be used for big meetings and events. The first major event accompanied the inauguration and took place on July 9, 1992. *Claas* organised a symposium on renewable resources, then as now a fascinating subject in which the company has always taken a leading role. Representatives of farming interests, industrial users and politicians from around Europe used the occasion to exchange ideas on the subject with a highly polished presentation by the *Claas* management team.

Nowadays the *Technoparc* is used frequently for press conferences, finance partner meetings, after sales and sales conferences. The fact that there is not a single pillar within the perimeters of the exhibition area enables a maximum of flexibility with no obstruction to vision and machines can be manoeuvred easily.

Since it was opened in 1992 some half a million guests have passed through the *Technoparc*. They have come from all over the world and whilst the majority are farmers, contractors and dealers there have been many other important guests from the world of science and many political leaders have visited here. Even cultural events have taken place with classical concerts and an audience of 800 people in the main exhibition area which underlines the good acoustic qualities of the building.

CLAAS TECHNOPARC

390 The updated Technoparc logo

Without a doubt the *Technoparc* will continue to figure as an ideal meeting place for the world of agriculture in the decades to come and reinforce the image of *Claas* as a leader in the field – close to the customer and open to dialogue.

EBERHARD WELLER

389 The Technoparc is used frequently for big events such as the dealer launch of the Lexion combine range some years ago

Appearances count – Design from Harsewinkel

For more than 20 years many aspects of the design of the *CLAAS* product range have originated in the town of Münster, not far from Harsewinkel. Design is like fashion, with new materials making it possible to create a new look or unique style. To do this successfully requires very close cooperation between the manufacturer and the design crew. Many innovative ideas from Münster have made their way onto the production lines in the *CLAAS* factories, as Paul Budde, the chief designer recalls in the following article.

As far as combines are concerned the first precursors of proper design can be traced back to the 1960s. The first designer of note is Louis L. Lepoix, who will go down in history as the man behind the remarkable new look of the *Bautz Titan* in 1967. This avant-garde machine featured a design with clear lines and no chassis. The sheet steel panels were extremely modern in their time and brought the whole subject of industrial design into the limelight.

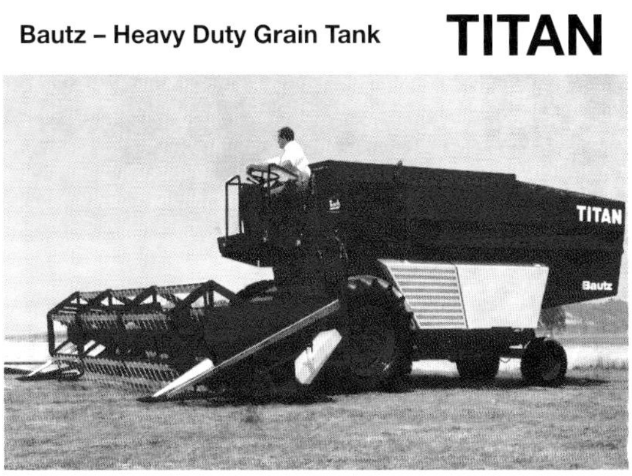

391 Sales brochure from 1967 shows the Bautz Titan designed by L. L. Lepoix

At about the same time *Claas* began working with the designer Ernest Hoffmann who had made a name for himself with clear and contemporary styling. His activity was however limited to external aspects of the design, rather than linking up with the functional aspects.

My involvement with *Claas* goes back to the end of 1982, when I was asked to design the control panel for the new *Dominator* combine range, followed by the cab which is still in use on the smaller models of this range. After this the whole bodywork was reviewed and for the first time we were able to have a 1:1 model built in the team rooms of the *Claas* R & D Department which amounted to a really new dimension in the design philosophy.

The agreed design proposal was constructed on the existing chassis as a prototype. The parts were cut out of hard foam with a modelling knife and the folds were made by hand over the edge of a table. After the drawing proposal had been made on A1 scale the panels were reworked and improved, twice on average. The smooth surface made it possible to paint the mock-ups to look like steel which gave them a really genuine look.

At that time we also presented cutter bar panels made of thermoplastic material which, as you

392 Plastic cutter bar housings as proposed in 1983

can imagine, led to a number of highly controversial discussions with the engineers at *Claas*!

Thanks to the availability of a relatively detailed model, the transition of the combine proposal

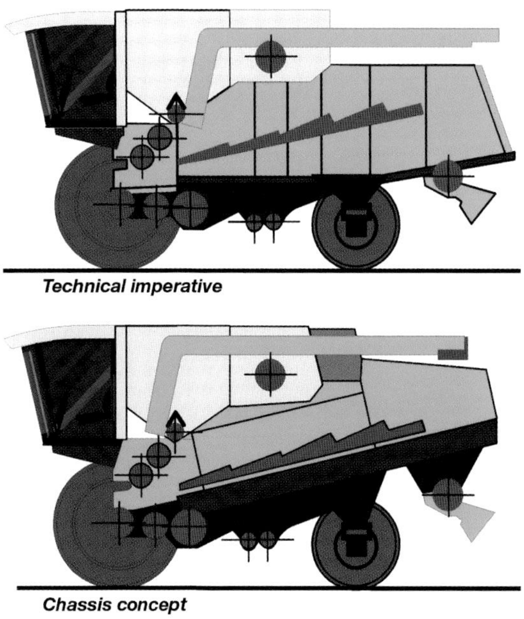

393 The unmistakable design of the Lexion stems from the modified chassis line. The lower incline angle matches the angle of the straw walkers and sieve box

to series production could be started immediately. Wherever changes were needed for manufacturing reasons they were tried out on the lightweight models first and then reviewed and discussed.

This live design process helped to speed up the detail work and limit the problem areas to a minimum. It was also possible to verify aspects such as accessibility and ease of service of those panels which covered the critical drive components.

In the years which followed other products such as the *Quadrant* big baler, the *Rollant* round baler, the *Lexion* and *Medion* combines were first presented as full-scale models in the primary design stage. On the *Jaguar 800* range we introduced the characteristic descending line of the panels from the rear to the front which makes *Claas* machines uniquely distinguishable. As part of the recent *Cougar* self-propelled mower project we formed the engine hood in glass fibre simultaneously to completion of the first machine.

Design for *Claas* subsidiaries

We began to work with the developers in Saulgau in 1983 because we all agreed that even a machine without big panels must be well-designed if we expect the customer to recognise the technological leadership which is built in and maybe even pay a premium price for it.

This is a perfect example of form and function. Profiles were changed, parts joined together and new structures were aimed at. This had ramifications across the board. For instance during the second year of our design consulting, one design proposal led to the development of the tedder CKL (Powerflow drawbar) suspension system in

394 First draft of a tractor to Claas corporate design standards

395 Quadrant 2200 as foam mock up

close cooperation with the Saulgau engineers. This in turn made it possible to widen the machines to accommodate more than eight rotors and reduce the weight at the same time. The basic telescopic tubes were then fitted with a braking system for functional reasons.

Initially the whole machine was painted green in Saulgau. We agreed to add the light grey *Claas* colour to underline the premium product technology and bring it into line more closely with the overall corporate design guidelines. From then on design reviews have been carried out on a two monthly basis.

The first project we carried out for the Metz baler plant some years ago was the *Quadrant 2200* which still has broadly the same design today. However we are also allowed to think about the possible design approach for the next generation of big balers, a task which is now

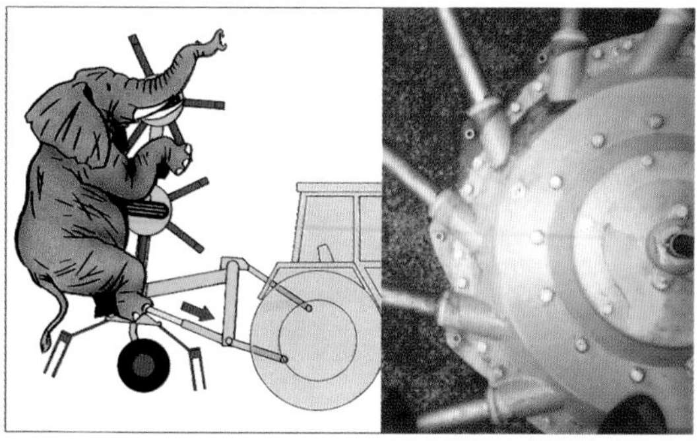

396 The Powerflow drawbar feature was visualised by the elephant

carried out virtually completely on the screen. This is thanks to the development of new generation 3-D design tools which produce extremely realistic results. During this process the balers are still on hand in our design studios so that we can carry out the detail optimisation on the machine in the most critical access areas.

Design for a new tractor range

Even before the ink was dry on the contracts between *Claas* and *Renault* we were given the go-ahead to start design work on the tractor range. The first virtual *Claas* tractors were designed on the screen using photos and sketches, colour schemes were modified and lettering defined in order to ensure compliance with corporate design with no delay. This task was handled in close cooperation with the design team at the R&D centre in Vélizy.

Operator ergonomics

Without a doubt the whole *Claas* product range stands out for ease of operation and intuitive control layouts which stem from a holistic approach and consistent design elements.

397 Cebis rotary switch inspired many copies

The design of the rotary switch on the *Lexion* combine is a prime example of what this means in practice. This driver can select a function and monitor the whole machine status intuitively and this was our response to the engineers' demands for improved ease of control. Our idea was to make a control group consisting of a single rotary 12 position switch coupled with a pair of +/- keys for adjustment. This would replace the complicated amal gam of 12 individual controls which were usually dispersed around the cab and required different action by the driver. The idea was the start but it had to work!

The functionality could only be achieved thanks to the persistence of the *Claas* electronic engineers who ensured that everything worked properly from the word go. Now similar systems are cropping up in the premium automobile sector.

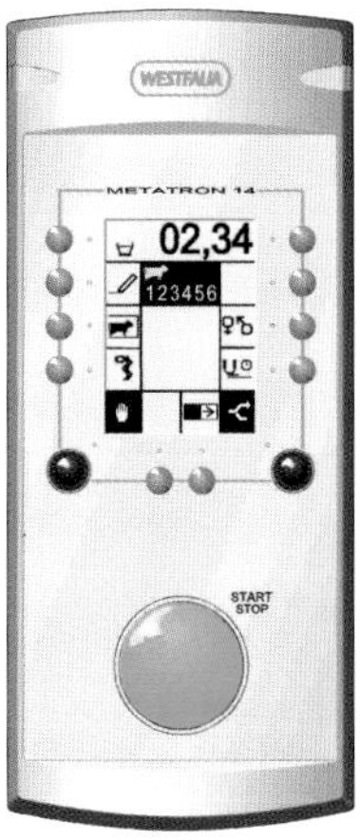

398 Control unit for a Wesfalia milking machine

The user interfaces before and after the arrival of the *Lexion* combine have evolved continuously with the *CEBIS* and *IMO* terminals on the combines, the *CIS* terminal on the *Jaguar* forage harvester and the multifunctional ACT. Apart from the ergonomic design and the look of the driver compartment on *Claas* harvesting equipment we are also active in other design areas.

399 Wooden concept cab mock up

This includes the *MMI* or *Man-Machine-Interface* which is where the human being communicates with the machine. Every indicator, control and response has to work properly in both directions. This is a major area of work in future and one which will provoke a lot of controversy between engineers and designers in order to achieve simple and functional control in the interests of the operator.

Colour scheme and product graphics

By this we refer to all of the logos, technical and safety information which is directly applied to the machine. First though, let me tell you how the *Claas* colour scheme came about. The current *Claas* green livery was instigated by Ernest Hoffmann in the 1960s and certainly set the

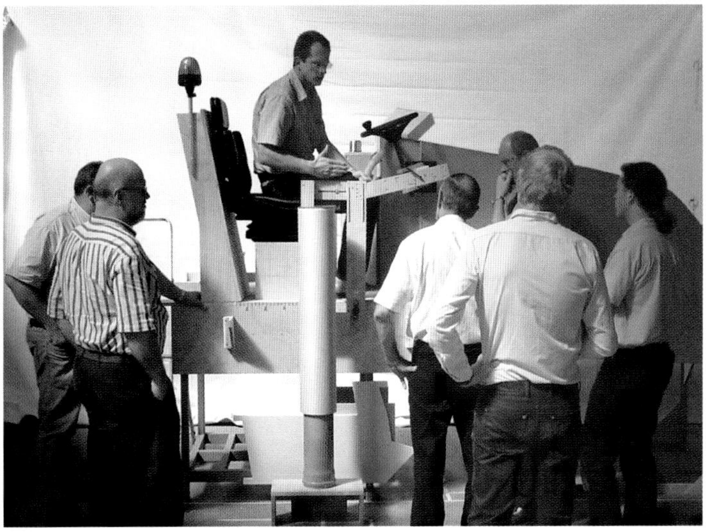

400 The design team evaluate an ergonomic layout

401 Virtual design draft for the Lexion ...

products apart from other brands. The proposal was certified by a report drawn up by the experts of the German *Institute of Colour Psychology*. This comprehensive report defined bright red as an additional colour for the brand logo and cutter bar reel plus a silver white colour for the cab and decorative stripes. This was the basis for the bright and tasteful three colour approach. It was designed to appeal to farmers and customers, which it has done from 1966 onward and it makes a *Claas* product immediately identifiable from far away whenever you see one in the field.

During the 1970s Ernest Hoffman also came up with the *Claas* logo which has remained largely unchanged to this day. The logo is positioned prominently on both sides of the machine on the light grey background, making it a basic element of the corporate design. It was first applied on the *Dominator* range of combines. The product name which originally used the same lettering is the logo has been replaced in recent times with their new dark grey lettering which harmonises well with the logo. This new layout provides a more neutral appearance and has no influence on the logo itself.

402 ... was turned into reality with the rounded rear panel

Since the safety and operating decals also have an effect on the appearance of the machine, we also take responsibility for this. Originally we collected all the various decals and that was enough to show that it was going to be necessary to review all of these functional and safety stickers. So we set about harmonising the appearance and created a catalogue of pictograms to represent various functions, actions and warnings. Every new safety or operational decal has to be agreed in advance to make sure that the graphic information can be interpreted correctly and with no misunderstanding.

When form, function and ergonomics can be fused together, the overall impression is clear and uncluttered. Even if the solutions we come up seem to be simple and obvious, there is

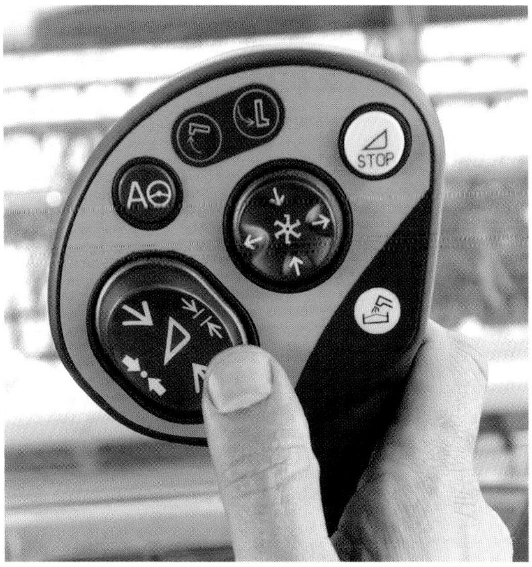

404 The multifunctional control lever is a masterpiece of design grouping the main drive functions in one place

403 The latest edition of the Lexion cab features steering column height and angle adjustment

405 CAD is an essential design tool today

usually a long gestation period and considerable discussion needed to get there. The intensive discussion on the function, handling and design is what gives every new product its appeal and increases the chances of its success in the marketplace.

Past and future design

Design options seem to us to be limitless with new materials increasing the spectrum open to us for exterior design. In the layout phase we manoeuvre exclusively in the virtual world, drawing ideas on the PC tablet. These drafts can be modified as much as needed and variants produced in the duplex system. Detailed design drafts are produced in 3 D animation programmes. Data is transmitted between us and the engineers involved in the development of the project, discussions take place on the screen and via Internet. To save time the same information can be made available on both screens whether it is moving film sequences, tables or lists.

Design has become more than a nice thing to have. It is the privilege of the leaders to be able to invest properly in this field and it will continue to play a vital part in the overall corporate strategy in future. We will do all we can to ensure that *Claas* products remain distinctive, ergonomically excellent and give the user a sense of pride at having bought the finest technology within the most imaginative design package.

PAUL BUDDE

406 The unique aggressive lines of the Jaguar contribute to the enormous success of this product range

65 years on and still going strong

This chronicle wouldn't be complete without a real life story of endurance and this one takes some beating. It's about a family called Weber. They run a farm in Merseburg in the eastern part of Germany. They bought an *MDB* combine in 1938 at the Leipzig agricultural fair and both the *MDB* and their 1935 *Lanz Bulldog* survived the war years, communist collectivisation and post-communism. The third generation of the family still keep these classics running. We visited this unusual family in a region which gives us an opportunity to describe some of the history of this region in the intervening years.

Our first encounter is with Gerhard Weber who makes it clear: "that machine will not leave this house as long as I live". The pensioner is referring of course to the *Claas MDB* combine which has been part of his life since it was bought in 1938. It is stored close by in the barn on the farm which has been in this family's hands for hundreds of years.

The family is one of only two full time farmers who are left in the two neighbouring villages of Upper and Lower Klobikau. In common with many rural communities in this part of the world it seems to have been left behind in time. This time warp is exemplified by the closeness of the houses which are lined up cheek by jowl along the narrow cobbled village high street. The entry to the farm which is now run by Frank Weber and his family is in keeping with the rest with an imposing arch followed by cobblestones.

The survival of this ancient road surface is not unusual, since there are other investment priorities for these farms which were left to decay for the over 40 years of communist domination. At the start of this process, redistribution of wealth was on the big agenda. Small farms were turned into collectives with the smallholders each retaining their share, at least on paper. Efficient large farms were turned into cooperatives whilst the owners who were considered to be enemies of the working class were disenfranchised.

Most of them fled to the west but those who didn't flee were frequently punished. Since everyone was working for the common good a large labour force was able to live from the farm operation, regardless of outputs and yields. They were forced to specialise either in cereals or animal production, regardless of where their former expertise really lay. At the same time the German Democratic Republic became the centre of production for a lot of farm equipment used in the eastern bloc.

407 The Lanz Bulldog on the Weber farm

When the Iron Curtain collapsed, these farms were in a dreadful state of disrepair and it took ages for ownership claims and structures to be cleared up. The machinery manufacturing sector declined rapidly and is virtually non-existent these days.

Back to the farm, which is peaceful today since we are here at the weekend and the machines are

408 Historic snapshot of the MDB in Klobikau

not working. The silence is broken only occasionally by passing motorists which is not surprising with just 500 inhabitants in the village. We enter the barn next to the house where the *Claas MDB* is stored in the semi-darkness next to the *Lanz Bulldog* tractor built in Mannheim in 1935. This pair of machines was the backbone of the

409 Contemporary Lanz Bulldog brochure

farm mechanisation here on the farm for many years, and the two of them have stayed inseparable to this day.

Gerhard Weber has resolved to keep it this way, having grown up surrounded by these historic machines. He has shared most of his working life with them and others through the most amazing periods of change and they have stuck together. In fact the classic combine and tractor are part of the family for him, for son Frank and grandson Jens. In particular the combine is a close friend and Gerhard loves to relate all kinds of stories about it.

Hans-Adolf Hahn lives near Leipzig and is an expert on old farm equipment. His specialities are products from *Hanomag, Sack, Claas* and *Lanz.* He gave us the lead which took us to the Weber farm. "*Claas*!? There's another old machine standing around nearby in the village".

Back in 1938 the *Claas MDB* made its first entry in the sleepy village. It was like a celebrity, one to be admired and applauded. Gerhard Weber was just a schoolboy then, eight years old in the town of Halle. An impressionable age, and as we all know memories of major events which impress us then don't fade with age.

The history books confirm that this was a time of prosperity in Germany as a whole, following the recession of the early 1930s and the economic policies of the Nazi regime. The farming community benefited from the fact that it had become politically important for the third Reich. Self sufficiency in food production was a prime target, and farm mechanisation would release labour for industrial and military purposes. The annual Farming Conference which took place in Bückeburg, Lower Saxony turned into a high profile propaganda event at which Adolf Hitler usually made an appearance.

The other propaganda event was the annual Leipzig Farm Show which took place at the Marktkleeberg fair grounds. This location is significant because eastern Germany was in those days the bread basket of the country, and it kept its significance as an agricultural region after the war. The fair became a showcase with farmers coming with their families to see the latest equipment and cultivation trends. They were encouraged to buy on the spot and many did so.

Gerhard's father came to the farm in 1926 from a neighbouring estate, marrying into the family. In line with customs his family's farm was to be inherited by the eldest son so Gerhard knew he

410 Setting up the cutter bar in modern times

had to move on. He brought with him a 10 ha dowry and a very open attitude to farm mechanisation which he shared with his father-in-law. The farm location in an area of extremely high soil quality gave them the necessary financial reserves to dream about investing in new style equipment. Before long they had developed a reputation in the region as extremely progressive, well-trained and dynamic farmers.

The local farm equipment dealer Karl Gäbler had been in the business a long while and knew all his customers personally. It doesn't come as a surprise that he kept closely in touch with Otto Weber and made a point of inviting him to the Leipzig farm show. Mr. Gäbler had been planning for a while to try and get Mr. Weber interested in the most modern harvesting machine in Germany, which was from *Claas* in Harsewinkel. Up till then there wasn't a single machine of this type in the locality. However Otto Weber was an early adopter of technology with a Stock belt drive tractor being acquired in 1928 and a *Lanz Bulldog* in 1935. He had been reading the farming journals and had kept himself well informed about what *Claas* was up to.

For the first time Otto Weber was able to see the *MDB* as large as life on the *Claas* exhibition stand. The performance specifications added up as did the price so the deal was concluded on the stand. The sum of 18,000 Reich Marks is reputed to have changed hands for the machine with plenty of accessories thrown in.

412 Bulldog and MDB ready for the road

When the combine harvester was delivered directly from the show a few days later it caused a sensation in the otherwise sleepy neighbourhood. The induction training took place with the dealer and as was usual in those days a representative of the company was to be dispatched directly from the plant. The owners were delighted when Dr. Walter Brenner, the combine's designer, turned up in person to ensure that the *Claas – Lanz* combination was correctly matched. The *Bulldog* PTO speed was measured at 540 rpm which was considered adequate.

The news spread fast – farmers and estate managers came from far and wide to see what this miracle machine was capable of. They came by car, by tractor and on horseback. Weber was very enthusiastic about his latest acquisition and the onlookers were highly impressed by what they saw. Weber saw himself as being the local lea-

411 Frank Weber at the wheel of his historic machines

413 Original "Claas patents" on the combine

der amongst his colleagues and the decision he had made enabled him to stay ahead of his rivals. In fact he bought a second *Claas MDB* combine a year later, a further *Lanz Bulldog* and a *Hanomag RL 20* which was the so-called "farmer's tractor".

Every farmer in Germany was forced to contribute to a maximum to the war effort. For the Weber farm their modern fleet of equipment was what was needed to meet their targets and do their bit to supply the population in the troublesome years to come. Otto Weber didn't have much opportunity to manage the business personally since he was called up and spent the war years patrolling on the nearby airbase.

Following the end of the war things got back to normal gradually under Soviet occupation and Gerhard Weber recalls that they produced excellent quality malting barley and peas which were sold in sacks. The team had their work cut out to keep up with the bagging unit on the *MDB*, he recalls.

The shadow of collectivisation in the German Democratic Republic fell on the farm and the family reluctantly decided to take the combine out of service and mothball it in the barn. This was a wise move since the Communists didn't appreciate products from the capitalist West and it would have landed on the scrap heap. The family ensured the survival of this technological masterpiece during the era of collective farming.

During the 25 years it was used regularly, the *MDB* never let the owners down. Only minor repairs were acquired along with the replacement of wear parts, which is pretty much as expected. For instance the threshing drum slats wore out after some years, the textile feed apron needed replacing as did a few of the bearings. All in all it turned out to be a very good return on investment.

When Frank took over the farm in the 1990s, the age of collective farming had passed and ownership regained by the family. He had to promise to care for the machines so dearly loved by his father and grandfather, which was an honour for him. After all he had grown up with them as well.

This farming business is not a typical huge scale cereals farm. After its return to private hands it has now grown to around 400 ha by renting some neighbouring fields. Their main activity is in cereals along with sugar beet. In addition there is a herd of 60 high-performance dairy cows which supply milk to the local dairy. The farm butts onto the former location of the open-cast lignite mining sites which have left behind them a number of lakes.

Surprisingly this region also produces a certain amount of wine and one of the neighbours with a very sunny location has planted 1.5 ha of grapes for sparkling wine production. The labels are reproduced below.

The survival of this early *MDB* combine is a rare combination of circumstances. It is one of the very few surviving pre-war machines from eastern Germany and we are happy to see it in such careful hands. *Claas* is proud of its long tradition and in the following chapter you will find out more about the efforts made to keep the past alive.

Dieter Tasch

Source:

Adapted from "The Pioneer", a journal of Lanz Bulldog enthusiasts in Schleswig- Holstein, volume 69, 1996.

414 Label from the local wine company

Keeping the Tradition alive

415 A Claas baler "as found" in a barn

Historical agricultural machinery attracts fans of all ages and walks of life. As such it is a significant image builder for those outside the world of farming. Whilst the restoration of a big machine like a combine harvester is often tricky, the effort is rewarded when it is displayed at a country fair or put on show in a museum. Early or unusual combines and other machines are sought after by collectors and museums around the world and practical demonstrations bring to life how these machines transformed farm working methods out of all recognition. This chapter describes the lengths Claas go to in order to keep the tradition alive. Another collecting fraternity focuses on scale models and here too there is a huge assortment which our editorial team set out to discover for you.

The Archives, Collector's items and the *CLAAS* Museum

The company decided to start collecting historical machines many years ago and landmark products have been restored over a number of years. Whilst they are normally exhibited in the *CLAAS* Museum which forms part of the *Technoparc* in Harsewinkel, these classics attract plenty of attention whenever they are presented at events. The *CLAAS* archives house all the documentation on historical machines and the company history, providing a complete record of the corporate history of *CLAAS*.

As a family company with a long tradition *Claas* had obvious reasons to try to preserve its historical machines. This was important in order to document not only its corporate history but also the long and often strenuous development towards today's modern production and state of technology. Unfortunately, many firms underestimate or even neglect this image factor completely.

A small team of pensioners and current employees of *Claas* has taken up the task of restoring exhibits to their former glory, primarily for visitors of the group HQ. The best place to admire the results is within the four walls of the corporate museum. Machines which embody historical milestones are purchased and first stored in a shop whilst awaiting attention.

Some historical exhibits had always stayed in the company's possession. However, until the end of the 1980s, they were procured at random and only on the initiative of a few people who recognised the importance of historical machines early on and played an active role in acquiring some of them for the company.

On April 1, 1990, a small team led by Wilhelm Kemper, himself a *Claas* old timer and co-author of this Chronicle, began restoring the old harvesting machines. Advertisements were put in the trade press in order to get hold of more *Claas* machines. The team restored the first combine harvesters in a newly designed workshop. Some of the first exhibits were a *Hercules* self propelled combine, a *Huckepack*, a seed drill, and the prototype of a tractor with a hydrostatic transmission.

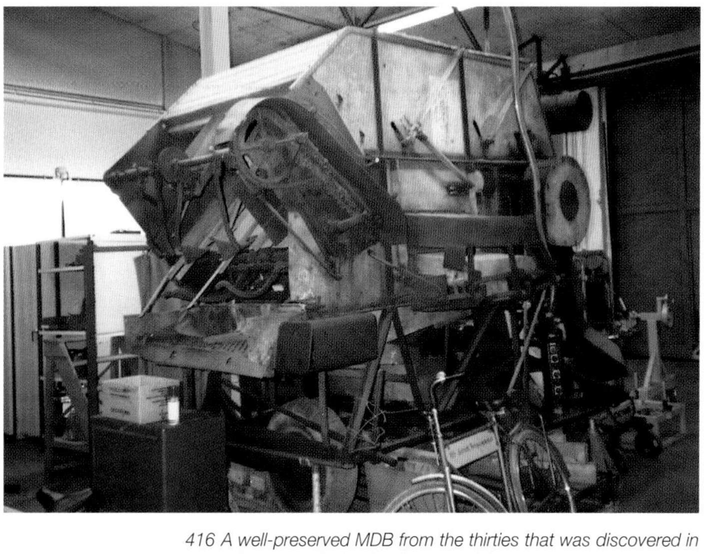

416 A well-preserved MDB from the thirties that was discovered in a barn on arrival at the Claas workshop ...

At the same time, the new exhibition centre for visitors, the *Technoparc* of today, was being built. At its formal opening in 1992, part of the building was dedicated to the past and the Marketing team turned it into the permanent home for the first exhibits of the museum which have been fascinating numerous visitors ever since.

Let's go back to 1990 when everything began. The advertisements had the desired effect so that a considerable collection of important *Claas* machines was built up without delay. The goal had always been to obtain an adequate cross-section of all machines produced by *Claas* so that today, not only the most important combine harvesters but also some balers and the *Jaguar SF 60* have returned into the possession of the company. More machines are offered to the team on a regular basis, and when they are in good condition they stand a chance of being added to the collection. Since *Claas* built more than 150 different types of combine harvesters alone and all exhibits have to be stored in a dry place, it's going to be impossible to acquire all these machines.

A systematic restoration process was developed that is still applied today. On the one hand, the machines are rebuilt so that they both look like new and also work properly. What's more, the aim is to show visitors how the machines function. Therefore, the threshing components of some of them were painted red, for instance, so that their mode of operation could be demonstrated more easily. In addition, information boards highlight the outstanding features of each machine including brief information about production volumes and dates. To make the information easier to digest, each area has information boards in a different colour. Visitors can watch films showing historical harvesting machines and, depending on their individual interests and how long they stay, are given the opportunity to find out all they want about the company's past.

Historical farm equipment in action

Special events call for special efforts to be made. In 2001, there was just such a special event: *Claas* celebrated a very special anniversary, 66 Years of Combine Harvesters. During the event, the Marketing team set out to show a cross-section of all *Claas* combine harvesters and other products in action to a cross section of business partners and international opinion formers. Of course, this also included an early *MDB* combine, and since the one in our museum was the showpiece of our celebration, we needed a second one. One of the exhibits in the Westphalian open air Museum in Detmold, which forms part of the *Landschaftsverband (Agricultural Association) Westfalen-Lippe*, was a functioning *MDB*, and the Association agreed to lend it to us. After it had been brought to Harsewinkel and was serviced, we did a test run and made the machine thresh some winter barley – it worked perfectly. Thus, we had no reason to worry when the celebration started at the end of July.

It goes without saying that we did a second test run before the celebration – this time with summer barley – to make sure that the *MDB* was working properly. Unfortunately, we found that the baler's ejector couldn't pull the bales off the trussing hook because the short straw became too brittle in the mid-summer heat. One of our team had to walk beside the machine and pull the bales off by hand. Despite all this, the demonstration was a success. After all, who's ever seen an *MDB* in action? Everyone was impressed by the cleanliness and quality it showed during the demonstration.

We demonstrated to our visitors the impressive developments in the field of grain harvesting with a chronological parade of our combine harvesters in action, including an *SF*, a *Compact*, a *Matador*, and a *Lexion 480*. Before the *MDB* was cleaned and returned to the museum, it was filmed in action. The rye harvest took place at the time, and the machine was working smoothly once again in this crop. The bales were neatly lined up on the field.

417 … where it will be completely overhauled and repainted

In the evening, when the filming was completed, the friends of the local harvest thanksgiving society (*Erntedankgemeinschaft*) from neighbouring Clarholz-Sundern who had given immense support to this event including bagging the harvest were quite relieved that they didn't have to do such hard work every day. Afterwards, they did their best to wash the dust down their throats. Everyone was enthralled by this vivid re-enactment of the 'good old days'.

The *SF* mentioned above is a special machine. Having been in our possession for quite some time, it was restored so that it could be used at the celebration and afterwards exhibited at the new *Technoparc* in eastern France. Thus, we could convey the long tradition of *Claas* to our prospective customers there. At the end of

418 It's important to pass on knowledge to the young generation of employees to ensure a transfer of expertise into the future

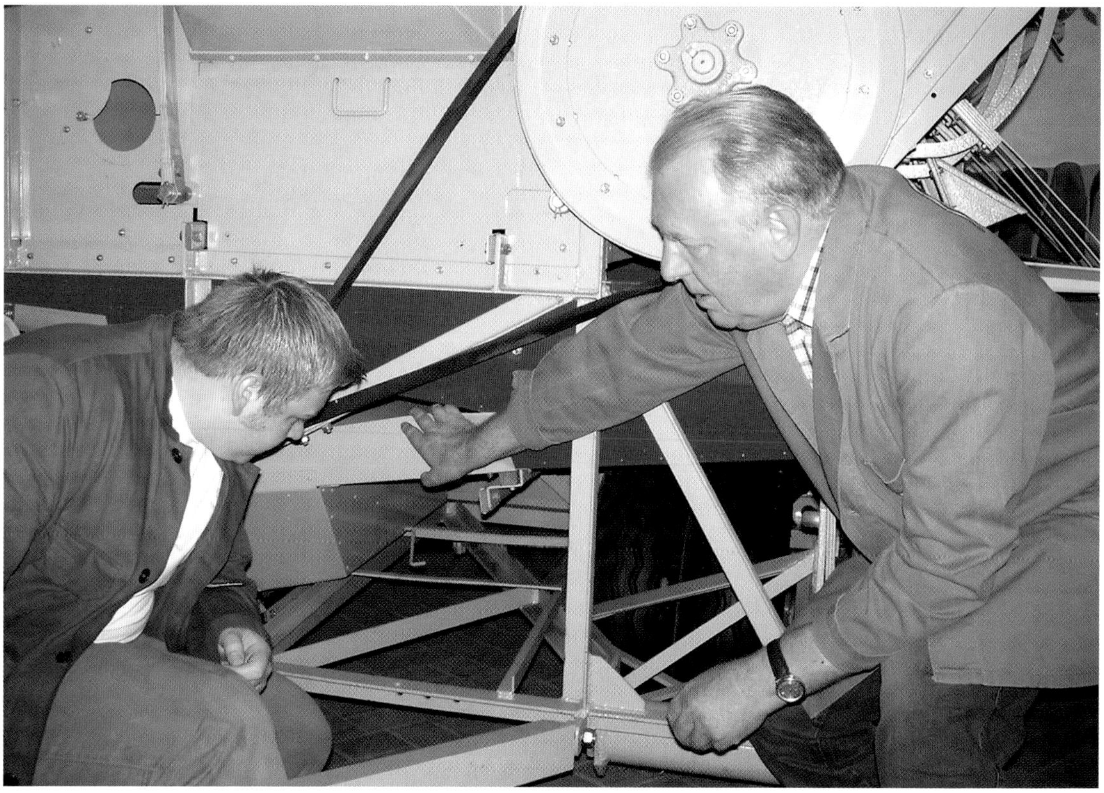

419 Franz Grothues explains the secrets of how the MDB works to a younger colleague

this foreign assignment, the machine was cleaned thoroughly and sent to the US where it now serves as an exhibit in our new factory in Omaha, Nebraska.

The devil is in the detail

When setting out on a restoration project it's difficult to know the extent of work. It is only possible to see how much the parts are worn out when every single component has been taken apart. Replacement parts have to be either purchased from outside or made in-house. It takes a lot of time and effort to assemble new bearings, straighten out bent parts, install new pipes and hoses and so on.

The process of derusting, priming and repainting requires a great deal of effort because all components, even riveted joints, are taken apart

420 Sometimes parts have to be modelled, here you see Karl "Charly" Heitmann in action

421 An old pick-up press, after it had been procured by Claas in 1998 ...

422 ... and a few hundred hours of work later in the museum together with the team.

to ensure that rust will not build up between the metal parts. When our restorers can look up the old drawings in our in-house documentation, the job of rebuilding is fairly straightforward. With the very old models such as the *MDB*, for instance, this was not possible. Every panel had to be removed and measured. We were very surprised about the way some parts were made because in those days they had to be manufactured by hand or with special tools since even a modern bending press would not be able to bend them. Nevertheless, these parts were crafted extremely well.

Although it takes many hours to restore an old combine, it is an exciting moment for the restorers when it can finally be displayed in all its splendour to museum visitors. The restorers are mostly former employees of our Service or R & D departments who know the machines inside out and are fully aware of which details are most important. If a spare part is no longer available or cannot be made in-house, it is procured by the individual departments. In this context, we would like to say that we owe a debt of gratitude to all those who have supported the process of restoration in so many ways.

The *Claas* Museum is developing on an ongoing basis. Among other things, we regularly exchange our machines and update the information on the information boards. Eberhard Weller, Manager of the *Technoparc* is responsible for continuously improving our exhibition. The unique atmosphere of the *Technoparc* is due to the coexistence of old and new technology in one place.

423 Striking display of the difference between generations – a Claas-Xerion with a Quadrant 2200 large square baler and a Hanomag R 22 with a Claas pick-up press at the Open Day of, 66 Years of Combine-harvesters' in 2001

424 Contemporary garb contributes to the old time feeling

426 Co-author Dr. Ludwig Caspers digging through the Claas archives

Documentation and archives

Equally important to preserving historical exhibits, documentation is a key to how a company and its products have developed. After Wilhelm Kemper had put the plan of a corporate museum into practice, he took up his next task: for some time now, he has been taking care of our inhouse archive together with Dr. Ludwig Caspers, who, like Wilhelm Kemper, doesn't mind being referred to as an old timer himself either.

Historical brochures and other documentation of importance for *Claas* such as catalogues, operating manuals, and parts lists, had originally been stored all over the place. With the inauguration of the central archives they were collected, numbered, and filed with a reference, so nowadays we are able to respond swiftly to customers' special requests. It only takes a quick search in our computer database, which we have created ourselves, to find the requested file.

For instance the *Claas* archives provided the basis for this book and they will be filled with even more documentation in the future. Therefore, we are making some of our young employees familiar with what we have collected so that they can continue the task we have begun.

Now as in the future, preserving our roots will form an important part of the corporate philosophy of *Claas*. The countless groups of visitors who come to our HQ in Harsewinkel each year in order to witness our modern production facilities are reminded of where we come from and the fascination of the development of our brand.

Martin Beckmann

425 Vintage kit in action is a crowd puller, here we see a Lanz Bulldog with a Claas MDB

Apollo Centrepiece of a New Museum

There has been a steady growth of interest in restoring old tractors and combine harvesters as a hobby over the last years. Some companies have also committed themselves to keeping their tradition alive by restoring selected machines. One of the few existing *CLAAS Apollo* forage dryers comes into this category. The *CLAAS* Saulgau team first dismantled it and then carefully restored it to exhibition standards, after which it made its way to its final home at the German Agricultural Museum (DLM), part of the Hohenheim University near Stuttgart. The story behind this extraordinary piece of equipment was described in more detail from page 97, whilst its last journey is related here.

Once it had been decided that the last surviving *Apollo* drying system would find a place in the Hohenheim Museum (DLM), the management of *Claas Saulgau* – in their capacity as the green harvest specialists within the group – volunteered to restore the whole chain of equipment in 2003 and 2004. This one was complete and also included the *Rapido* loader wagon. The unit picked for restoration was the one which had worked from 1976 on a test station belonging to the Hohenheim University.

The drying project was discontinued two years later as a result of the spectacular rise in the oil price and only small quantities were dried in the following years. In 1992 it was decided that the whole complex consisting of the dryer and pellet maker, the *Rapido* loader wagon and portioning system would have to be scrapped. Fortunately this decision was reversed at the last moment thanks to the efforts of Hermann Wandel, the university's expert on farmyard mechanisation and board member of the museum. We think it is the last complete unit and the consensus was finally reached that this unique exhibit should be reserved for the museum. However it took another 10 years for this to happen, during which time the *Apollo* spent most of its time gradually rusting away outside.

Restoration in Saulgau

The decision to carry out the restoration was certainly facilitated by the construction of a new museum building dedicated to harvesting and sponsored by Helmut Claas. The unique *Apollo* would be able to take centre stage here. During

427 Hubert Buhne is an Apollo expert, here he is dismantling the machine

428 The Rapido loader wagon nearing completion in Saulgau

the winter of 2002 / 2003 all the components of this bulky system were transported to Saulgau where it was inspected by the restoration team. The project was supervised personally by the General Manager. Individual groups were set up to restore the individual components with enthusiastic support from the apprentice shop.

429 Erwin Spehn inspects the restored cooling conveyor

Work first began on May 5, 2003 with the *Rapido*. This machine was unusual in that it was designed for working both in grass and maize. Once the crop had gone through the chopper it was offloaded just like a loader wagon. It took just a week to dismantle, following which the parts were sandblasted or sandpapered, welded, filled and painted. As is usual with this sort of project more problems were encountered than expected.

Fortunately many spare parts were available still and the drawings were also on hand for tricky situations. Other components were rebuilt by hand. Several suppliers including *EFTEKA*, *Vredestein* and *Walterscheid* provided materials and parts free of charge. The portioning system was very difficult to fix since the wooden parts had deteriorated due to the long period of open air storage.

Early in 2004 the other components including the huge drying unit with its engine, burner and the pellet press were started on. Whilst we decided not to restore everything to a usable condition, we thought it would be important to render the drying drum serviceable for demonstration purposes. At this point some colleagues were detached from Harsewinkel for the disassembly and rebuilding of the *Apollo* drying unit.

Part of the work had to be transferred to the engineering test shop since this was the only place

430 *The Agricultural Museum (DLM) near Stuttgart, a well known meeting point*

with suitable 3.2 tonne overhead gantry cranes to manoeuvre the drying drum. The worst job was cleaning the inside of the drying drum because it was cramped and extremely dusty in there.

Finally the whole restored set of equipment was assembled on the factory yard exactly as it was when it was new. The date was May 27, 2004. After it had been photographed the unit was shipped to Hohenheim, with part of the transport requiring special low loaders. When the new museum building was opened on June 9, 2004 the *Apollo* was definitely the centre of attraction and has stayed so ever since.

Martin Beckmann, Günter Schlagenhauf

Harvesting takes pride of place at Hohenheim

Hohenheim, home to the *German Agriculture Museum* (or *Deutsches Landwirtschaftsmuseum*), is the first of its kind with a building dedicated to cereals and forage harvesting. The concrete and wood structure is 900 m² in area and the roof which goes up to eight metres in height can house the large exhibits and also fits in nicely with the overall look of the campus. The architect was instructed to design a functional building which wouldn't be out of place in rural surroundings. When you enter the building your attention centres on the last surviving *Claas Apollo* displayed prominently in the middle. This piece of history is impressive both in size and the quality of the restoration. It also brings to mind how this project fascinated both the farming and the scientific communities in the 1970s.

The *McCormick* reaper from 1831 is another outstanding exhibit, because it started the era of

432 *General view of the Hohenheim harvest building*

mechanisation of the cereals harvest and is the forerunner of the *Epple-Buxbaum* type of reaper and the *Lanz-Wery* reaper-trusser. Early threshing is depicted with flails, threshing sledges,

431 *Poster for the opening of the new harvest exhibit in Hohenheim*

433 McCormick reaper from 1831

By the mid-1950s the pull type combine era was coming to an end with farmers impressed by the performance of self-propelled units represented here by the *Massey Harris 726* built in 1953. The *Claas Huckepack* was another invention which they scrutinised closely, although it never really caught on. Its history has been described in detail on page 53 ff. On the other hand *Claas* combines such as the *Columbus* or *Mercur* were extremely successful as were the small farmer combines such as the *IH 8-61* and *Deere-Lanz 150* which sold in large numbers as harvest mechanisation became a universal requirement in the 1960s.

stationary threshing machines (*Lanz*) and mobile threshers (*Dechentreiter*). Then there are three exhibits which originated in Harsewinkel. These include a so-called high-performance straw baler which really belongs to the era of the reapers. Of course no proper exhibition would be complete without the presence of the *MDB*, since this marks the beginning of the combine age. The *Claas Super* from 1951 is the first combine to be used in the region, making it of particular interest for the many visitors who come here from the surrounding countryside.

435 Claas MDB, 1936 vintage

434 Claas "High Performance" straw baler for stationary harvesters

436 Mercur self propelled Claas combine

438 Apollo in all its glory

Recent combining history is represented by a *Deutz Fahr 1002*. This one is 25 years old and spent some years as a test machine for Hohenheim University. With 2,900 litres grain tank and 3.30 metre cutting width it looks smart and – in common with most exhibits here – is a runner. In response to many requests, the combine department has been supplemented recently with a *Claas Dominator*. With this move the most successful combine of the period has made its first entry into a museum.

Even if the grass harvesting exhibits are relatively small, mowers from *Epple-Buxbaum, Krupp* and *Lanz* are significant, as are the *Niemeyer-Heuma* and *Bautz* brand rake swathers. Whilst they each have different functions, they all contributed to taking the backbreaking effort out of farmers' lives. Other milestones of this

437 Rapido loader wagon, Apollo and the cooling conveyor as centrepiece of the new museum building

439 Helmut Claas opened the historic harvest centre officially on June 9th 2004. On his left Professor Dieter Kutzbach, Dean of the Agricultural Faculty of Hohenheim University and on the right, Dr. Klaus Herrmann, DLM Director

genre are, for instance, the first generation loader wagon, the Weichsel Hamster plus the Speiser trailed forager, the original *Jaguar*. The *Claas* self propelled *Jaguar* is represented by the *SF 60* exhibit, much to the joy of many of our guests. Thanks to support from the *Claas* team in Saulgau, Klaus Haegele, Erwin Spehn and Anton Meier, the whole *Apollo* set up has been positioned where everyone can look at it from all sides.

The exhibition is rounded off with full size cut-aways from the University's Agricultural Institute and a historical wall chart with 33 large depictions from the history of farming. The harvest centre of the museum sponsored both by Dr. Helmut Claas and the *Claas* Company, breaks new ground in museum design and we are pleased with the positive response we've had from our guests. This shows that we are on the right track with our approach which focuses on originality of the exhibits.

KLAUS HERRMANN

441 The Rapido in the new hall of harvesting

440 The Claas team responsible for rebuilding the Apollo pose with the exhibit in Hohenheim

Collectibles for All Ages

Models come in all shapes and sizes and different versions are available for children, fans of the brand and collectors alike. *CLAAS* has many years of experience in working with specialised manufacturers around the world to produce a highly desirable range of products in all shapes and sizes. Not only are these models available in the *CLAAS* shop and at many dealer outlets, they are also popular items in toy shops and the like. We trace the history of the development of models from simple beginnings ending up with today's highly realistic range.

There is a long tradition of model making in Germany in general, and in the Nurnberg region in particular. The origins of the farm equipment model range go back over more than 50 years.

The first reasonably accurate model was made of plastic and came from a German company called *Wiking*. In 1951 the first large-scale models for farming equipment were produced for *Hanomag* and *Normag* on 1:40 and 1:25 scale which soon became the standard for the sort of models from other manufacturers too.

442 Early Columbus kit turned up in the 1990s

By 1966 over 30 different plastic models had been created by a variety of manufacturers for 17 different farm equipment manufacturers. The accuracy of these promotional models was nothing like the metal and wooden models sold by model shops to retail customers at that time. During all this time there was just one miniature combine in Germany which was created by the *Rex* Company on the basis of a *Lanz* design.

The *Claas Columbus* model based on early plastic promotional models

A second attempt to make a combine harvester model had in fact been made in the 1950s. This was based on the *Claas Columbus* and the result was a highly detailed miniature on a scale of 1:50. The cutter bar came complete with a rotating reel and tines and the intake auger turned as well. This version had a grain tank with a fixed discharge auger. The large cooling air screen and filter were made to look just like they were on the typical *VW* engine layout. Both the rounded cover and the mounting plate on which the petrol engine was fixed can be identified on the model. However, no attempt was made to reproduce the engine.

In the 1990s an antique auctioneer called *Brinckmann* based in Paderborn was found to be selling this model as a kit. According to him it had never gone into production and he proclaimed that "this was one of the first plastic precision models made after 1945". Both the scale that was advertised and the model name were incorrect, which could be excused since this person was really an antique dealer. The customer received all the individual parts in a plastic bag. Assembly was accompanied simply by a photograph and two side views on the assembly instructions which were printed on cardboard.

Matchbox Matador from 1967

In 1959 the well known toy maker *Matchbox* in England started production of combine models based on an *MF* design, followed closely by

443 Early Matchbox Matador Gigant with unusual paint scheme

444 Gama models were of a high standard as these early Dominator models shows

Corgi in 1960. In 1967 *Matchbox* went on to produce a model of the *Claas Matador Standard* on a scale of 1:75. Over the years, model makers have found it difficult to adhere closely to corporate identity and accurate scale. This one, for instance, was painted red. When measuring the wheelbase the scale changed to 1:106. The reel rotated on the otherwise rigid cutter bar and there was no steering wheel fitted.

At the same time *Matchbox* came up with a second *Claas* model in their King Size range. The *Matador Gigant* served as the base and was reduced on a scale of 1:66 measured by the wheelbase. The proportions were much more accurate than on the smaller version and a tiny *Matchbox* driver was seated at the wheel. The hollow discharge auger could even be swivelled. This model was sold in three different dark green colours which were nothing like the original plus a red version. All of these models had the *Claas* logo including the famous round knotter symbol. These were simple, low-cost models for a mass-market and were some way off the quality expected from collectors.

The first real *Claas* models from *Gama*

Model building in Germany was spearheaded by names which are still familiar today such as *Schuco*, *Märklin* and *Wiking*. *Gama* is also one of these, founded in 1882 by Georg Adam Mangold, whose name lives on abbreviated in the company title. *Gama* produced metal toys up until the 1960s when plastic and die cast models were then added in the nick of time. During

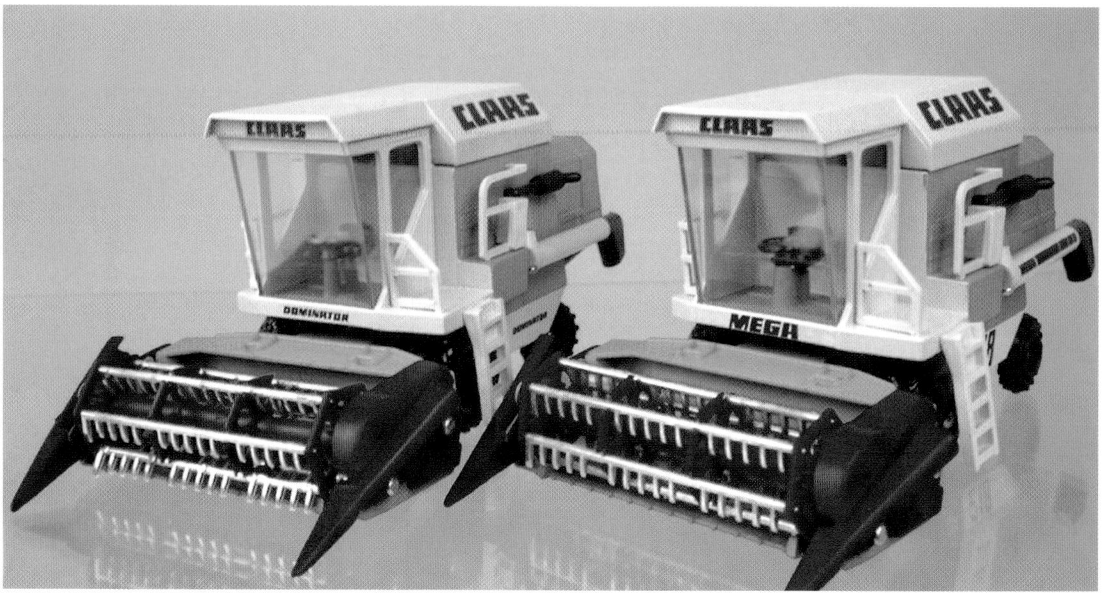

445 These Dominator 8 series models set new detailing standards

the 1970s *Gama* developed close relationships with *Claas* and many interesting products evolved from this cooperation.

For instance the *Dominator 100* combine was reproduced on a 1:50 scale. This was a die cast model with a green cab, the three side window panels were well detailed and the flat profile, off-white roof clearly identifiable. The plastic steps came complete with open handrails whilst the height adjustable cutter bar featured three reel sections and a rotating multifinger intake auger. The reel was also detailed with metal tine bars. For the first time a *Claas* model became available with prominent crop dividers. The *Gama 423* model could be steered by a knob fitted over the air filter.

Gama then updated the model with the changeover to the *Dominator 105*. They paid a lot of attention to detail with the changeover, including the new two section side window design and kept the line with the engine cowling and grain tank. The handrails on the steps had be-

446 Dominator model in MF livery for North America

come smaller and so they were left out of the new model. The roof panel included the folding edges which were a prominent part of the new design. The engine compartment was completely redone in line with the original, the exhaust was modelled accurately with a separate section and the wheelbase was lengthened.

The model was given a new number – 2331 – to demonstrate that it was a completely new product, although the wheels and cutter bar had been taken over from the previous model. It was just given the name of *Dominator* with no number.

Another review was made following the introduction of the *Dominator 8* series. This product upgrade introduced the next range of cabs, whilst other changes made by the model maker were more superficial. The forward pillar was narrowed and painted black to emphasise the panoramic nature of the cab design. *Gama* didn't

447 Forager models from Gama – the SF 80 with the later 600 series on the left

make separate glass sections, since the 90° bend came close enough to reality. The modified side glass panels were included as was the cab roof design which had been modified noticeably once again. The colour scheme was also changed, since the cab was now painted white. This model kept going for a long time and in the 1990s was still popular as the *Mega 218*.

There had been combine models in blue for the North American market during the coorporation with *Ford*. When *Claas* signed the distribution agreement with *MF* in North America, a further model variant was introduced. This time the *Gama* model was also produced in red livery and called the *MF 8460* alongside the standard version.

In the 1970s a *Jaguar* self-propelled forage harvester from *Gama* took its place on the same lines as the *Dominator*. The *SF 80* model and a green cab located on the left with a flat roof and three side windows similar to the *Dominator 100* model. The engine cover was flat and the model could also be steered by a knob over the air filter. At first it had the number 428 which was later changed into 2332. The model was fitted with a maize header.

448 Large plastic model of the flagship Commandor 116 CS

449 Beautifully engineered Atles tractor model by Bruder

The forager was also updated on a regular basis in line with the product. When the *Jaguar 600* series took over, a lot of changes were made. The maize header was modified, the cab moved to the centre and given the new roof design in line with the real thing. The lines fell away towards the rear and gave a good likeness to the actual machine.

Apart from the 1:50 models *Gama* also added other products which were linked to *Claas*. These included a red single axle loader wagon with a white forage extension on top, the *Rollant 62* round baler, a six rotor tedder and a conventional baler.

The *Commandor 116* was the top of the line combine and deserved its own model, which it got with a large 1:27 version. This was made almost completely of plastic and in line with increased combine size the cutter bar was removable so a trailer became part of the package. The crop dividers were also correctly detailed whilst the reel was divided into four sections and fitted with metal tine bars. Behind this the multifinger intake auger was fitted.

This model could also be steered with the knob which also doubled up as the air filter. This version was fitted with steerable wheels, in contrast with the smaller models where the axle was rigid and the whole unit pivoted. In common with the 1:50 scale models the rear access ladder could be lowered.

Rugged and accurate models from *Bruder*

The *Bruder* Company has usually specialised in larger scale models. The company brought out their first model for *Claas* in 1986. This was based on the contemporary *Dominator*. This model which is still available today was made to 1:24 scale. The *Claas Lexion 480* followed in 1998 with an opening grain tank and cutter bar trailer on 1:20 scale. Following this in April 2002 this company came out with their first 1:16 scale model of the *Rollant 250 RC* round baler. The next entry to the market was in 2003 with a *Jaguar* 1:16 scale model fitted with a maize header and partially glazed cabin. With the completion of the *Renault Agriculture* takeover, the *Claas Atles 935 RZ* tractor was selected for modelling in 2004 and this is a superb model with all the glass panels, opening doors and high-quality finish, as the picture shows. In addition *Bruder* offer a mini version of this model as a key ring.

450 Jaguar 695 models from Siku with cutter bar and maize header

451 Ranger 911 T telescopic handler

A brief encounter with *Britains*

Britains originated in England and managed to gain broad acceptance of their 1:32 scale which was adopted by *Hausser* with *Siku* following in 1983. This was thanks to their very broad range of tractor and implement models. In 1988 the *Claas Jaguar 690* was launched as a battery driven version in the Powerfarm range. This model was discontinued a year later, after which it was offered without the electric motor. It came with a pick-up, a properly glazed cabin and looked very good. From 1988 *Britains* added a tipping trailer in *Claas* colours on their own initiative.

Another model worthy of note was the *Valmet 8950* tractor which appeared in *Claas* colours with a white cab during the period in which the company had close links with *Claas* in several European markets.

Siku advance from toys to collectors' models

This company was originally set up by Richard Sieper in 1921 and whilst originating as a foundry they occupied themselves with thermoplastic processing as early as 1937. The company attempted to break into the toy market in 1951, followed by a vehicle range in 1954. They switched over to die cast models in 1963 and following the lead set by *Britains* they launched a 1:32 Farmer range 20 years later which was a direct competitor to *Britains*.

It was only in the 1990s that *Claas* products were included in their model line up. Alongside the *Jaguar 695 Mega* with a cutter bar there was a tipping trailer and an automatic loader wagon. In 1994 *Siku* added the *Liner 770* swather and the maize header was added to the Jaguar model.

In 1995 the *Ranger 911 T* telescopic handlers as well as a large baler were added with a round baler following a year later. *The Lexion 480* was introduced shortly afterwards with a 1:20 scale tipper trailer made of plastic and even a triple mower combination.

In 1998 *Siku* embarked on a programme to improve the detail accuracy of their Farmer range, for instance by the addition of glass panels to the cabs. The *Xerion 3000* also benefited from this improved model building standard with a cab which emulated the three positions of the real machine. The Dutch farm model collectors club *LCN* ordered a special edition of the *Xerion* model as a *Xerion 2500* and *Siku* finally added the *Rollant 250 RC* to its extensive farm equipment range.

In 2003 *Siku* upgraded the *Lexion 480* model by adding full glass panels to the cab, exemplary interior detail and mirrors. The cutter bar was improved and the ladder complete with hand rail were properly detailed. To mark the 400,000[th] combine a special edition was produced with metallic silver paint finish.

The *Targo* telescopic handler was another new product which *Siku* managed to model successfully and additionally built a 1:58 version.

Tim

This is one of the many new companies based in China. This one offers the *Lexion 480* as a simplified toy based on the *Siku* model 4150.

Large scale belt drive tractors from *NZG*

The *NZG* Company was founded Nurnberg by two former employees of the *Gescha-Strenco* Company in 1968. Their most important customers for many years were *Caterpillar* and their German distributor *Zeppelin*. It doesn't come as

452 Smart Cat Lexion model with belt drive

453 Collector's MDB model from Norscot behind a Lanz tractor

a surprise that *NZG* focused on *Cat* models which included a 1:16 version of the *Challenger* belt drive tractor from 1997. When *Claas* got involved with marketing the *Challenger* in Europe, the *Claas Challenger 45* model was not long in coming. The model was an impressive 34 cm long with a good-looking belt drive and fully detailed rear lifting system.

Collectors' models from *Norscot*

This company based in America originally specialised in merchandising for *Caterpillar*. Following this they took over the marketing for the *Cat* die cast miniature range exclusively. When *Claas* and *Cat* joined forces new models were added such as the 1:32 version of the big *Challenger 85E* belt drive tractor in *Claas* livery.

The small 1:64 scale is popular in North America so the *Claas Challenger 55* and the *Lexion 480* with belt drive were both produced and adapted to the local conditions with a *Cat Lexion 485* version with the yellow paint scheme. Another two 1:32 models were added in 2001. The first of these is the best *Jaguar 880* forage harvester model to date with a removable pick-up. The second is an attempt to revive the past with a model of the 1936 *MDB* on which the whole *Claas* success story begins. This model is extremely finely detailed with an accurate cutter bar design including the apron, the main housing complete with the bagging stand and the straw baler. The 1:64 range was rounded off with the introduction of the *Claas Challenger 75* model in 2002.

Norscot later fitted the *Jaguar* model with the *RU 600* row independent maize header started production of the popular 1:32 scale *Lexion 580* in 2004. This updated version features a highly accurate copy of the design and colour scheme.

The latest *Jaguar* from *Westend*

Another recent addition was shown in the first time at the 2003 *AGRITECHNICA* exhibition. The *Jaguar 900* model has been made by this supplier to the same standard as the *Norscot* ones and features a removable maize attachment. This can even be interchanged with the *RU 600* attachment on the Norscot model.

High-quality *Claas* tractor models from *Universal Hobbies*

This producer is based in France with a background of working for *Renault*. In 2001 they started with a 1:32 scale model of the *Renault Atles* tractor and followed this with other *Renault* models including the *Celtis*. After the takeover by *Claas* the appropriate model was quickly adapted to the new look.

454 The Norscot Jaguar 880 and more recent Westend Jaguar 900 model with interchangeable headers

455 Four models, four producers: Celtis – Universal Hobbies; Challenger 85 – Norscot; Valtra – Britains; Xerion 3000 – Siku

French models from *CTF*

This company began in 1997 and specialised in extremely finely detailed 1:32 scale models. Among these we find the *Matador Gigant* and then the *Matador Standard* combines. Since then their name has changed to Tractoys, but they continue to produce the models to the same high standard including the Europa combine, which also comes on the 1:32 scale. The model is available in both green and metallic silver colours and is based on the diesel engined version.

Tyro Toys

The company produces models branded Tyroller in Bavaria and is currently the only producer of trailed *Claas* combine models. The range of 1:32 scale models includes the *Super* and the *Junior* versions and they can be ordered with different colour schemes.

HO scale from *Marks*

This company announced in 1994 the production of a well detailed version of the *Claas* Europa combine on this very small scale. This model was offered both in light green and silver finish. They added a version with a bagging stand in the year 2000.

Wiking led the way

The company was an early leader in the business and produced models of cars, trucks, buses, fire engines and tractors. This explains why *Wiking*, now part of *Siku*, is the only producer of high-volume assembled HO miniatures based on *Claas* products. This began with a tipper trailer which was modelled in 1995 with a *Corto 270 F* mower being added in 1997 to put on the tractor models.

Three years later in 2000 *Wiking* came up with a *Lexion 480* combine harvester model, in 2001 a *Rollant* round baler to 1:87 and 1:160 scales. The *Lexion 480* model was enhanced with a cutter bar trailer in 2002 and at the end of 2003 the triple mower was miniaturised on 1:87 basis. The company also produced a version of the *Lexion* in silver to mark the occasion of the jubilee mentioned earlier.

1:87 kits from *Kibri*

Whilst the history of this toy company can be traced back to 1895, they turned their attention to plastic products in the 1950s. In 1976 *Kibri* presented the first 1:87 scale vehicle models. *The Lexion 480* was introduced in 1998 as a kit complete with cutter bar. This was followed soon by a version with maize header plus a

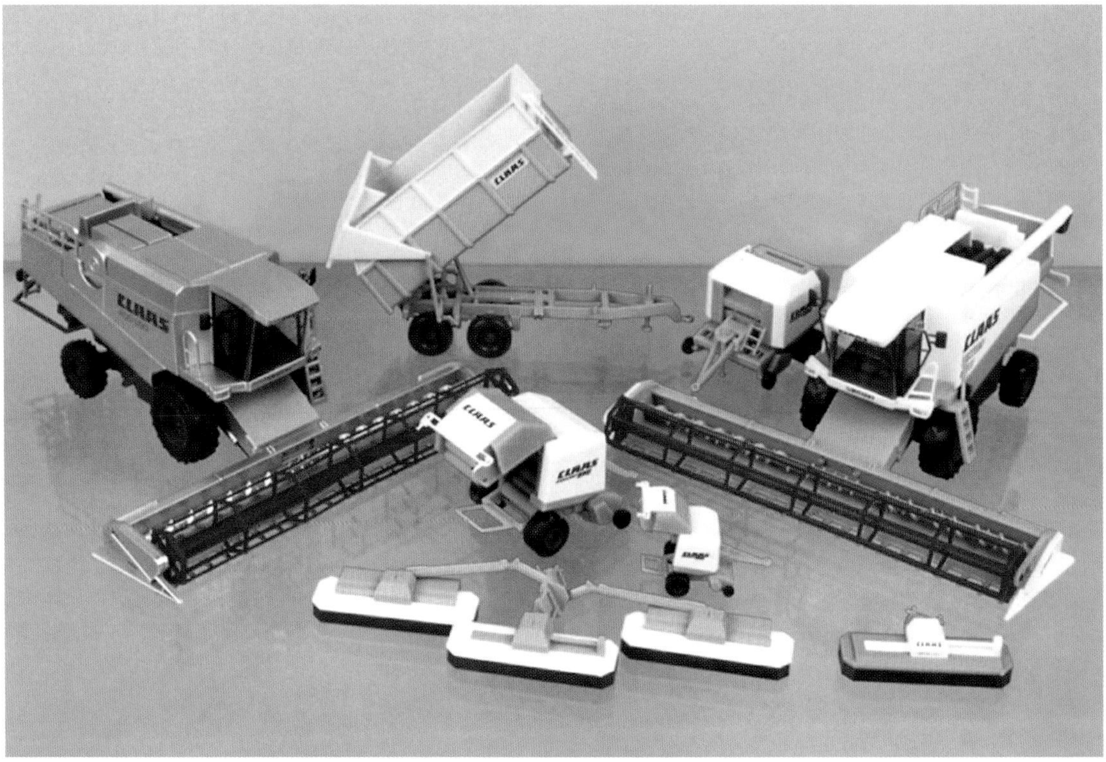

456 The Wiking range including the silver Lexion no. 400,000

model of the *Rollant* round baler, a *Cat Lexion* version with cereals cutter bar and belt drive. In 2002 the *Cat Lexion* was also given a maize header plus a special *Lexion* series in red and white which was made available for sale exclusively by the *MC* toy dealer organisation.

They also offered on their own initiative an HO scale *Jaguar* model with maize header in kit form plus a version of the *Volto 740* on the same size. In 2004 *Kibri* took on the challenge of producing a 1:160 *Lexion* model with cutter bar and a maize header to follow. The *Jaguar* range was extended with an optional cutter bar or grass pick-up.

The world of model makers knows no limits, with new farm equipment models appearing regularly to enthuse young and old and contribute to the status of farming in the community as a whole. It's encouraging to see that historical models are gaining in significance.

This review of the world in miniature also marks the end of this chronicle and if you've read everything, you will now be able to better appreciate the enormous skills and expertise of *Claas* as it has developed over the years.

Johannes Schwörzer

457 Europa combine model from CTF comes in a wooden box

Appendix

458 Claas Xerion with full implement set up

CLAAS Combine Harvester Model Register

Model	Production dates: Start	Production dates: Finish	Threshing system: Width (mm)	Threshing system: Type	Cutter bar: width (m)	Grain tank: Bagging stand	Grain tank: Capaci (l)
MDB (HT)	1936	1946			2.1	x	
Super	1946	1955	1,250		2.1	x	
Super 500	1955	1966	1,250		2.1	x	
Super Automatic	1958	1978	1,250		2.1		1,700
Junior	1953	1969	1,250		1.5	x	
Junior Automatic	1959	1973	1,250		1.8		1,100
Garant	1967	1970	1,060		2.4		1,800
Hercules	1953	1954	1,250		2.4	x	
Selbstfahrer	1955	1963	1,250		2.6	x	
Huckepack	1957	1960	800		2.1	x	
Europa	1958	1968	800		2.1	x	1,700
Columbus	1958	1970	800		1.8	x	1,100
Matador Gigant	1960	1969	1,250		3.0		2,155
Matador Standard	1962	1968	1,250		2.6	x	1,700
Mercur	1962	1968	1,060		2.6	x	1,700
Senator	1966	1972	1,250		4.2		3,200
Senator R	1968	1971	1,250		4.2		3,200
Comet	1967	1970	800		1,8		1,350
Consul	1967	1981	1,060		2.6	x	2,000
Cosmos	1967	1971	800		2.1		1,700
Protector	1968	1972	1,250		2.6	x	2,000
Corsar	1969	1975	800		2.4		1,700
Ford 620	1967	1971	1,060		2.6	x	2,000
Ford 630	1967	1970	1,250		3.6		2,700
Ford 640	1966	1972	1,250		4.2		3,200
Mercator	1967	1970	1,250		3.6	x	2,700
Mercator 50	1973	1981	1,250		2.6		2,000
Mercator 60	1973	1981	1,250		3.0		2,500
Mercator 70	1968	1974	1,250		3.6		3,000
Mercator 75	1975	1982	1,250		3.6		3,000
Mercator R	1974	1982	1,250		4.2		3,200
Compact 20	1970	1972	580		1.7		850
Compact 25	1970	1980	960		2.1		1,100
Compact 30	1975	1981	960		2.4		1,900
Dominator 80	1970	1974	1,320		4.5		3,400
Dominator 100	1971	1974	1,580		5.1		5,500
Ford 622	1971	1972	1,060		2.6		2,000
Ford 632	1971	1976	1,250		3.6		2,700
Dominator 85	1975	1980	1,320		3.9		4,000
Dominator 85 H	1976	1979	1,320		4.5		3,000
Dominator 105	1975	1981	1,580		5.1		5,500
Dominator 56	1978	1982	1,060		2.7		2,500
Dominator 66	1979	1985	1,060		3.0		2,500

ine (hp)	Separation system				Cleaning system		
	Type	No. of racks	Aera- (m²)	Separation intensifier	Sieve area (m²)	Double ven- tilated step	Turbine fan
PT	Swing motion	1	1.63		1.76		
PT	Swing motion	1	4.20		2.15		
PT	Swing motion	1	4.20		2.15		
PT	Swing motion	1	4.20		2.15		
PT	Swing motion	1	4.20		1.80		
PT	Swing motion	1	4.00		1.80		
PT	Offset motion	4	2.9/3.15		2.05		
56	Offset motion	4	3.00		0.98		
56	Offset motion	4	3.00		0.98		
2 + 34	Offset motion	3	2.20		1.26		
45	Offset motion	3	2.20		1.26		
27	Offset motion	3	1.70		1.26		
87	Offset motion	4	4.50		3.15		
62	Offset motion	4	4.00		3.15		
52	Offset motion	4	2.90		2.05		
105	Offset motion	4	4.75		3.20		
105	Offset motion	4	4.75		3.20		
29	Offset motion	3	1.70		1.26		
68	Offset motion	4	3.55		2.05		
38	Offset motion	3	2.2/2.38		1.44		
68	Offset motion	4	4.20		3.15		
52	Offset motion	3	2.70		1.56		
68	Offset motion	4	3.55		2.05		
95	Offset motion	4	4.20		3.15		
105	Offset motion	4	4.75		3.20		
95	Offset motion	4	4.20		3.15		
68	Offset motion	4	4.20		3.15		
95	Offset motion	4	4.20		3.15		
105	Offset motion	4	4.75		3.15		
105	Offset motion	4	4.75	1 IS	3.20		
105	Offset motion	4	4.75		3.20		
24	Offset motion	3	1,40		1.15		
34	Offset motion	5	2.30		1.95		
50	Offset motion	5	2.30		1.95		
120	Offset motion	5	5.15		3.30		
170	Offset motion	6	7.00		4.20		x
60	Offset motion	4	3.55		2.05		
95	Offset motion	4	4.20		3.15		
120	Offset motion	5	5.15	2 IS	3.50		
150	Offset motion	5	5.15	2 IS	3.50		
175	Offset motion	6	7.00	2 IS	4.25		
85	Offset motion	4	4.15		3.00		
102	Offset motion	4	4.15	1 IS	3.40		

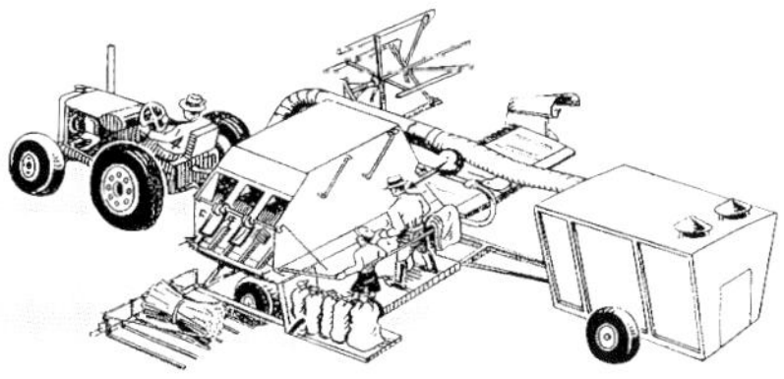

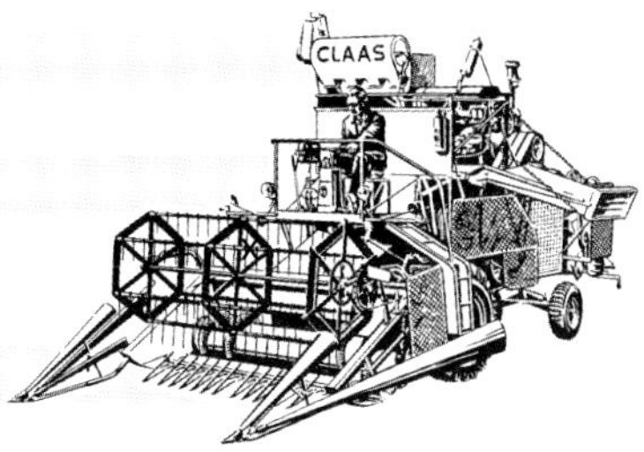

Model	Production dates		Threshing system		Cutter bar	Grain tank	
	Start	Finish	Width (mm)	Type	width (m)	Bagging stand	Capaci (l)
Dominator 76	1978	1985	1,060		3.6		4,200
Dominator 76 H	1979	1981	1,060		3.6		2,500
Dominator 76 R	1979	1979	1,060		4.5		4,200
Dominator 86	1980	1985	1,320		3.9		4,600
Dominator 96	1978	1985	1,320		4.5		5,200
Dominator 96 RABA	1982	1982	1,320		4.5		5,200
Dominator 106	1978	1987	1,580		5.1		6,500
Dominator 112 CS	1983	1985	1,320		4.5		6,000
Dominator 114 CS	1983	1985	1,320		5.1		7,000
Dominator 115 Cs	1985	1985	1,320		5.1		7,000
Dominator 116 CS	1981	1985	1,580		6.0		8,000
Ford 625	1978	1978	1,060		2.7		2,500
Ford 635	1978	1980	1,320		3.9		4,000
Ford 642	1978	1979	1,580		5.1		5,500
Ford 645	1978	1980	1,320		4.5		5,200
Ford 655	1978	1978	1,580		5.1		6,500
Dominator 76 USA	1981	1984	1,060		3.6		4,200
Dominator 96 USA	1981	1984	1,320		4.5		5,200
Dominator106 USA	1981	1985	1,580		5.1		6,500
Dominator 38	1981	1991	800		2.4		2,100
Dominator 48	1981	1994	1,060		2.6		2,400
Dominator 58	1981	2003	1,060		3.0		2,700
Dominator 68	1981	2004	1,060		3.0	x	3,200
Dominator 68 R	1986	1996	1,060		4.2		3,200
Dominator 78	1986	1998	1,060		3.6		4,200
Dominator 78 H	1989	1995	1,060		3.6		4,200
Dominator 88	1986	2000	1,320		3.9		4,600
Dominator 88 Maxi	1989	1995	1,320		3.9		5,200
Dominator 98	1985	2000	1,320		4.5		5,200
Dominator 98 H	1990	1999	1,320		4.5		5,200
Dominator 98 Maxi	1989	1995	1,320		4.5		6,200
MF 8450	1992	1993	1,320		4.5		5,200
Dominator 108	1986	2000	1,580		5.1		6,500
Dominator 108 Maxi	1989	1995	1,580		5.1		7,500
Dominator 118	1992	1994	1,580		5.1		7,500
MF 8460	1993	1995	1,580		5.1		6,500
COMMANDOR 112 CS	1987	1987	1,320		4.5		6,000
COMMANDOR 114 CS	1986	1989	1,320		5.1		7,000
COMMANDOR 115 CS	1986	1990	1,320		5.1		7,000
COMMANDOR 116 CS	1986	1991	1,580		6.0		8,000
COMMANDOR 228 CS	1992	1995	1,580		6.0		10,000
Croptiger	1990	....	500		2.1		1,200
Dominator MEGA 202	1994	1995	1,320	APS	3.9		5,200
Dominator MEGA 203	1994	1995	1,320	APS	4.5		6,200
Dominator MEGA 204	1994	1995	1,320	APS	4.5		6,200
Dominator MEGA 208	1993	1995	1,580	APS	5.1		7,500
Dominator MEGA 218	1993	1995	1,580	APS	6.0		7,500
Mega 202 II	1996	2003	1,320	APS	3.9		5,200
Mega 204 II	1996	2003	1,320	APS	4.5		6,200
Mega 208 II	1996	2003	1,580	APS	5.1		8,000
Mega 218 II	1996	2003	1,580	APS	6.0		8,000

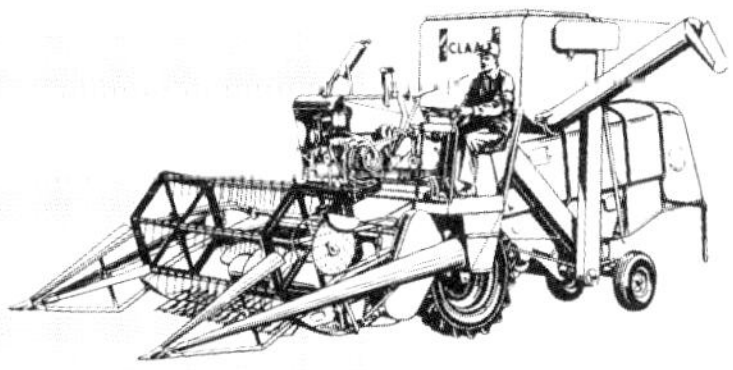

gine (hp)		Separation system			Cleaning system		
	Type	No. of racks	Aera- (m²)	Separation intensifier	Sieve area (m²)	Double ventilated step	Turbine fan
120	Offset motion	4	4.65	2 IS	3.2/3.4		
150	Offset motion	4	4.65	2 IS	3.40		
120	Offset motion	4	4.65	2 IS	3.40		
120	Offset motion	5	5.15	2 IS	4.25		
150	Offset motion	5	5.80	2 IS	4.25		
150	Offset motion	5	5.80	2 IS	4.25		
170	Offset motion	6	7.00	2 IS	5.10		x
170	8 cylinder			4.70	x	x	
221	8 cylinder			4.70	x	x	
250	8 cylinder			4.70	x	x	
276	8 cylinder			5.65	x	x	
85	Offset motion	4	4.14		3.20		
150	Offset motion	5	5.15		3.50		
170	Offset motion	6	7.00		4.20		
150	Offset motion	5	5.80		4.00		
170	Offset motion	6	7.00		4.80		x
120	Offset motion	4	4.65	2 IS	3.2/3.4		
150	Offset motion	5	5.80	2 IS	4.25		
170	Offset motion	6	7.00	2 IS	5.10		x
65	Offset motion	3	2.75		2.20		
75	Offset motion	4	3.65		3.00		
85	Offset motion	4	4.15	1 IS	3.00		
100	Offset motion	4	4.15	1 IS	3.00		
100	Offset motion	4	4.15	1 IS	3.00		
120	Offset motion	4	4.65	2 IS	3.40		
120	Offset motion	4	4.65	2 IS	3.40		
120	Offset motion	5	5.15	2 IS	4.25		
160	Offset motion	5	5.15	2 IS	4.25		
150	Offset motion	5	5.80	2 IS	4.25		
150	Offset motion	5	5.80	2 IS	4.25		
200	Offset motion	5	5,80	2 IS	4.25		
150	Offset motion	5	5.80	2 IS	4.25		
180	Offset motion	6	7.00	2 IS	5.10		x
221	Offset motion	6	7.00	2 IS	5.10		x
260	Offset motion	6	7.00	2 IS	5.10		x
180	Offset motion	6	7.00	2 IS	5.10		x
180	8 cylinder			4.70	x	x	
221	8 cylinder			4.70	x	x	
250	8 cylinder			4.70	x	x	
276	8 cylinder			5.65	x	x	
330	8 cylinder			5.65	x	x	
58	TAF			1.56			
160	Offset motion	5	5.15	2 IS	4.25		
170	Offset motion	5	5.80	2 IS	4.25		
200	Offset motion	5	5.80	2 IS	4.70	x	x
235	Offset motion	6	7.00	2 IS	5.65	x	x
270	Offset motion	6	7.00	2 IS	5.65	x	x
160	Offset motion	5	5.15	2 IS	4.25		
221	Offset motion	5	5.80	2 IS	4.70	x	x
235	Offset motion	6	7.00	2 IS	5.65	x	x
270	Offset motion	6	7.00	2 IS	5.65	x	x

Model	Production dates		Threshing system		Cutter bar	Grain tank	
	Start	Finish	Width (mm)	Type	width (m)	Bagging stand	Capaci (l)
Lexion 405	1997	2001	1,420	APS	4.5		5,500
Lexion 410	1997	2003	1,420	APS	4.5		6,300
Lexion 415	1997	2001	1,420	APS	5,4		6,500
Lexion 420	1997	2003	1,420	APS	5.4		7,300
Lexion 430	1997	2003	1,420	APS	5.4		7,800
Lexion 440	1997	2003	1,700	APS	6.0		8,100
Lexion 450	1997	2003	1,700	APS	6.6		8,600
Lexion 460	1997	2003	1,700	APS	7.5		9,600
Lexion 470	2001	2003	1,420	APS	7.5		9.600
Lexion 480	1996	2003	1,700	APS	7.5		10,500
CAT Lexion 450	1998	2002	1,420	APS	6.0		8,600
CAT Lexion 460	1998	2002	1,700	APS	7.5		9,600
CAT Lexion 465	1998	2001	1,700	APS	7.5		9,600
CAT Lexion 460R	2001	2003	1,420	APS	6.0		9,600
CAT Lexion 470R	1998	2003	1,420	APS	7.5		9,600
CAT Lexion 475R	1999	2003	1,420	APS	7.5		9,600
CAT Lexion 480R	1998	2003	1,700	APS	9.0		10,500
CAT Lexion 485R	1998	2003	1,700	APS	9.0		10,500
Medion 310	2001	.....	1,320		3.9		5,800
Medion 320	2001	2002	1,320		4.5		6,500
Medion 330	2002	....	1,320		5.1		7,200
Medion 340	2001	....	1,580		6.0		8,200
Mega 350	2004	....	1,320	APS	3.6		7,200
Mega 360	2004	....	1,580	APS	4.5		8,200
Mega 370	2005	....	1,580	APS	4.5		8,200
Dominator 130	2005	....	1,060		3.0	x	3,200
Dominator 140	2005	....	1,060		3.0		3.200
Dominator 150	2005	....	1,060		3.6		4,000
Lexion 510	2004	....	1,420	APS	4.5		7,300
Lexion 520	2004	....	1,420	APS	4.5		7,800
Lexion 530	2004	....	1,420	APS	5,4		8,600
Lexion 540C	2004	....	1,700	APS	5.4		8,100
Lexion 540	2004	....	1,700	APS	6.0		8,600
Lexion 550	2004	....	1,700	APS	6.0		9,600
Lexion 560	2004	....	1,700	APS	6.6		10,500
Lexion 570	2004	....	1,420	APS	7.5		9,600
Lexion 580	2004	....	1,700	APS	9.0		10,500
CAT Lexion 560	2004	....	1,420	APS	7.5		10,500
CAT Lexion 560R	2004	....	1,420	APS	7.5		10,500
CAT Lexion 570R	2004	....	1,420	APS	7.5		10,500
CAT Lexion 575R	2004	....	1,420	APS	7.5		10,500
CAT Lexion 580R	2004	....	1.420	APS	9.0		11,800
CAT Lexion 585R	2004	....	1,420	APS	9.0		11,800
CAT Lexion 590R	2004	....	1,700	APS	12.0		12,500

October 2004

APS: Acceleration and Pre-Separation

gine (hp)	Separation system				Cleaning system		
	Type	No. of racks	Aera- (m²)	Separation intensifier	Sieve area (m²)	Double ven- tilated step	Turbine fan
170	Offset motion	5	5.54	2 IS	4.40		
190	Offset motion	5	5.54	2 IS	4.40		
200	Offset motion	5	6.25	2 IS	4.80	x	x
220	Offset motion	5	6.25	2 IS	4.80	x	x
240	Offset motion	5	6.25	2 IS	4.80	x	x
250	Offset motion	6	7.48	2 IS	5.80	x	x
275	Offset motion	6	7.48	2 IS	5.80	x	x
300	Offset motion	6	7.48	2 IS	5.80	x	x
339	Twin rotor			4.80	x	x	
375	Twin rotor			5.80	x	x	
256	Offset motion	5	6.25	2 IS	4.80	x	x
290	Offset motion	6	7.48	2 IS	5.80	x	x
290	Offset motion	6	7.48	2 IS	5.80	x	x
290	Twin rotor			4.80	x	x	
340	Twin rotor			4.80	x	x	
340	Twin rotor			4.80	x	x	
400	Twin rotor			5.80	x	x	
400	Twin rotor			5.80	x	x	
196	Offset motion	5	5.80	2 IS	4.25		
200	Offset motion	5	5.80	2 IS	4.25		
220	Offset motion	5	5.80	2 IS	4.25		
258	Offset motion	6	7.00	2 IS	5.10		x
231	Offset motion	5	5.80	2 IS	4.25	x	x
258	Offset motion	6	7.00	2 IS	5.10	x	x
279	Offset motion	6	7.00	2 IS	5.10	x	x
121	Offset motion	4	4.15	1 IS	3.00		
121	Offset motion	4	4.15	1 IS	3.00		
141	Offset motion	4	4.15	1 IS	3.00		
220	Offset motion	5	6.25	MSS	4.40		
260	Offset motion	5	6.25	MSS	4.80	x	x
286	Offset motion	5	6.25	MSS	4.80	x	x
260	Offset motion	6	7.48	MSS	5.80	x	x
286	Offset motion	6	7.48	MSS	5.80	x	x
321	Offset motion	6	7.48	MSS	5.80	x	x
340	Offset motion	6	7.48	MSS	5.80	x	x
401	Twin rotor			4.80	x	x	
480	Twin rotor			5.80	x	x	
290	Offset motion	5	6.25	MSS	4.80	x	x
290	Twin rotor			4.80	x	x	
340	Twin rotor			4.80	x	x	
340	Twin rotor			4.80	x	x	
400	Twin rotor			5.10	x	x	
400	Twin rotor			5.10	x	x	
462	Twin rotor			6.20	x	x	

TAF: Tangential-Axial-Flow

IS: Intensive Separation
MSS: Multifinger Separation System

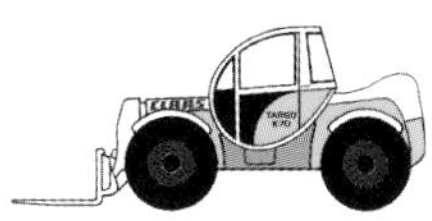
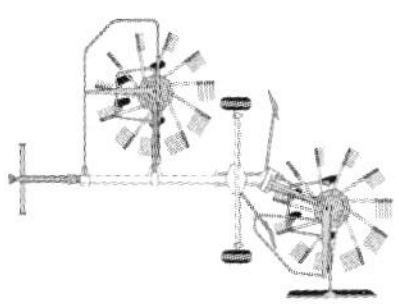

CLAAS Historic Timeline

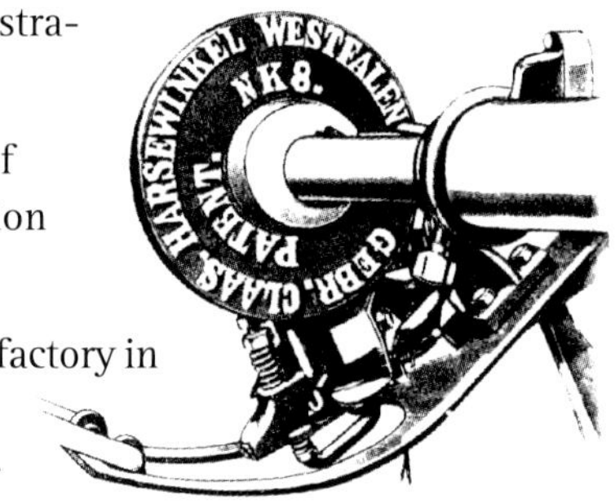

460 The patented Claas knotter was unmistakable

1913 August Claas applies to the Herzebrock authorities for registration of his company in Clarholz.

1914 The commercial court in Rheda confirms the registration of Bernhard, August and Franz Claas Jr. and their incorporation as *Claas Bros.*

1919 On July 7th the *Claas brothers* purchase the defunct brick factory in Harsewinkel for 13,000 Marks and following the physical transfer of the company, they commence straw trusser production.

1921 First Claas patent on an improved knotter for reliable straw binding.

1922 First representative – Wilhelm Kock – takes up a franchise in Hamburg.

Business relationship established with *Trier & Küas* in Wiesbaden, later Trier, *Fils & Cie* in Paris.

1923 First plant expansion with the addition of four new assembly buildings.

Company first in England with *Claas* products exhibited at the Royal Show.

1924 First presentation of *Claas* products at the DLG show, which took place this year in Hamburg.

The *Claas* brand straw trusser is awarded the prime silver DLG medal during the DLG congress.

Production of fertiliser spreaders commences.

1928 The firm set up their own tool making activity.

Death of Franz Claas Senior on May 15th.

1929 *Claas* machines are displayed at the World Fair in Barcelona.

1930 Professor Vormfelde of the Bonn University Agricultural Institute firms up plans with August Claas to build the first European style combine, followed by Dr. Walter Brenner's move to Harsewinkel.

Production of straw trusser no. 10,000 on July 19th.

1932 The 15,000th straw trusser (*Claas Patent Fortschritt*) leaves the assembly line.

First field trial with front cutting combine.

1934 The first *pick-up* baler is built.

1935 Production of the 20,000th Claas straw trusser on October 15th.

1936 Introduction of the *Claas MDB*, the first combine harvester built in and for Europe. The pull type combine is successfully tried out – Victory of Zschernitz – in East Germany and then is ready to go into production.

1937 The straw trusser sales continue to boom with number 35,000 coming out this year.

1939 August Claas announces the creation of the *Claas* old age and widows' pension fund.

Outbreak of war on September 1st. Forerunner of the company journal "Der Knoter" which is sent to the *Claas* soldiers called up for military service.

459 Smoking chimneys in 1930 indicate high activity levels

1942 Production of the 1,000th *MDB* combine.

Development of the *Super* combine takes shape with first prototypes being tested a year later.

1943 The company is ordered to cease production and switch over to supporting the military effort by making shell and bullet cases.

1945 Capitulation of the 3rd Reich quickly followed by start of production of seed drills.

1946 First Emergency Harvest Action in the Rhine valley around Aachen and introduction of the *Super* combine.

1947 First 13 combines exported to England following confiscation and evaluation by the British authorities of a Super the year before.

Repeat of the Emergency Harvest Action.

1948 Topping out at the "*Christophorus Hütte*", a foundry near to Harsewinkel as reconstruction starts in earnest.

"*Der Knoter*" makes its appearance as the staff journal.

1949 Accumulated unit sales now add up to 100,000 consisting of spreaders, seed drills, straw balers, trussers and of course combines.

1950 August and Helmut Claas visit South America (Argentina, Brazil, Uruguay) to see the products in the field first hand and start recruiting distributors. Successful field operation with *Claas* combines in Brazil.

464 Founding father August Claas (1887 to 1992) with his son Helmut as Franz Claas Senior (1859 to 1928) looks on. Photo shot in 1969

1952 Majority of combines are now sold abroad with 1,500 *Super* sales to the UK alone.

Hercules, the company's first self propelled combine harvester, is presented to coincide with August Claas' 65th birthday and goes into volume production in 1953.

1953 The *Super Junior* is added as a smaller version of the *Super* combine.

1954 The *Claas Super* gets an enthusiast reception in South Africa.

1955 Launch of the *SF 55* combine harvester.

1956 The Paderborn axle and transmission plant is inaugurated.

1957 The *Huckepack* comes onto the market.

1958 The self propelled combine range is augmented with the *Europa* and *Columbus* models.

1961 Phase out of the *SF* combine and launch of the *Matador*.

1962 Production starts at the new baler plant in Metz, France.

Helmut Claas is appointed to the board of the company.

The 100,000th combine leaves the plant.

1963 The *Mercur* is lauched to broaden the *Europa* combine offering.

1966 The *Matador Gigant* receives a gold medal in Moscow.

Launch of new look *Senator* combine with styling and new light green livery in Europe, introduced as the *Ford 640* in North America in blue.

461 Bronze DLG medal awarded for the Super

462 Silver DLG medal went to the Super Junior

463 The self propelled combine was distinguished with gold

465 August Claas opening the Claas rail terminal in Harsewinkel in 1966

1967 The *Consul* is launched with integral chassis as well as the *Mercator.*

1968 Combine number 200,000 is handed over to a farmer in Scotland.

The *Claas* machine tool and plant division (*CFT*) is founded.

1969 Addition of a full forage harvest equipment range following takeover of the *Josef Bautz* Company in Saulgau plus the *Jaguar* technology and name from the *Speiser* Company.

1970 The most successful combine range ever is heralded by the introduction of the *Dominator 80.*

1971 The development of the sugar cane harvester opens up new markets in tropical and sub tropical regions.

1972 Contract signed with the Algerian government for local production of the *Mercator* under licence.

1973 The first *Jaguar* self propelled forage harvester sees the light of day.

1976 *Claas* launches the first round baler – the *Rollant* family is born.

1978 The company opens links to the Peoples' Republic of China with an exhibition in Beijing. In 1979 *Claas* gets a large order for a range of machines including combines.

The *Dominator 6* series is launched.

The company is turned into an "oHG" or unlimited company with Helmut Claas as Managing Director.

1982 Incorporation of the foundries under the mantle of *Claas Guss.*

Joint venture agreement signed with *Escorts* in India for production and marketing of the *Crop Tiger* combine.

1983 Launch of the next generation *Jaguar 600* series.

1984 The *Dominator CS* forced separation combine becomes the new flagship, later it evolves into the *Commandor* range.

The *CMG* is the mantle for a newly established employee share owning scheme which accumulates a large volume of capital over the years.

1985 Presentation of the *Dominator 78* to *108* range.

1986 New domestic sales and service company (*Claas Vertriebsgesellschaft*) is inaugurated.

1988 Premiere of the *Quadrant* large square baler.

1992 New plant opened in nearby Beelen for expansion of the company's machine tool and plant manufacturing division *Claas Fertigungstechnik.*

Opening of the *Technoparc* in Harsewinkel, the corporate visitors' centre and museum.

1993 Launch of the *Mega* combine range with the advanced *APS* threshing system.

Jaguar 800 series carries on the self propelled forager success story.

1994 Development of *AGROCOM* initiated to provide farmers and contractors with IT based decision making tools.

466 Helmut Claas, large scale farmer and contractor

1995 The Lexion range is rapidly recognised as the highest performing combine ever with hourly throughputs of 40 t/h and more. Therefore, an entry into the *Guiness World Records* was made.
The company is transformed into *Claas KGaA* (share owning partnership).

1996 The Harsewinkel, Paderborn and Metz plants are turned into independent operating units.

1997 Takeover of the factory in Törökszentmiklos, Hungary and creation of the wholly owned *Claas* Hungaria subsidiary. Manufacture of assemblies such as cutter bars concentrated here.
Factory remodelling in Saulgau completed and new painting centre inaugurated .

1998 Construction of the Parts Logistics Centre in conjunction with *Stute Verkehrslogistik* begins in Hamm and takes up operation in 2000.
Restructuring of *AGROCOM* with focus on the whole spectrum of agricultural IT solutions and relocation to Bielefeld.
The *Lexion* is voted "machine of the year" by the farming press.

1999 Inauguration of the *Claas* Foundation with support for promising farm graduates.
Completion of the new combine plant in Omaha, Nebraska.
Creation of a new financing arm *Claas Financial Services SAS* or *CFS* for short.

2000 The *Jaguar 800* range is updated incorporating many new features to reinforce global market leadership.
First *Claas* bale wrapper / baler combination – *the Uniwrap* – makes its debut.

2001 Phase out of the *Dominator* name which lives on inside the updated *Medion* range.
Groundbreaking for comprehensive factory overhaul and modernisation programme in Harsewinkel which takes till 2003 to complete.

2003 The product range is strengthened with the addition of tractors following the acquisition of *Renault Agriculture* assets.
Combine number 400,000 – a *Lexion 480* – leaves the plant.
Presentation of the new *Lexion 500* series at the *AGRITECHNICA* in Hanover.

2004 The 20,000th self propelled forager is produced .
Groundbreaking for new combine plant in Krasnodar, Russia.

Selected by: Martin Beckmann, Ludwig Caspers, Horst-Dieter Görg, Wilhelm Kemper

467 Main entrance to company HQ in Harsewinkel with showcase Lexion combine

CLAAS World harvest schedule

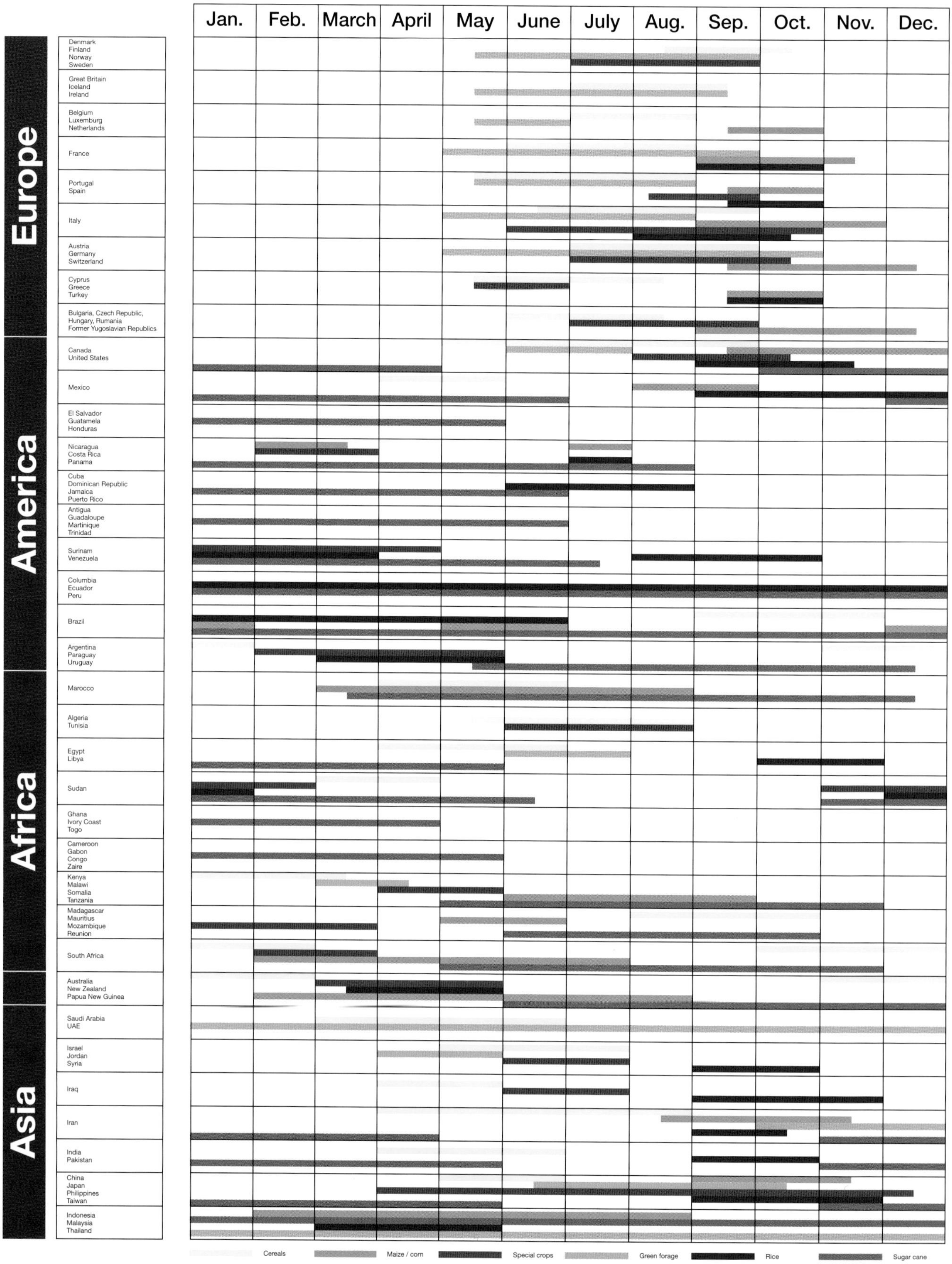

Jan.
Feb.
March
April
May
June
July
Aug.
Sep.
Oct.
Nov.
Dec.
Europe
Denmark Finland Norway Sweden
Great Britain Iceland Ireland
Belgium Luxemburg Netherlands
France
Portugal Spain
Italy
Austria Germany Switzerland
Cyprus Greece Turkey
Bulgaria, Czech Republic, Hungary, Rumania Former Yugoslavian Republics
America
Canada United States
Mexico
El Salvador Guatamela Honduras
Nicaragua Costa Rica Panama
Cuba Dominican Republic Jamaica Puerto Rico
Antigua Guadaloupe Martinique Trinidad
Surinam Venezuela
Columbia Ecuador Peru
Brazil
Argentina Paraguay Uruguay
Africa
Marocco
Algeria Tunisia
Egypt Libya
Sudan
Ghana Ivory Coast Togo
Cameroon Gabon Congo Zaire
Kenya Malawi Somalia Tanzania
Madagascar Mauritius Mozambique Reunion
South Africa
Australia New Zealand Papua New Guinea
Asia
Saudi Arabia UAE
Israel Jordan Syria
Iraq
Iran
India Pakistan
China Japan Philippines Taiwan
Indonesia Malaysia Thailand
Cereals
Maize / corn
Special crops
Green forage
Rice
Sugar cane

Take no risks – demand original CLAAS parts

467 The world harvest schedule

Acknowledgements

Firstly we would like to thank all of our contributing authors, many of whom provided not only texts but also photographic material.

At Claas we were assisted by Paul Curzon, Martin Dammann, Simone Engelmeier, Helmut Homberg, Ingo Lindenblatt, Eva-Maria Mense, Henning-Christian Paulsen, Nicole Samol, Konrad Siegers, Barbara Schlickbernd, Andrea Schwarze, Simone Suder and Stephan Vormbrock.

We wish to mention the contributions made by former employees including Dr. Gustav Ackermann, Günther Danker, Karl Düpjohann, Franz Grothues, Josef Hügelmeyer, Folkert Krull, Heinrich Schlingmann, Robert Schocke and Helmut Wiesner with their various ideas, pictures and other tips.

Dieter Althoff painted the introductory water paintings for us.

Ursula Wendorf and Dr. Rudolf Haberland provided us with documents on "Victory at Zschernitz" along with Christa Söte née Specht who helped with the details on her father Bernhard.

A number of pictures were acquired from Eckhard Möller from the Harsewinkel archives.

Jacques Gouet was of assistance with the history of Renault Agriculture, in particular thanks to his Encyclopaedia of the Renault Tractor.

The team led by Andreas Asche at the Phoenix advertising agency in Laatzen worked overtime to produce the creative layout, enhance the pictures and create the text.

Peter Seifried as the lecturer of the German Chronicle. Willi Heinemann, Jürgen Lining, Matthias Meiburg, Manfred Wagner and Josef Meier Westmeier for technical and editorial consulting.

The Mundschenk Druck- und Verlagsgesellschaft for print production.

Finally thanks to our families who supported us patiently during this production period.

Harsewinkel July 2005

Horst-Dieter Görg, Wilhelm Kemper

List of Contributors

Here is a brief thumbnail of the contributors, most of whom worked for *CLAAS* and are now in retirement. They are listed alphabetically with their year of birth, what they did and where they are now. If you would like to know more and contact any of them, please contact Horst Biere at *CLAAS*. His E-mail address is included below.

1. Bernd Albrecht, 1940, most recently Manager at *CLAAS Parts Distribution*, passed away a few months after the chronicle was completed

2. Martin Beckmann, 1965, employed in production planning / technical services at the *CLAAS* plant in Harsewinkel

3. Hasso Bertram, 1936 worked in basic research at *CLAAS* from 1968 to 1975 including the Apollo project, later magazine editor. Retired and living in Dexheim near Mainz

4. Horst Biere, 1948, is responsible for corporate communication for the *CLAAS Group*, lives in Oerlinghausen, (biere@claas.com)

5. Bernard Blömer, 1939, former *CLAAS Group* Service Manager lives in Harsewinkel, retired

6. Stefan Böttinger, 1959, *Agrocom* development, resident of Bielefeld

7. Hans Budde, 1946, *CLAAS Fertigungstechnik*, resident of Bielefeld

8. Paul Budde, 1951, independent designer from Münster

9. Ludwig Caspers, 1933, spent many years in combine development and retired where he lives locally at Clarholz-Herzebrock

10. Gerhard Clostermeyer 1938, was in the baler development team, now retired, lives in Gütersloh

11. Johannes Dammann, 1935, long serving combine engineer, retired and living in Harsewinkel

12. Christian von Davier, 1955, responsible for exhibitions and events of the *CLAAS Group*, resident of Harsewinkel

13. Erick Eckermann, 1937, freelance author on automotive history, veteran car judge and exhibition designer, lives in Seeshaupt, autohistorica@t-online.de

14. Günter Ellermann,1936, formerly export manager and now retired, lives in Schloß Holte-Stukenbrock

15. Astrid Enge, 1976, former PA to the Chairman of the Supervisory Board, now pursuing her MBA studies at the Paris *HEC*, lives in Detmold

16. Hans Fischer, 1922, retired Service Manager, Versmold

17. Nils Fredriksen, 1941, best known as *Xerion* development engineer, now working for *CIT* and resident of Harsewinkel

18. Horst-Dieter Görg, 1959, PR and event freelancer, vehicle collector and engineering historian, resident in Hildesheim, h-dieter.goerg@t-online.de

19. Jacques Gouet, 1940, has spent many years in the *Renault Agriculture* service organisation, publisher of the *Encyclopédie du tracteur Renault* and founder member of the "Amicale des tracteurs Renault" and is retired in Le Mans

20. Franz Heidjann, 1937, now retired in Harsewinkel after many years in combine development

21. Heinrich Hemker, 1929, former engineering manager, chairman of the *CLAAS Pensioners' Club*, retired, Harsewinkel

22. Klaus Herrmann, 1947, academic head and manager of the "*Deutsches Landwirtschaftsmuseum*", the museum section of the Hohenheim University, lives in Stuttgart, kh650@uni-hohenheim.de

23. Wolfgang Hornberger, 1933, managed the Paderborn plant for many years and spends his retirement in Paderborn

24. Wilhelm Isenberg, 1941, was Regional Sales Manager in Germany, retired, lives in Harsewinkel

25. Johannes Jansen, 1934, former Regional Sales Manager in Germany, retired, lives in Marienfeld

26. Wilhelm Kemper, 1924, was factory manager in Harsewinkel for many years, in retirement he maintains the *CLAAS* archives, lives in Harsewinkel

27. Ernst Klinger, 1931, helped develop the forage harvester, resident in Harsewinkel

28. Heinz König, 1931, specialist for drive design, retired in Harsewinkel

29. Josef Löchte, 1936, was responsible for factory planning before his retirement to Bad Rothenfelde

30. Rolf Meuther, 1948, General Manager of *CLAAS* in Saulgau where he also lives

31. Jens Möller, 1960, development planning and validation in the *CLAAS* self propelled product division, lives in Rheda-Wiedenbrück

32. Gerhard Meyer, 1927, for many years Metz factory manager, retired, lives in Saarburg

33. Gerhard Meyer, 1955, resident of Halle and in charge of training in the self propelled product division

34. Norbert Ortkras, 1935, is now a Harsewinkel based pensioner and a long serving member of the development team

35. Hillrich Otten, 1942, development of *Xerion* and *CLAAS* Special Products and resides locally

36. Meinolf Reiher, 1929, was in overall charge of the Schloß Holte plant and now retired, lives in Paderborn

37. Heinrich Reinharz, 1927, managed production at Schloß Holte and went into retirement in Harsewinkel

38. Heinrich Rinklake, 1920, an early member of the *CLAAS* development team, lives in Harsewinkel

39. Heinrich Roderfeld, 1926, former *CLAAS* development engineer, Harsewinkel resident

40. Karl Rupprecht, 1937, best known for cutter bar engineering, lives in retirement in Hilter

41. Günter Schinkel, 1944, now management of *CLAAS Guss*, works and lives in Bielefeld

42. Günther Schlagenhauf, 1950, works and lives in Saulgau, also produces the *Bautz Chronicle*

43. Johannes Schwörzer, 1959, teacher and expert author for "modell" magazine and is located in Tübingen

44. Wilhelm Strothmann, 1938, for many years Metz factory manager, retired, lives in Saarburg

45. Dieter Tasch, 1928, former journalist, author and chief reporter of the *Hannoversche Allgemeine paper*, lives in retirement in Hanover

46. Manfred Wagner, 1929, a founder member of the advertising and PR department, has stayed in Harsewinkel for his retirement

47. Eberhard Weller, 1955, takes care of visitor groups of the *CLAAS Group* in Harsewinkel where he also lives

48. Ludger Wiemann, 1940, was previously involved in quality management for *CFT* and is a retired person resident in Beelen

Photos

Company and private collections:

Dieter Althoff:	6, 31, 70, 145, 199, 248, 303, 356, 414, 457
Martin Beckmann:	415 - 419, 425, 426
Horst Biere:	1, 429 - 440
Eberhard Weller:	325 - 326, 380 - 381
Paul Budde:	391 - 394, 398 - 400, 404, 405
Claas:	5, 19 - 30, 32 - 36, 39 - 50, 52, 55 - 69, 71 - 102, 104 - 127, 130 - 130, 132, 135 - 144, 147, 149 - 186, 188 - 198, 225 - 233, 247, 249 - 251, 253, 255 - 259, 263 - 299, 304 - 324, 328 - 340, 342, 343, 345 - 355, 357 - 368, 370 - 376, 379, 382 - 390, 395 - 397, 401 - 403, 408, 420 - 424, 458 - 464, 466, 467
Erik Eckermann:	7 - 18,
Nils Fredriksen:	234 - 246
Jacques Gouet / Renault-Encyclopädie:	200 - 224
Johannes Schwörzer:	441 - 456

Individual sources:

Advertise: 3; Bernhard Blömer: 341, 344; Ludwig Caspers: 254; Christian von Davier: 369, 377, 378; DLG: 2; Horst-Dieter Görg: 409 - 412, 456; Franz Grothues: 187; Haberland family album: 51, 53, 54; Harsewinkel city archives: 37; Franz Heidjann: 131, 133, 134; Ernst Klinger: 146, 148; Anton Mayer: 427, 428; Norbert Ortkras: 103; Jürgen Prahl: 465; Meinolf Reiher: 260 – 263; Heinrich Roderfeld: 128, 129; Manfred Schön: 300 – 302; Harald Sievers: 4; Christa Söte: 327; Manfred Wagner: 251; Frank Weber: 406, 407, 413

Layout, picture scanning, processing and restoration plus print preparation:
PHOENIX Advertising, Service & Consulting Ltd. & Co. KG
Weetzener Landstraße 112 · D-30966 Hemmingen-Westerfeld
Telephone +49 (0) 5 11 - 52 489 489 · Fax +49 (0) 5 11 52 489 305
info@phoenix-werbeagentur.com · www.phoenix-werbeagentur.com

English version: William Howard

Proof reader: Oliver Walston

Production:
Mundschenk Druck- und Verlagsgesellschaft mbH
Harburger Straße 63 · D-29614 Soltau
Telephone +49 (0) 51 91- 8 08-0 · Fax +49 (0) 51 91- 8 08-1 45
info@mundschenk.de · www.mundschenk.de

Distribution
Old Pond Publishing
Dencora Business Centre · 36 White House Road · Ipswich IP1 5LT
Telephone +44 (0) 1473 238200 · Fax 44 (0) 1473 238201
www.oldpond.com

and CLAAS Internetshop (www.claas.com)

Printed in Germany 2006, 1. Edition

ISBN 1-905523-49-1 / ISBN 978-1-905523-48-8

Lexion 580

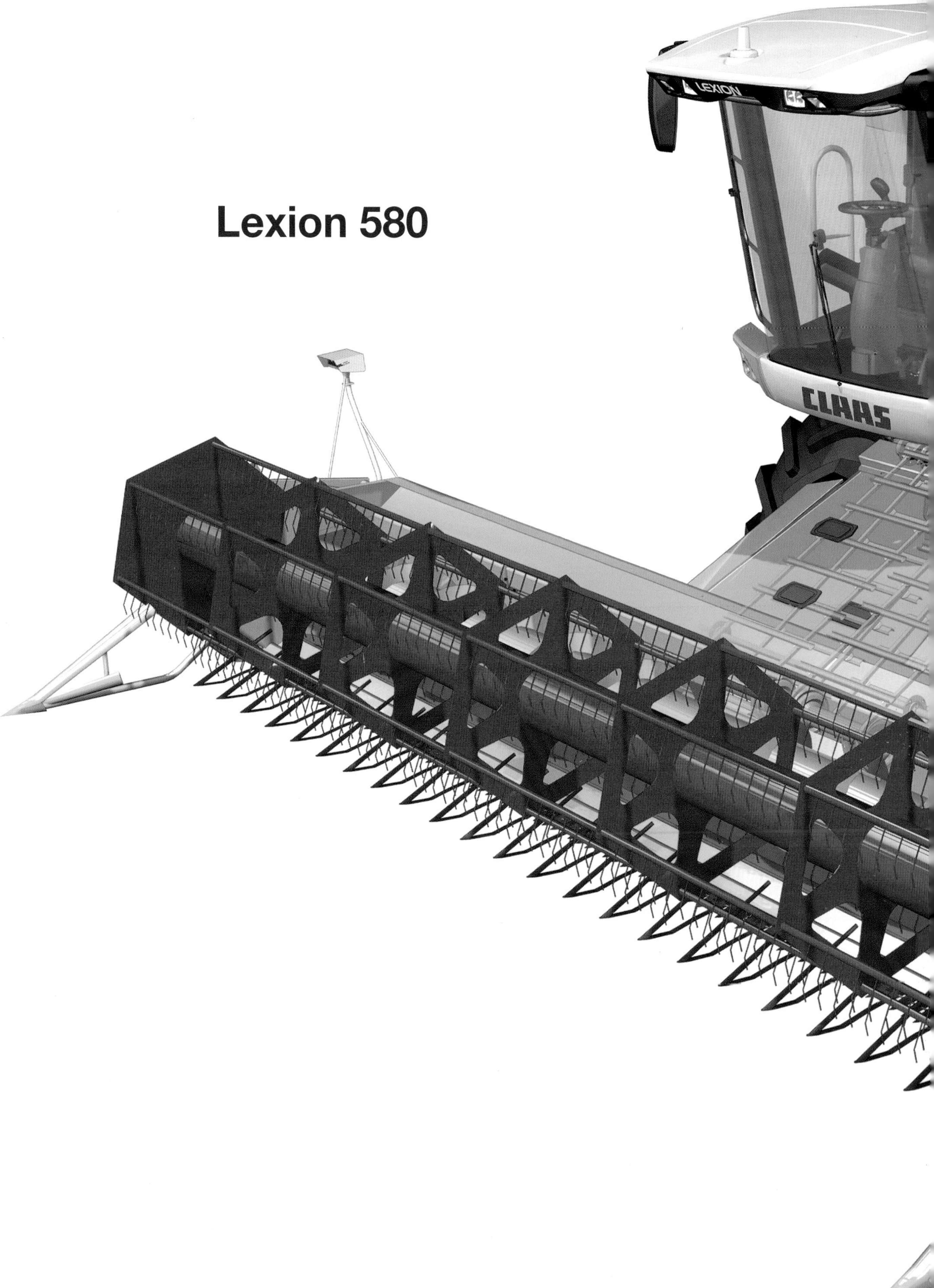